Time Out

The Little Black Book

of London

timeout.com

D0766907

Published by Time Out Guides Ltd, a wholly owned subsidiary of Time Out Group Ltd.
Time Out and the Time Out logo are trademarks of Time Out Group Ltd.

ISBN: 978-1-905042-32-6

Distribution by Seymour Ltd +44 (0)20 7429 4000
For further distribution details, see www.timeout.com

Printed and bound by Cayfosa-Quebecor, Ctra de Caldes km3, 08130 Sta Perpetua de Mogoda,
Barcelona, Spain

While every effort and care has been made to ensure the accuracy of the information contained in this
publication, the publisher cannot accept responsibility for any errors it may contain. All rights reserved.
No part of this publication may be reproduced, stored in a retrieval system, or transmitted in any form or
by any means, electronic, mechanical, photocopying, recording or otherwise, without prior permission
of Time Out Group Ltd.

© **Copyright Time Out Group Ltd 2008**
All rights reserved

Time Out Guides Limited
Universal House
251 Tottenham Court Road
London W1T 7AB
Tel + 44 (0)20 7813 3000
Fax + 44 (0)20 7813 6001
Email guides@timeout.com
www.timeout.com

Editorial
Editor Elizabeth Winding
Copy Editor Yolanda Zappaterra
Listings Editor Cathy Limb
Researchers Shane Armstrong, Alex Brown
Proofreader Karen Mulkern
Indexer Jackie Brind

Managing Director Peter Fiennes
Financial Director Gareth Garner
Editorial Director Sarah Guy
Series Editor Cath Phillips
Editorial Manager Holly Pick
Assistant Management Accountant Ija Krasnikova

Design
Art Director Scott Moore
Art Editor Pinelope Kourmouzoglou
Senior Designer Henry Elphick
Graphic Designers Gemma Doyle, Kei Ishimaru
Ad Designer Jodi Sher

Picture Desk
Picture Editor Jael Marschner
Deputy Picture Editor Katie Morris
Picture Researcher Gemma Walters
Picture Desk Assistant Marzena Zoladz

Advertising
Commercial Director Mark Phillips
Sales Manager Alison Wallen
Advertising Sales Annabel Bates, Ben Holt,
Jason Trotman
Advertising Assistant Kate Staddon

Marketing
Marketing Manager Yvonne Poon
Marketing Designers Anthony Huggins,
Nicola Wilson

Production
Group Production Director Mark Lamond
Production Manager Brendan McKeown
Production Controller Damian Bennett
Production Coordinator Julie Pallot

Time Out Group
Chairman Tony Elliott
Group General Manager/Director Nichola Coulthard
Time Out Communications Ltd MD David Pepper
Time Out International Ltd MD Cathy Runciman
Group IT Director Simon Chappell
Head of Marketing Catherine Demajo

Contributors Tim Arthur, Simone Baird, Nuala Calvi, Katie Dailey, Dan Jones, John Lewis, Charmaine Mok, Jenni Muir, Meryl O'Rourke, Candice Pires, Kate Riordan, Cyrus Shahrad, Daniel Smith, Caroline Stacey, Peter Watts, Yolanda Zappaterra.

The Editor would like to thank Jessica Cargill-Thompson, Henry Elphick, Susan Greenwood, Emma Howarth, Jenni Muir, Cath Phillips, Candice Pires, Andrew Shields and Anna Spencer, plus all the *Time Out* contributors whose work provided a basis for this book, and everyone who came up with suggestions and recommendations.

Illustrations Anna Spencer (www.raspberrykisses.co.uk)

© **Copyright Time Out Group Ltd**
All rights reserved

Introduction

No matter how well you know London, certain mysteries remain – such as knowing where to head for a post-last orders drink, or who to call when your boiler breaks down. In a city with hidden delights around every corner, it pays to have a well-stocked contacts book: the café that serves the finest full English in town; the manicurist that beauty editors swear by; the computer repair genius who'll speed across town to save the day.

We've ransacked our address books for the city's best shops, services, venues and contacts, with useful information and quirky finds to cover every eventuality – whether you're in search of circus classes for the kids or a romantic dinner reservation for two. From secret gardens and brilliant breakfast spots to where to buy a custom-blended lipstick, host a private cinema sceening or pick up the best birthday cakes in town, this is the ultimate insider's guide to London living.

It's not an A-Z of London's shops, bars, restaurants, museums and galleries, or a sightseeing guide – and instead of focusing on the familiar, we've tried to seek out the unexpected and the overlooked. It's about the practicalities of living in the capital, and its many unexpected pleasures – because however long you've lived in London, there's always something new to discover.

Contents

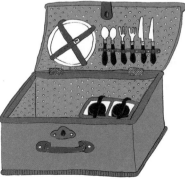

The ultimate sourcebook for decoration

THE HOUSE DIRECTORY

www.thehousedirectory.com

UP THE CREEK
COMEDY CABARET CLUB

Up The Creek Greenwich
302 Creek Road, Greenwich, London, SE10 9SW
Open Fri: 8:00pm till 2:00am Sat: 7:00pm till 2:00am
020 8858 4581

Comedy, bar, disco and restaurant
Thai food @ reasonable prices...

Summer offer: 20% Discount
on all Friday/Saturday tickets by
mentioning (Time Out 20 Offer)

www.up-the-creek.com

About the guide

LISTINGS

We've tried to make this book as useful – and user-friendly – as possible. Addresses, telephone numbers, websites, transport information, opening times and admission prices are included in the listings, along with price categories for cafés and restaurants. We've indicated how much an average main course costs by using one to four £ signs (£-££££), representing budget, moderate, expensive and luxury.

While every effort has been made to ensure the accuracy of information within this guide, the publishers cannot accept responsibility for any errors it may contain. Businesses can change their arrangements at any time, so before you go out of your way, we strongly advise that you phone ahead to check opening times, prices and other particulars.

Certain shops, restaurants, pubs and services are marked with a star symbol ★ – which indicates that we consider them to be particularly worthy of note.

CREDIT CARDS

If credit cards are not accepted, we've said so; otherwise, establishments should accept major credit cards (MasterCard, Visa and usually AmEx).

TELEPHONE NUMBERS

All telephone numbers listed in this guide assume that you are calling from within London. If you're ringing from outside the city, you will need to use the area code (020) before the phone number. If you're calling from abroad, dial your international access code, then 44 for the UK; follow that with 20 for London, then the eight-digit number.

ADVERTISERS

No payment or PR invitation of any kind has secured inclusion in this guide, or influenced its content. No establishment appears because it has advertised in any of our publications. The editors select the venues and activities listed, and reviews were compiled before any advertising space was sold. The opinions given in this book are those of Time Out writers, and are entirely independent.

WHAT DO YOU THINK?

Did we miss anything? We welcome suggestions for services and places you think we should include in future editions, and take note of your criticism of our choices. You can email us at guides@timeout.com.

ALL GO PLUMBING

Registered plumbing company
Bathroom Installations, Heating and Drainage
24 hour service
Please call **0800 083 2215** or **07956 934345**

alanwgood@aol.com
www.allgoplumbing.co.uk

Mangal 1 *KEBAB* RESTAURANT

- STARTERS RANGE FROM £1.50-£5.00 •
- KEBABS START FROM £6.50-£9.00 •

10 Arcola Street • London • E8 2DJ
(off Stoke Newington Road)
Tel: 020 7275 8981 • www.mangal1.com

Life's 2 Short

Too much to do and too little time?

Life's 2 Short can help with travel, property maintenance, personal admin and much more. No membership or joining fees. Use us on a one-off basis or more regularly – it's up to you.

"They'll fix your boiler, renew your parking permit and find you a babysitter with mind-boggling efficiency and great charm." *Telegraph*

"It's always rewarding to find companies that make life easier." *Elle*

info@lifes2short.co.uk   0800 066 5373   www.lifes2short.co.uk

Going Out

139

BEAUTY

FASHION

PARTIES

FOOD

HEALTH

ECO

OUTDOORS

HOME

CHILDREN

PETS

TRANSPORT

RESOURCES

Cinema

London's alternative cinema scene is thriving in small or unusual sites – if you know where to look.

Independent cinemas

We've focused on smaller indie cinema gems, but you can't go wrong with the grandes dames of London's cinema scene – the **BFI Southbank** (Belvedere Road, SE1 8XT, 7928 3232, www.bfi.org.uk) and the **Barbican** (Silk Street, EC2Y 8DS, 7638 8891, www.barbican.org.uk).

CENTRAL

Curzon Soho
99 Shaftesbury Avenue, W1D 5DY (7292 1686/booking line 0870 756 4620/www. curzoncinemas.com). Leicester Square tube. Tickets £8-12; £9 reductions.
Arguably the city's leading indie cinema, the Curzon Soho also boasts a bar and a street level café, run by the fab Konditor & Cook.

ICA
The Mall, SW1Y 5AH (7930 0493/www. ica.org.uk). Charing Cross tube/rail. Tickets £7-£8; £6-£7 reductions.
Two cinemas show an eclectic variety of feature-length films and shorts, as well as hosting talks by film industry luminaries.

Prince Charles
7 Leicester Place, WC2H 7BP (7494 3654/ www.princecharlescinema.com). Leicester Square tube. Tickets £4-£5; £1.50-£3.50 reductions.
This place has been known to sell seats for as little as £1, but it's always cheap.

Renoir Cinema
The Brunswick, WC1N 1AW (7837 8402/ www.curzoncinemas.com). Russell Square tube. Tickets £7-£10; £5-£7 reductions.

The two-screen Renoir Cinema shows an international array of arthouse releases, and has changing art exhibitions in its bar.

Rex Cinema
21 Rupert Street, W1V 7FE (7287 0102/ www.rexbar.co.uk). Leicester Square/ Piccadilly Circus tube. Tickets call for membership details.
It's members only at the Rex (£250/yr) – but screenings are then free, and you can invite three guests. After the film, head to the opulent '30s-style bar downstairs.

NORTH

Phoenix
52 High Road, N2 9PJ (8444 6789/www. phoenixcinema.co.uk). East Finchley tube. Tickets £8; £5 reductions.
Screenings at East Finchley's single-screen art deco treasure include the latest indie flicks, and films accompanied by live music.

Screen on the Hill
203 Haverstock Hill, NW3 4QG (7435 3366/ www.screencinemas.co.uk). Belsize Park tube. Tickets £9.50; £6-£7 reductions.
Recently refurbished, the Screen on the Hill now has a new screen, roomy seats and a Dolby sound system.

EAST

Rich Mix
35-47 Bethnal Green Road, E1 6LA (7613 7498/www.richmix.org.uk). Liverpool Street tube/rail. Tickets £3-£7; £4.50-£5.50 reductions.
Shoreditch's cultural foundation screens big-budget releases alongside unconventional festival fare, and there's a large bar.

CINEMAS WITH SOFAS

The Electric Cinema
191 Portobello Road, W11 2ED (7908 9696/www.electriccinema.co.uk). Notting Hill Gate tube. Sofas £30 for 2.
Book early to secure one of the Electric's two sofas, then relax with a bloody mary. Bliss.

Everyman Cinema Club
5 Holly Bush Vale, NW3 6TX (0870 066 4777/www.everymancinema.com). Hampstead tube. Sofas £30 for 2.
Leather sofas and armchairs, footstools, wine and canapés make for a perfect date venue.

The Exhibit
12 Balham Station Road, SW12 9SG (8772 6556/www.theexhibit.co.uk). Balham tube. Sofas £10 for 2.
No less than 24 leather sofas for two, plus a great drinks menu.

thefilmworks
Odeon Greenwich, Bugsby Way, SE10 0QJ (0871 2244 007/www.odeon. co.uk). North Greenwich tube. Sofas £18-£20 for 2 people.
Upgrade to the gallery and it's a different world. Stretch out and enjoy the ample legroom, drink in hand.

Rio Cinema
107 Kingsland High Street, E8 2PB (7241 9410/www.riocinema.org.uk). Dalston Kingsland rail. Tickets £6-£8; £3.50-£6 reductions.
The Rio screens everything from major releases to Turkish, Kurdish and gay cinema.

SOUTH

Dulwich Paradiso Film Society
East Dulwich Tavern, 1 Lordship Lane, SE22 8EW (8299 1136/www.paradisofilm.co.uk). East Dulwich rail. Tickets £4, plus £1 annual membership. No credit cards
This community-run society holds left-of-mainstream screenings on Tuesdays during the spring and autumn.

Ritzy Picturehouse
Brixton Oval, Coldharbour Lane, SW2 1JG (0871 704 2065/www.picturehouses.co.uk). Tickets £6.50-£8.50; £5.25-£7.25 reductions.
Kids' Club, cheap offers for over-60s and autism-friendly screenings all feature here.

WEST

Cine Lumière
17 Queensferry Place, SW7 2DT (7073 1350/www.institut-francais.org.uk).
South Kensington tube. Tickets £7-£9; £5-£7 reductions.
Founded in 1910 to introduce Londoners to artists and writers from across La Manche, London's French cultural institute shows European and World cinema classics.

Coronet Cinema
103 Notting Hill Gate, W11 3LB (7727 6705/ www.coronet.org.uk). Notting Hill Gate tube. Tickets £7; £4.50 reductions.
In its days as a theatre, Ellen Terry and Sara Bernhardt trod the boards here, but contemporary Londoners know it as the last cinema where you could enjoy the film through a haze of cigarette smoke.

Riverside Studios
Crisp Road, W6 9RL (8237 1111/www. riversidestudios.co.uk). Hammersmith tube. Tickets £7.50; £6.50 reductions.
The Riverside is famed for its inspired double bills – a bargain at £7.50. The airy café and terrace are lovely in summer too.

Tricycle
269 Kilburn High Road, NW6 7JR (7328 1000/www.tricycle.co.uk). Kilburn tube. Tickets £5-£8; £1.50-£7 reductions.
This well-loved cultural centre offers a lively mix of theatre, visual arts and cinema.

GOING OUT
BEAUTY
FASHION
PARTIES
FOOD
HEALTH
ECO
OUTDOORS
HOME
CHILDREN
PETS
TRANSPORT
RESOURCES

GOING OUT

BEAUTY

FASHION

PARTIES

FOOD

HEALTH

ECO

OUTDOORS

HOME

CHILDREN

PETS

TRANSPORT

RESOURCES

Private hire

Whether you're after a lavish screening of your favourite Hepburn film with your 200 closest friends or a cosy viewing of an old family holiday, venues across the city provide facilities to suit all budgets.

Big cinemas – including the **Prince Charles**, **Rio** and **Electric** (*see p12-p13*) plus chains such as **Screen Cinemas** (7472 5093, www.everymancinemaclub. com) – also hire out auditoriums. Note that not all prices include screening rights, which start at £100.

The Fleapit
49 Columbia Road, E2 7RG (7033 9986/ www.thefleapit.com). Liverpool Street tube/ rail. Capacity 50. Cost £100 Tue-Thur; £150 Fri-Sat.
Housed in a converted warehouse, this café-bar is an East End creative hub. 'The Pit' can be hired for art events and parties, with its own projector screen and Bose sound system.

The Garrison
99-101 Bermondsey Street, SE1 3XB (7367 6351/www.thegarrison.co.uk). London Bridge tube. Capacity 30. Cost £50 Mon-Wed; £100 Thur-Sun.
This buzzy gastropub offers intimate screenings on a decent-sized screen (5ft x 4ft) in its cosy, living room-like basement.

One Aldwych ✷
1 Aldwych, WC2B 4RH (7300 0700/www. onealdwych.com). Covent Garden tube. Capacity 30. Cost £95-£125/hr.
The slick screening room features 35mm hotel projection with Dolby SR wide screen and cinemascope; popcorn's on the house.

Phoenix Cinema
For listings see p12. Capacity 255. Cost £200-£1,800.
Available for hire outside normal screening hours, the Phoenix is a big hit for children's parties. Romantics take note: it was once hired for an audience of two to watch *Gone with the Wind*.

The Rex
For listings see p12. Capacity 75. Cost £250/hr-£350/hr
This smart members' club has a state-of-the-art screening room and plush bar for hire. Watch your chosen film in the lap of luxury, or play shoot 'em ups on the big screen.

Roxy
128-132 Borough High Street, SE1 1LB (7407 4057/www.roxybarandscreen.com). Borough or London Bridge tube. Capacity 220. Cost £200/hr.
Book ahead at this spacious bar, whose four-metre screen has full projection capabilities. Great cocktails and lovely staff make it a very popular choice.

16mm Café
19 D'Arblay Street, W1F 8ED (7287 8892/ www.16mm-soho.com). Oxford Circus tube. Capacity 16. Cost varies
The downstairs room at this warmly welcoming little café can be used to show films on its four-metre screen, while the owners are happy to arrange refreshments.

The Soho Hotel
4 Richmond Mews, WC2H 9HB (7559 3000/www.firmdalehotels.com). Tottenham Court Road tube. Capacity 45 & 100. Cost £250/hr.
Two luxurious screening rooms are available at the Soho Hotel – and also at its sister operations, the Covent Garden Hotel and Charlotte Street Hotel.

City Secret

Sign up for **Secret Cinema** (www. secretcinema.org) and you could be in for a surprise. Monthly mystery screenings take place in the most unlikely of locations, from derelict theatres to children's playgrounds. Subscribers are only given details on the morning of the event – but rest assured, you won't be watching an anodyne Hollywood rom com.

Cousin Jill's is an exclusive and unique, stylish karaoke lounge situated in the Heart of Mayfair.

Cousin Jill's Karaoke Lounge
Basement, 42 Albemarle Street
London W1S 4JH

Tel: 020 7499 9969
Web: www.cousinjills.com

The Mucky Pup

39 Queen's Head St. N1   www.myspace.com/themuckypupn1   0207-226-2572

FREE JUKEBOX   LIVE MUSIC   NO TV   SMOKING AREA
REAL ALES   SUNDAY ROAST   PUB FOOD   QUIZ NIGHTS

A RARE BREED OF PUB

ribon
Japanese Restaurant

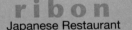

• Private KARAOKE PARTIES (Reservations Only)
• A great venue for Hen Nights, Birthday Parties and Work do's
to warm your vocal chords with the Karaoke and awaken your
taste palettes with the Japanese cuisine.

www.ribonrestaurant.co.uk
6 Holborn Viaduct London EC1A 2AE • 020 7329 3252 / 3254

DOORS BY JAS M.B.   8 GANTON STREET   LONDON   W1F 7QP
Telephone +44 (0)20 7494 2288
Facsimile +44 (0)20 7494 2287

www.doorsbyjasmb.com

GOING OUT

BEAUTY

FASHION

PARTIES

FOOD

HEALTH

ECO

OUTDOORS

HOME

CHILDREN

PETS

TRANSPORT

RESOURCES

Clubbing

Dance like there's no tomorrow, or sample the city's buzzing alternative scene.

Alternative nights out

The city's alternative clubbing scene is ever-changing, with trends shifting in the twirl of a nipple tassel. Here's our pick of the current crop of clubs and promoters; for the latest overview, check out *Time Out London* (www.timeout.com).

As most of the nights we've chosen are held at various venues, we've listed the websites where you'll be able to find details of upcoming events.

Book Slam
www.bookslam.com. Admission £8.
Invariably a sell-out, this monthly literary soirée is leagues ahead of your average book club. Major authors read from recently published works, while spoken word and slam poets step up alongside soon-to-be big musical names. Venues vary, but line-ups are constantly impressive: one recent event saw Irvine Walsh and Alabama 3 sharing the bill.

Cabaret Room at Bistrotheque
For venue listings see p96. Admission £5-£20.
The small cabaret room at Bistrotheque is much loved by edgier performance artists. Drag superstar Jonny Woo leads a talented and ever-increasing collective of drag queens, bear burlesquers and surreal performers.

Hula Boogie
8672 5972/www.hulaboogie.co.uk. Admission £7.
When the grey-on-grey weather gets you down, there's a tiny bit of the sunny South Pacific to be found in… Kennington. One Sunday a month sees Hula Boogie – a colourful, floor-stomping rock'n'roll party that's hosted by Miss Aloha and Reverend Boogie – take over the South London Pacific Tiki Bar (340 Kennington Road, SE1 14L, 7820 9189). If the hula and jive classes can't get you moving, nothing will.

I Knit London
www.iknit.org.uk. Admission free.
Knitting circles might sound like something your gran once went to, but young Londoners are flocking to I Knit London's gatherings in their droves. Events alternate between the I Knit shop (106 Lower Marsh, SE1 7AB, 7261 1338) and various central London pubs, and are particularly popular with gay knitters.

Jewdas
www.jewdas.org. Admission varies; check online for details.
Purveyors of the sort of biting Jewish satire that isn't for everyone (four members of the group were arrested in 2007, due to the controversial content on their flyers), Jewdas is a collective of, well, really funny Jews. It holds irregular events in venues across the capital, often loosely tied to Jewish high holidays. The twisted entertainment on offer might include rabbinical lap dances, mass conversions, klezmer bands and other arty offerings; expect the unexpected.

Killing Kittens
www.killingkittens.co.uk. Admission varies; check online for details.
Girls who like boys but sometimes like girls too will love Killing Kittens, the monthly party for London swingers, held in a secret location. Participants are strictly vetted (young, attractive couples and single girls only), and the girls say what goes. You can keep your kit on, but the brave plunge straight in to the bacchanalia.

Lady Luck Club

www.ladyluckclub.co.uk. Admission varies; check online for details.

There's one constant in London's constantly shifting clubbing scene, and that's the suave Mr El Nino: DJ, promoter and founder of Lady Luck. With its strict 'vintage glamour' door policy, the long-running monthly grindfest attracts folk who live and breathe the scene, and know how to move to 1940s, '50s and '60s underground sounds. The night's current home is a three-floored East End strip joint, where occasional burlesque performers and live music add to the heady atmosphere.

London Rollergirls

www.londonrollergirls.com. Admission £5-£6.

Enormously popular in Depression-era America, and now the subject of a worldwide revival, roller derby is a sometimes violent girls-only sport on skates. In a nutshell: two teams race around a track, each trying to block the other team's key player, called a jammer. What makes it a riot, though, are the girls' punk-meets-burlesque costumes, the themes chosen by the teams, and the fund-raising rockabilly parties held most months.

Oh My God I Miss You! ★

www.ohmygodimissyou.com. Admission £8-£10.

With seemingly endless imagination, the Oh My God I Miss You! team transforms the Bethnal Green Working Men's Club (44-46 Pollard Row, E2 6NB, 7739 7170, www. workersplaytime.net) each month for its themed parties. Go Go Grind rewinds to a 1960s television set, filled with dancers on podiums and girls in miniskirts, while the Birthday Club is like no party you went to as a small child. Always dress to the theme.

Torture Garden

www.torturegarden.com. Admission £18-£32.

All roads in London's fetish scene lead to Torture Garden, arguably the world's biggest S&M club. The monthly balls aren't half as intimidating as fetish virgins assume: people dress in sleazy vintage as well as small bits of rubber, and there's a zero-tolerance policy on leches.

EARLY OPENING

Been out at night and still wide awake? Carry on the excess with a cheeky breakfast pint at one of the city's early-opening pubs.

Smithfields' **Fox & Anchor** (115 Charterhouse Street, EC1M 6AA 7250 1300, www.foxandanchor. com, opens 7am) is in sparkling form after a 2007 refurb, while on the other side of the market, the **Hope** (94 Cowcross Street, EC1M 6BH, 0871 984 1334, opens 6am) has also been serving the traders for years. In the market itself, the **Cock Tavern** (East Poultry Avenue, EC1A 9LH, 0871 984 1318, opens 5.30am) offers fine ales, with or without such brekkie stalwarts as kippers and smoked haddock.

Borough Market has a decent drinking spot in the **Market Porter** (9 Stoney Street, SE1 9AA, 7407 2495, www.markettaverns.co.uk, opens 6-8.30am Mon-Fri), where film buffs can enjoy the fact that scenes from *Mission Impossible* were shot here.

If you're heading for Petticoat Lane or Brick Lane, a good stopping-off spot is the **Market Trader** (50 Middlesex Street, E1 7EX, 7247 3459, opens 8am Sun).

Non-market-related drinking can be had at the oddly-named **Only Running Footman** (5 Charles Street, W1J 5DF, 7499 2988, opens 7.30am) in Mayfair, while at Kings Cross, **06 St Chad's Place** (6 St Chad's Place, WC1X 9HH, 7278 3355, www.6stchadsplace.com, opens 8am Mon-Fri) occupies a modish, stripped-down warehouse. Further afield, the **George** (159 High Street, E11 2RL 8989 2921, opens 9am) in Wanstead is run by Wetherspoons, and remains an exceedingly handsome hostelry.

GOING OUT

BEAUTY

FASHION

PARTIES

FOOD

HEALTH

ECO

OUTDOORS

HOME

CHILDREN

PETS

TRANSPORT

RESOURCES

GOING OUT

BEAUTY

FASHION

PARTIES

FOOD

HEALTH

ECO

OUTDOORS

HOME

CHILDREN

PETS

TRANSPORT

RESOURCES

Address Book Secrets
Jodie Harsh
DJ & party organiser

I like Thursday's **Smash and Grab** at Punk (14 Soho Street, W1D 3DN, 0871 223 1242, www.myspace.com/smashandgrabnight). People like Kate Moss and Lily Allen go there, but you don't have to be on the guestlist to get in. There's a young, rock'n'roll vibe and it's got a lot of zebra prints and fibre-optics. Much debauchery goes on in the red velvet chill-out area out back.

Bungalow 8 (45 St Martin's Lane, Covent Garden, WC2N 4HX, 7300 5592, www.bungalow8london.com) is quite strict on the door and really discreet. I love the interior – it's all black and white stripy walls that give you a headache, like being in a big Jaeger carrier bag. They do the best cocktails in town too.

Before you head out on the pull for the evening, a great place to line your stomach is the **Rivington Grill** (28-30 Rivington Street, EC2A 3DZ, 7729 7053, www.rivingtongrill.co.uk). It's in the beating heart of Shoreditch and they do really good champagne and oysters, for a bit of an aphrodisiac on a night out.

All the drag queens and trannies get their shoes done at the **Little Shoe Box** (89 Holloway Road, N7 8LT, 7607 1247, www.thelittleshoeboxonline.com), as it does made-to-measure shoes. It's particularly good for big shiny platforms. I don't buy that sort of thing myself – I've got more style than that. Luckily I'm a size eight, so I can buy women's shoes from **Terry de Havilland** (see p58).

My favourite place for party outfits is **Kokon To Zai** (57 Greek Street, W1D 3DX, 7434 1316, www.kokontozaishop.com). It's a little boutique that sells all sorts of crazy designs and is owned by Marjan Pejoski, who did Bjork's swan dress. It's also got really good accessories, which are always the most important thing in an outfit.

In Shoreditch, the new branch of **Beach Blanket Babylon** (19-23 Bethnal Green Road, E1 6LA, 7749 3540, www.beachblanket.co.uk) is a loungey kind of club where they play mainly electro, set in a really grand building that was an old warehouse, with big oil burners outside.

I run a club night, Issue, on the first Sunday of the month at **Shoreditch Electricity Showrooms** (39a Hoxton Square, N1 6NN, 7739 3939, www.issueclub.blogspot.com) – which has an amazing light-up dance floor in its basement. The night's called Issue because the theme is a magazine where you're the editor. There's a photographer who'll let you style your own shoot, a psychic like Mystic Meg, an agony aunt and guest 'editors' on the decks every week.

All the gays have to go to **Fire** (38-42 Parry Street, SW8 1RT, 7820 0550) once in their lives. It's a club that stays open until 4pm the next day; you can go there at midday and there will be people there who've been partying all night. God knows how they must feel when they stumble out into the Vauxhall daylight on Sunday afternoon.

Clubs

Where we've listed specific nights held at particular clubs (such as Jaded at AKA), the opening times given are for that particular club night, rather than the club's general opening hours.

Best for...
A tearing sound system

Fabric
77A Charterhouse Street, EC1M 3HN (7336 8898/www.fabriclondon.com). Farringdon tube/rail. Open 10pm-6am Fri; 10pm-7am Sat. Admission £13-£16.
When Fabric opened in 1999, the Bodysonic speaker system under its floorboards left punters lost for words – not that they'd have heard them anyway – and its spine-melting, trouser-flapping bass still wipes the dancefloor with every other club in London.

See also *End, 18 West Central Street, WC1A 1JJ (7419 9199/www.endclub.com).*

Best for...
Freaky electro fun

Bugged Out @ End
End, 18 West Central Street, WC1A 1JJ (7419 9199/www.buggedout.net). Holborn or Tottenham Court Road tube. Open 11pm-7pm Sat. Admission £12-£17.
Bugged Out has proved one of the most popular nights to rock the End, thanks to its bubbly yet bleeding-edge brand of techy electro euphoria, with appearances by everyone from Daft Punk to Dave Clarke, Squarepusher to Simian Mobile Disco.

See also *Trailer Trash @ On The Rocks (www.clubtrailertrash.com).*

Best for...
Messy after-parties

Jaded @ AKA
AKA, 18 West Central Street, WC1A 1JJ (7836 0110/www.akalondon.com).

Tottenham Court Road tube. Open 5.30am-noon Sun. Admission £8-£12.
Anyone still on the dancefloor at 5.30am clearly wants to stay there until lunchtime – and now they can thanks to Jaded, which combines spine-tingling electro mayhem with all manner of sleep-deprived skylarking. No wonder plenty of people stay in the night before then head here after breakfast.

See also *Breakfast @ EGG (www.myspace.com/breakfastategg).*

Best for...
An eclectic booking policy

Plastic People
147-149 Curtain Road, EC2A 3QE (7739 6471/www.plasticpeople.co.uk). Liverpool Street or Old Street tube/rail/8, 55 bus. Open 10pm-2am Thur; 10pm-4am Fri, Sat; 8-11.30pm Sun. Admission £5-£10.
Complaints about clubs regurgitating the same floor-filling formats should be checked in at the door. An innovative programme sees everything from Sunday dubstep sessions to nights where bedroom producers air their works, plus atmospheric one-off shows from the likes of Four Tet and Carl Craig.

See also *Herbal, 10-14 Kingsland Road, E2 8DA (7613 4462/www.herbaluk.com).*

Best for...
Clubbing with a garden

Cargo
83 Rivington Street, EC2A 3AY (7749 7840/www.cargo-london.com). Old Street tube/rail/55 bus. Open noon-1am Mon-Thur; noon-3am Fri, Sat; 1pm-midnight Sun. Admission £6-£12.50.
Having the option of grabbing five minutes of fresh air is an important clubbing asset, and not just for smokers. Cargo's garden is one of London's finest, with seating aplenty, heat lamps for chill winter evenings and free yard parties throughout the summer.

See also *EGG, 200 York Way, N7 9AP (7609 8364/www.egglondon.net).*

GOING OUT
BEAUTY
FASHION
PARTIES
FOOD
HEALTH
ECO
OUTDOORS
HOME
CHILDREN
PETS
TRANSPORT
RESOURCES

BEAUTY

FASHION

PARTIES

FOOD

HEALTH

ECO

OUTDOORS

HOME

CHILDREN

PETS

TRANSPORT

RESOURCES

Best for...
Jungle fever

Hospitality @ Heaven

Heaven, Under the Arches, Villiers Street, WC2N 6NG (7930 2020/www.hospital records.com/hospitality). Embankment tube or Charing Cross tube/rail. Open 10pm-6am Fri. Admission £16-£18.

Hospitality's move to Heaven has revitalised the capital's drum 'n' bass scene. The main room brings anthemic madness from Hospital Records' own soldiers and big name DJs such as Andy C; upstairs it's more cerebral and sinister, courtesy of labels like Subtitles or Commercial Suicide.

See also *Ram Records @ End (www.ramrecords.co.uk).*

Best for...
Underground sounds

Forward @ Plastic People

Plastic People, 147-149 Curtain Road, EC2A 3QE (7739 6471/www.ilovefwd.com). Liverpool Street or Old Street tube/rail/8, 55 bus. Open 8.30am-12.30pm Sun. Admission £5-£7.

The jury remains out on how well dubstep translates from the studio to the dancefloor, but there's no denying it's one of the freshest, most fiercely experimental things happening in London's clubs, or that Forward is the most exciting night at which to catch it in action.

See also *DMZ @ Mass (www.myspace.com/dmzuk).*

Best for...
Hands-in-the-air house

Defected in the House
@ Ministry of Sound

Ministry of Sound, 103 Gaunt Street, off Newington Causeway, SE1 6DP (0870 060 0010/www.defected.com). Open 11pm-7am Sat. Admission £15.

A safe option for those seeking a slice of Ibizan excess without resorting to the extortionate swank of Pacha, bi-monthly Defected in the House brings big-name DJs to a club that's currently undergoing something of a renaissance.

See also *Dusted @ Pacha (www.pachalondon.com).*

Best for...
Old-skool rave

Raindance @ seOne

SeOne, Weston Street, SE1 3QX (7407 1617/www.raindanceravefestival.com). London Bridge tube/rail. Open 9pm-8am Sat. Admission £20.

Nu rave may have been getting all the press in recent years, but Raindance brings back the old skool sounds to a crowd that was popping pills when Klaxons fans were still gnawing on rusks.

See also *Bang Face @ Electrowerkz (www.bangface.com).*

Best for...
Eclectic hip hop nights

Battlejam @ Cargo

For club listings see p19 (www.myspace.com/ battlejam). Admission £10-£12.

Motor-mouth of the moment Beardyman conducts the chaos at this gloriously free-form night, which mixes hip hop and beatbox with scratch wackiness, innovative audience interaction and off-the-wall humour.

See also *Breakin' Bread @ Jazz Café (www.breakinbread.org).*

Best for...
Gay clubbing

Popstarz @ Sin

144 Charing Cross Road WC2H 0LB (0871 971384/www.popstarz.org). Tottenham Court Road tube. Open 10pm-4am Fri. Admission £7 or free before 11pm.

The easy-going, affable Popstarz has found a winning formula: indie music (bands followed by DJs), credible pop and crunching electronic carnage across three rooms.

Comedy

You can be spoon-fed comedy on telly, but why not discover it first?

GOING OUT
BEAUTY
FASHION
PARTIES
FOOD
HEALTH
ECO
OUTDOORS
HOME
CHILDREN
PETS
TRANSPORT
RESOURCES

CENTRAL

Amused Moose Soho
17 Greek Street, W1D 4DR (7287 3727/ www.amusedmoose.com/shows). Leicester Square or Tottenham Court Road tube. Shows 7.30pm-4am Sat. Admission £7-£15.
The grande dame of the comedy world, Hils Jago, runs her clubs with military precision, with a good mix of big names and the best of the current crop of newcomers.

Comedy Camp
Barcode, 3-4 Archers Street, W1D 7AP (0870 060 0100/www.comedycamp.co.uk). Leicester Square or Piccadilly Circus tube. Shows 8.30pm Tue. Admission £8 plus £2 membership.
This intimate, straight-friendly gay club is one of the best nights out in town. Resident host and promoter Simon Happily only books fabulous acts: Jo Caulfield, Harry Hill and Graham Norton have all performed here.

Comedy Store
1A Oxendon Street, SW1Y 4EE (0844 847 1728/www.thecomedystore.co.uk). Leicester Square or Piccadilly Circus tube. Shows 8pm-10.30pm Tue-Thur, Sun; 8pm & midnight Fri, Sat. Admission £13-£18.
Apart from the corking bills every Thursday to Saturday, check out the brilliant Comedy Store Players (Wed, Sun) or the fantastic Cutting Edge Team (Tue). The Gong Show on the last Monday of the month is also not to be missed.

Funny Side of Covent Garden
Corner Store, 32-35 Wellington Street, WC2E 7BN (0870 446 0616/www.thefunny side.info). Covent Garden or Leicester Square tube. Shows 7.30pm Wed-Sat; 6.30pm Sun. Admission £12.50.

Five nights a week this award-winning club puts on a terrific line-up of well-established comedians in its medium-sized space.

Soho Theatre
21 Dean Street, W1D 3NE (0870 429 6883/www.sohotheatre.com). Tottenham Cout Road tube. Shows vary. Admission £10-£17.50.
Soho Theatre has become one of the best places to catch major comedy talents breaking out of their normal club sets to perform more substantial solo shows.

NORTH

Cockadoodle Comedy Club
Cock Tavern, 125 Kilburn High Road, NW6 6JH (7624 1820/www.cocktavern.com). Kilburn Park tube. Shows 9pm Sat. Admission £8.50.
Roland and Claire Muldoon's club is a friendly affair with excellent food. Having run the Hackney Empire for years, these two know how to put together an enticing bill.

Downstairs at the King's Head
2 Crouch End Hill, N8 8AA (8340 1028/ www.downstairsatthekingshead.com). Finsbury Park tube/rail then W7 bus. Shows 8pm Thur-Sun. Admission £4-£9. No credit cards.
Founded back in 1981, this Crouch End venue is still run with huge enthusiasm by the immensely knowledgeable promoter Pete Grahame. It's a friendly sort of place.

Hampstead Comedy Club
143 Adelaide Road, NW3 3NL (7633 9539/ www.hampsteadcomedy.co.uk). Chalk Farm or Swiss Cottage tube. Shows 8pm Sat, Sun. Admission £9.50; £8.50 reductions. No credit cards.

Ivor Dembina, host of this Saturday night club, hates the sound of people scoffing food during a show, and detests the idea of a disco afterwards. Instead, he invests everything in booking exciting, interesting acts.

Hen and Chickens
109 St Paul's Road, Highbury Corner, N1 2NA (7704 2001/www.henandchickens. com). Highbury & Islington tube/rail. Shows times vary. Admission £7-£10. No credit cards.
This dinky black box theatre (seating just 54) above the cosy Hen and Chickens Pub is the place to see great solo shows and catch major acts trying out their material before they head out on tour. Recent performers include Jimmy Carr, Frankie Boyle and Rhona Cameron.

EAST

Comedy Café
66 Rivington Street, EC2A 3AY (7739 5706/www.comedycafe.co.uk). Liverpool or Old Street tube/rail. Shows 8pm Wed, Thur, Sat; 7pm Fri. Admission £8-£15. Free Wed. No credit cards.
At this purpose-built Shoreditch club you're given a table for the evening and have to dine; the menu offers hearty burgers, pies and meze. Comedian and host Noel Faulkner mainly keeps to the back room now, but his influence can be felt in the emphasis on inviting bills and satisfied punters.

Theatre Royal Stratford East
Gerry Raffles Square, E15 1BN (8279 1160/www.stratfordeast.com). Stratford tube/rail. Shows 8pm Mon. Admission free.
Set in the opulent surroundings of the Theatre Royal, this little gem of a night is held every Monday and is completely free. The gig takes place in the long bar upstairs and has some great line-ups – especially considering you're not paying a penny to see them.

SOUTH

Banana Cabaret
The Bedford, 77 Bedford Hill, SW12 9HD (8682 8940/www.bananacabaret.co.uk).
Balham tube/rail. Shows 8pm Fri, Sat. Admission £13-£16. No credit cards.
Satisfaction's guaranteed every Friday and Saturday in the roundhouse setting of Balham's Bedford Arms. Comics enjoy playing here, and the bills are always strong.

Up the Creek
302 Creek Road, SE10 9SW (8858 4581/www.up-the-creek.com). Greenwich DLR/rail. Shows 8pm Fri–Sun. Admission £5-£15; £3-£12 reductions. No credit cards.
Originally set up by the legendary Malcolm Hardee, this extraordinary purpose-built Greenwich club is still a superb spot. It's famous for its lively atmosphere, where only the strongest comics survive, though the 'Sunday Special Club' is more laid-back.

WEST

Bearcat Comedy
28 Winchester Road, TW1 1LF (8891 1852/www.bearcatcomedy. co.uk). St Margaret's rail. Shows 8pm Sat. Admission £12, £10 members. No credit cards.
Out in suburban Twickenham, this is one of London's oldest clubs, with an impressive list of past performers.

Headliners
George IV, 185 Chiswick High Road, W4 2DR (8566 4067/www.headliners comedy.com). Turnham Green tube. Shows 9pm Fri, Sat. Admission £10; £7.50 reductions. No credit cards.
Surprisingly perhaps, Headliners is the only purpose-built comedy club in West London – but it's a good one. At the helm is the highly experienced Simon Randall, who also operates the Ha Bloody Ha night at nearby Ealing Studios.

Music

Some of the capital's smaller musical gems, from melodious acoustic nights to belting karaoke clubs.

Acoustic nights

Bedford
77 Bedford Hill, SW12 9HD (8682 8940/ www.thebedford.co.uk). Balham tube/rail. Shows 7.30pm Mon-Thur. Admission free.
Above-average musos take to the stage in the Bedford's Elizabethan-style balconied theatre – Paolo Nutini cut his teeth here, while Pete Townshend and Willy Mason have both chosen it for secret shows.

Cavendish Arms
128 Hartington Road, SW8 2HJ (7627 0698/www.thecavendisharmsstockwell.co.uk). Stockwell tube. Shows 7pm daily. Admission £5. Free on selected evenings.
The recently refurbished Cavendish Arms is one of South London's most passionate purveyors of live acoustic music. The first-class PA ensures the charming rear room venue sounds as good as it looks.

Cross Kings
126 York Way, N1 0AX (7278 8318/ www.thecrosskings.co.uk). Kings Cross tube. Shows 8pm daily. Admission £10. Free on selected evenings.
In an area forging towards the future, the Cross Kings parties like it's 1969. Communal living room aesthetics meet hallucinatory art-house inclinations, and regular music nights mingle with day-long festivals.

Green Note
106 Parkway, NW1 7AN (7485 9899/www. greennote.co.uk). Camden Town tube. Shows 9pm Wed-Sun. Admission £4-£10.
This vegetarian restaurant and bar hosts a programme of suitably thoughtful live music – from folk and blues to jazz and country. The small space makes for a warm and intimate atmosphere, but means queues around the block when big acts are treading the boards.

Slaughtered Lamb ★
34-35 Great Sutton Street, EC1V 0DX (7253 1516/www.electroacousticclub.com). Barbican tube. Shows 8.30pm Mon-Thur. Admission £6-£8.
The Lamb's Electroacoustic Club nights pull in emotionally charged balladeers from around the UK to the Lamb's diminutive, candlelit downstairs room.

Troubadour
263-267 Old Brompton Road, SW5 9JA (7370 1434/www.troubadour.co.uk). Earls Court tube. Shows 8pm Tue, Wed, Fri. Admission £7. No credit cards.
Its sound system may be far from satisfying, but the cellar at this characterful pub is a live music mecca that has hosted the legendary likes of Hendrix and Dylan.

12 Bar Club
22-23 Denmark Street, WC2H 8NL (7240 2120/www.12barclub.com). Tottenham Court Road or Leicester Square tube. Gigs 7pm daily. Admission £3-£15. No credit cards.
The 12 Bar boasts one of London's most intimate stages, with ground floor seating and a snug gallery. Blues, folk and rock acts perform nightly.

Regal Room
Distillers Arms, 64 Fulham Palace Road, W6 9PH (8748 2834/www.theregalroom. com). Hammersmith tube. Shows 7.30pm Tue, Wed, Fri, Sat. Admission free.
A rather glamorous venue above a less-than-glamorous boozer, the Regal Room offers a well-edited roster of artful acoustic acts.

GOING OUT
BEAUTY
FASHION
PARTIES
FOOD
HEALTH
ECO
OUTDOORS
HOME
CHILDREN
PETS
TRANSPORT
RESOURCES

Jazz

In addition to the venues listed, the **100 Club** (100 Oxford Street, W1D 1LL, 7636 0933, www.the100club.co.uk) hosts occasional trad jazz sessions, the **Pigalle** (215 Piccadilly, W1J 9HN, 0845 345 6053/ 7644 1420, www.vpmg.et/pigalle.com) specialises in the jazzier end of pop and cabaret, and the **Jazz Café** (5 Parkway, NW1 7PG, 7485 6834, www.jazzcafe.co.uk) lives up to its name about half a dozen times a month. Both the **Barbican** and the **South Bank Centre** (for both, see p12) also host dozens of big jazz names every year, including the bulk of the **London Jazz Festival** (www.londonjazzfestival.org.uk).

See www.timeout.com or www.jazzinlondon.net for details on current events.

Bull's Head
373 Lonsdale Road, SW13 9PY (8876 5241/www.thebullshead.com). Barnes Bridge rail. Gigs 8.30pm Mon-Sun; 1-3.30pm, 8.30-11pm Sun. Admission £5-£12.
The rows of seating at this riverside boozer may resemble a school assembly hall, but acoustics are good and the music is of a high standard; regulars include pianist Stan Tracey and sax maestro Peter King.

The Klinker
Various venues (www.iotacism.com/ klinkerizer). Admission £5; £3 reductions.
This left-field night, held at three London venues, offers a mix of improvised music, poetry, performance art, beardy men and Super8 films; check online for details.

Pizza Express Jazz Club
10 Dean Street, W1D 3RW (0845 602 7017/ 7439 8722/www.pizzaexpresslive.com). Tottenham Court Road tube. Gigs 9pm daily. Admission £15-£25.
This 120-capacity basement hosts excellent swing, mainstream, contemporary and fusion residencies from the likes of Lea DeLaria and Mose Allison. Tip: if it's sold out, you may be able to cadge a seat at the bar.

Le QuecumBar
42-44 Battersea High Street, SW11 3HX (7787 2227/www.quecumbar.co.uk). Clapham Junction rail. Gigs 8pm Mon-Sat; call for details Sun. Admission £5-£15. Free before 8pm.
This lovely art deco bar and brasserie attracts a surprisingly young crowd with top drawer Gypsy jazz, alongside old-school swing, crooners, Balkan folk and ragtime.

Ronnie Scott's
47 Frith Street, W1D 4HT (7439 0747/ www.ronniescotts.co.uk). Leicester Square tube. Gigs 7.30pm daily. Admission (non-members) £20-£46 Mon-Sat.
After a 2006 change in ownership, tickets, food and booze are pricey at this Soho legend and the delightful upstairs and basement bars are now costly private members' clubs. Acoustics and sightlines are perfect though, and it's still the best place to see the greats.

606 Club
90 Lots Road, SW10 0QD (7352 5953/ www.606club.co.uk). Earl's Court or Fulham Broadway tube/11, 211 bus. Gigs times vary; call for details. Admission £8-£12.
There's no entry fee at this charmingly ramshackle 150-capacity venue: instead, the bands are funded from a 'music charge' that's added to your bill at the end of the night. Note alcohol can only be served with food.

Spice Of Life
6 Moor Street, Cambridge Circus, W1D 5NA (7739 3025/www.spiceoflifesoho.com). Gigs times vary; call for details. Admission free-£6.
The basement of this old-school boozer hosts excellent mainstream jazz singers and instrumentalists, with weekly open mic nights.

Vortex Jazz Club ★
11 Gillet Street, N16 8JN (7254 4097/www. vortexjazz.co.uk). Dalston Kingsland rail. Gigs 8.30pm daily. Admission £4-£12.
In new premises since 2005, the Vortex still draws a boho crowd. Line-ups remain as varied as ever, with left-field musicians mixing with cabaret divas and folkies.

Karaoke

Bloomsbury Lanes
Basement of Tavistock Hotel, Bedford Way, WC1H 9EU (7183 1979/www.bloomsbury bowling.com). Russell Square tube. Open noon-midnight Mon-Thur; noon-3am Fri, Sat; 1-11pm Sun. Room hire £40-£60/hr.
Two no-frills, retro-style rooms overlook the bowling lanes. There's an abundance of tunes to choose from but limited time to belt 'em out, with a maximum two-hour time slot.

Cousin Jill's
42 Albemarle Street, W1S 4JH (7499 9969/ www.cousinjills.com). Green Park tube. Open 5pm-1.30am daily. Admission from £25.
A Mayfair institution, Cousin Jill's boasts three polished private rooms (from £360/ 3hrs) and a 5,000-strong catalogue of songs. For bigger bashes, you can book out the whole club.

The Dolphin
165 Mare Street, E8 3RH (8985 3727). London Fields rail. Open 4pm-2am Mon-Thur; 4pm-4am Fri; noon-4am Sat; noon-2am Sun. Admission £5 after 11pm. No credit cards
With a beguilingly mixed crowd of arty, alternative types and old geezers, this Hackney boozer packs them in for a weekend sing-song – generally on Saturday night.

Hot Breath Karaoke @ The Legion
The Legion, 348 Old Street, EC1V 9NQ (7729 4441/www.hotbreathkaraoke.com). Old Street tube/rail. Open 5pm-midnight Tue. Admission free.
Every Tuesday, the uproarious Hot Breath gives Hoxtonites the chance to belt out some joyously cheesy hits – PJ & Duncan, anyone?

Karaoke Box
18 Frith Street, W1D 4RQ (7494 3878/ www.karaokebox.co.uk). Leicester Square or Tottenham Court Road tube. Open noon-midnight Mon-Sat; noon-11pm Sun. Admission free Mon-Wed, £3 after 6pm Thur-Sat.
Regulars avow Karaoke Box is the best of the bunch, thanks to its value for money, friendliness and – vitally – reliable mics.

K-Box
Cranbourn Mansions, 7-9 Cranbourn Street, WC2H 7AG (7287 8868/www.k-box.co.uk). Leicester Square tube. Open 6pm-late Mon-Sat; 6-11pm Sun. Room hire from £40/2hrs.
Japanese cocktails help loosen the vocal cords at this four-floor temple to karaoke, along with gloriously tacky '80s videos.

Lucky Voice
52 Poland Street, W1F 7NH (7439 3660/ www.luckyvoice.co.uk). Oxford Circus tube. Open 5.30pm-1am Mon-Thur; 3pm-1am Fri, Sat; 3-10.30pm Sun. Room hire £20-£110/hr.
Kitsch pink lighting and sleek, dimly lit private rooms make Lucky Voice the swishest karaoke joint in town. Some of the rooms have stashes of props (think hats, wigs and toy tambourines) to inspire you.

Ribon
6 Holborn Viaduct, EC1A 2AE (7329 3254/ www.ribonrestaurant.co.uk). St Paul's tube. Open 6-10.30pm Mon-Sat. Room hire £20-£50/hr.
The karaoke at this pleasingly authentic (if unpretty) Japanese restaurant kicks off from about 6pm for parties who have booked.

The Social
5 Little Portland Street, W1W 7JD (7836 4992/www.thesocial.com). Oxford Circus tube. Open 6pm-1am Thur. Admission free.
Baggy jeans and bling are optional but highly appropriate at the Social's monthly hip hop-themed karaoke knees-up. Free entry, yo.

Tiroler Hut
27 Westbourne Grove, W2 4UA (7727 3981/ www.tirolerhut.co.uk). Bayswater or Royal Oak tube. Open 6.30pm-1am Tue-Sat; 6.30-11.30pm Sun.
This kitsch-tastic eaterie serves solid Alpine fare and has musicians playing and yodelling every night. It's not karaoke as such, but group sing-a-longs are encouraged.

GOING OUT

BEAUTY

FASHION

PARTIES

FOOD

HEALTH

ECO

OUTDOORS · HOME

CHILDREN

PETS

TRANSPORT

RESOURCES

GOING OUT

BEAUTY

FASHION

PARTIES

FOOD

HEALTH

ECO

OUTDOORS

HOME

CHILDREN

PETS

TRANSPORT

RESOURCES

Pubs & bars

Cocktail bars, quiz nights, late-opening bars and much more.

Beer gardens

CENTRAL

Chapel
48 Chapel Street, NW1 5DP (7402 9220/ www.thechapellondon.com). Edgware Road tube. Open noon-11pm Mon-Sat; noon-10.30pm Sun.
Hedges screen busy Old Marylebone Road from the Chapel's beer garden, where you can wash down (unponcey) gastropub fare with a pint of Adnams or Addlestones' cloudy cider.

Coach & Horses
26-28 Ray Street, EC1R 3DJ (7278 8990/ www.thecoachandhorses.com). Farringdon tube/rail. Open noon-11pm Mon-Fri; 5-11pm Sat; noon-4pm Sun.
This Farringdon gastropub offers top-notch English and French country food, and a sterling list of beers. There's also a small but appealing garden with a handful of tables.

Crutched Friar
39-41 Crutched Friars, EC3N 2AE (7488 3243). Tower Hill tube. Open 10am-11pm Mon-Fri.
The neatly tucked-away garden is perfect for leisurely summer lunches in the City. Staff are friendly, and the wine list affordable.

NORTH

Albert
11 Princess Road, NW1 8JR (7722 1886). Chalk Farm tube. Open 11am-11pm Mon-Sat; noon-10.30pm Sun.
Everyone's welcome in this 11-table garden – kids and dogs included. There's loads of standing room, and a suitably bucolic apple tree growing in the middle of it.

Albion ✈
10 Thornhill Road, N1 1HW (7607 7450). Highbury & Islington tube/rail. Open 11am-11pm Mon-Fri; 10am-11pm Sat; 10am-10.30pm Sun.
The Albion's serene, sizeable garden is a thing of beauty, with its shady veranda, flower beds and wooden tables and chairs.

Compton Arms
4 Compton Avenue, N1 2XD (7359 6883). Highbury & Islington tube/rail. Open noon-11.30pm Mon-Sat; noon-10.30pm Sun.
Diminutive it may be, but the Compton has a lovely little paved courtyard, full of greenery and with space for about 25 drinkers.

Engineer
65 Gloucester Avenue, NW1 8JH (7722 0950). Chalk Farm tube. Open 9am-11pm Mon-Sat; 9am-10.30pm Sun.
The garden at this perennially trendy Primrose Hill pub is small but inviting, with lots of blooms. Kids are welcome.

Flask
77 Highgate West Hill, N6 6BU (8348 7346). Archway or Highgate tube. Open noon-11pm Mon-Sat; noon-10.30pm Sun.
Tables in the front garden fill up alarmingly fast on clement days, so get there early to bag a spot, then camp out for the day. If you're in luck, the barbecue may make an appearance.

Red Lion & Sun
25 North Road, N6 4BE (8340 1780/www. theredlionandsun.com). Highgate tube. Open noon-midnight Mon-Wed; noon-2am Thur-Sat; noon-1am Sun.
Recently refurbished, Highgate's Red Lion & Sun offers two beer gardens, with a courtyard at the back and larger patio area at the front.

EAST

Approach Tavern
47 Approach Road, E2 9LY (8980 2321).
Bethnal Green tube/rail. Open noon-11pm
Mon-Thur, Sun; noon-midnight Fri, Sat.
This classic East End boozer with a
contemporary twist has a large, pleasant patio,
good beer and hearty, unpretentious food.

Prospect of Whitby
57 Wapping Wall, E1W 3SH (7481
1095). Shadwell tube. Open noon-11pm
Mon-Wed; noon-midnight Thur-Sat;
noon-10.30pm Sun.
With views of the river and Canary Wharf,
both the flagstoned riverside garden and
rooftop terrace are generally packed on
summer weekends.

The Royal Inn on the Park
111 Lauriston Road, E9 7HJ (8985 3321).
Mile End tube then 227 bus. Open noon-
11pm Mon-Sat; noon-10.30pm Sun.
With a beer garden backing on to Victoria
Park, an alfresco pint at this Victorian pub is
a delight. There are barbecues in high season,
and heaters for nippy evenings.

SOUTH

The Crooked Billet
14-15 Crooked Billet, SW19 4RQ (8946
4942/www.thecrookedbilletwimbledon.co.uk).
Wimbledon tube/rail. Open 11am-11pm
Mon-Thur; 11am-midnight Fri, Sat; noon-
10.30pm Sun.
On summer afternoons, Pimms-quaffing
customers bask in the Billet's lush garden, or
order a picnic hamper (from £19.95-£37) to
consume on Wimbledon Common.

The Crown & Greyhound
73 Dulwich Village, SE21 7BJ (8299 4976/
www.crownandgreyhound.com). North
Dulwich rail. Open 11am-11pm Mon-Wed,
Sun; 11am-midnight Thur-Sat.
The Dog's two-tier garden and terrace come
into their own on warmer days, when you can
enjoy the barbecue or scoff a substantial
Sunday lunch.

The Duke of Edinburgh
204 Ferndale Road, SW9 8AG (7326 0301).
Brixton tube. Open noon-11.30pm Mon-Fri;
noon-midnight Sat; noon-10.30pm Sun.
Happy kids, leafy trees and plenty of picnic
tables characterise this superior pub garden.

The Dulwich Wood House
39 Sydenham Hill, SE26 6RS (8693 5666).
Sydenham Hill rail. Open noon-11.30pm
Mon-Wed; noon-midnight Thur-Sat;
noon-11pm Sun.
This elegant Young's pub has a charming,
part-decked garden running around its side,
which also hosts the odd jazz session.

Leather Bottle
538 Garratt Lane, SW17 0NY (8946
2309/www.leatherbottlepub.co.uk).
Earlsfield rail. Open 11am-midnight
Mon-Sat; noon-11pm Sun.
This has to be one of London's largest beer
gardens, with a 450-drinker capacity.
Handily, it's partially covered in case of rain.

WEST

The Grand Junction Arms
Canal Bridge, Acton Lane, NW10 7AD
(8965 5670). Harlesden tube. Open noon-
3pm, 6pm-midnight Mon-Fri; noon-
midnight Sat; noon-10.30pm Sun.
The attractive three-part garden here has a
decked balcony overlooking the canal.

The Old Ship
25 Upper Mall, W6 9TD (8748 2593/www.
oldshipw6.co.uk). Hammersmith tube. Open
8am-11pm Mon-Thur; 8am-midnight Fri,
Sat; 9am-10pm Sun.
One of the most coveted spots in the capital
during the Boat Race, the Old Ship's terrace
is a lovely place to drink at any time.

The Swan
1 Evershed Walk, W4 5HH (8994 8262/
www.theswanchiswick.co.uk). Chiswick Park
tube. Open 5-11pm Mon-Fri; noon-11pm
Sat; noon-10.30pm Sun.
Despite its tucked-away location, there's a
real buzz about this accomplished gastropub.

BEAUTY

FASHION

PARTIES

FOOD

HEALTH

ECO

OUTDOORS

HOME

CHILDREN

PETS

TRANSPORT

RESOURCES

GOING OUT

BEAUTY

FASHION

PARTIES

FOOD

HEALTH

ECO

OUTDOORS

HOME

CHILDREN

PETS

TRANSPORT

RESOURCES

Cocktail bars

CENTRAL

For innovative cocktails in deliciously
opulent surrounds, the bar at **Hakkasan**
(*see p95*) is well worth investigating.
So too is the low-lit basement bar at
Crazy Bear (*see p95*), also in Fitzrovia
– just don't quaff too many cocktails
before attempting to negotiate the
famously disorientating mirrored loos.

Christopher's Martini Bar

*18 Wellington Street, WC2E 7DD (7240
4222/www.christophersgrill.com). Covent
Garden tube. Open 11.30am-midnight Mon-
Thur; 11.30am-1am Fri, Sat; 11.30-
10.30pm Sun.*
Sit back in one of the plush booths and enjoy
the exceptional martinis and inventive
contemporary cocktails, such as the Morning
Dew – a delicious blend of Plymouth gin,
elderflower cordial, apple juice, lime and mint.

Milk & Honey

*61 Poland Street, W1F 7NU (7292 9949/
www.mlkhny.com). Oxford Circus tube. Open
Non-members 6-11pm Mon-Fri; 7-11pm Sat.*
Members bar Milk & Honey is open to all
comers at certain times, if you call ahead.
Sours, swizzles, punches and fizzes (from
£7.50) are first-rate.

Polo Bar

*Westbury Hotel, New Bond Street, W1S 2YF
(7629 7755/www.westburymayfair.com).
Bond Street or Oxford Circus tube. Open
11am-midnight Mon-Sat; noon-midnight Sun.*
Polo eschews the bland international style of
many hotel bars in favour of a gorgeous art
deco look that's just the right side of opulent.

NORTH

Gilgamesh

*Stables Market, Chalk Farm Road, NW1
8AH (7482 5757/www.gilgameshbar.com).
Chalk Farm tube. Open noon-3pm, 6pm-
2.30am Mon-Fri; noon-2.30am Sat, Sun.*

Once you've gawped at the Babylonian-style
decor, turn your attention to the lapis lazuli
bar and fruity house cocktails (from £9.50).

25 Canonbury Lane

*25 Canonbury Lane, N1 2AS (7226 0955).
Highbury & Islington tube/rail. Open 5pm-
midnight Mon-Thur; 4pm-1am Fri; noon-
1am Sat; 1pm-12.30am Sun.*
The premises may be small, but the baroque,
chandelier-lit interior has plenty of character.
Cocktails are a mere £6.50 each.

EAST

Loungelover

*1 Whitby Street, E1 6JU (7012 1234/www.
loungelover.co.uk). Liverpool Street tube/rail.
Open 6pm-midnight Mon-Thur, Sun;
5.30pm-1am Fri; 6pm-1am Sat.*
This famously louche lounge offers a unique,
upmarket ambience. Cocktails, listed by
genre in a leopardskin menu, are around £9.

Sosho

*2 Tabernacle Street, EC2A 4LU (7920
0701/www.sosho3am.com). Moorgate or
Old Street tube/rail. Open noon-midnight
Tue; noon-1am Wed, Thur; noon-3am Fri;
7pm-4am Sat; 9pm-4am Sun.*
Sosho delivers expert bartenders and quality
cocktails (£6.50), ranging from green tea
highballs to classic caipirinhas.

SOUTH

Dusk

*339 Battersea Park Road, SW11 4LF (7622
2112/www.duskbar.co.uk). Battersea Park
rail. Open 6pm-12.30am Tue, Wed; 6pm-
1.30am Thur; 6pm-2am Fri, Sat.*
Genial staff make top-notch cocktails (£6.50)
at this appealing bar – which doesn't take
itself too seriously, despite the slick decor.

Hide Bar ★

*39-45 Bermondsey Street, SE1 3XF (7403
6655/www.thehidebar.com). London Bridge
tube/rail. Open 10am-midnight Mon, Tue;
10am-1am Wed, Thur; 10am-2am Fri;
5pm-2am Sat.*

Expect meticulously-mixed cocktails in laid-back surrounds. If you're tired of mohitos and margaritas, choose from one of the bar's books of 1920s cocktails.

Inc Bar
7A College Approach, SE10 9HY (8858 6721/www.incbar.com). Cutty Sark DLR. Open 6pm-1.30am Wed, Thur; 7pm-3am Fri, Sat; 5pm-midnight Sun.
The longest cocktail list in south-east London offers almost three dozen classic and imaginatively mixed drinks (£6-£6.50).

Lost Society
697 Wandsworth Road, SW8 3JF (7652 6526/www.lostsociety.co.uk). Clapham Common tube/Wandsworth Road rail. Open 5pm-11pm Tue, Wed; 5pm-1am Thur; 5pm-2am Fri; noon-2am Sat; noon-11pm Sun. Admission £5 after 9pm Fri, Sat.
Lost has something of a roaring '20s feel, with art deco touches at every turn and glamorous cocktails of yesteryear (juleps, pina coladas).

WEST

On All Saints Road, **Ruby & Sequoia** (*see p32*) also serves up a mean cocktail.

Lonsdale
48 Lonsdale Road, W11 2DE (7727 4080/ www.thelonsdale.co.uk). Ladbroke Grove or Notting Hill Gate tube. Open 6pm-midnight Mon-Thur; 6pm-1am Fri, Sat; 6-11.30pm Sun.
The spirit of Dick Bradsell, undisputed king of the London mixologists, lives on at his former stamping ground, with a splendid, sweeping cocktail menu.

Montgomery Place
31 Kensington Park Road, W11 2EU (7792 3921/www.montgomeryplace.co.uk). Ladbroke Grove tube. Open 5pm-midnight Mon-Fri, Sun; 2pm-midnight Sat.
Any bar that takes its inspiration from the Rat Pack is aiming pretty high, but the cocktails at this slinky bar pass with flying colours.

HAPPY HOURS

Akbar
77 Dean Street, W1D 3SH (7437 2525/www.redfort.co.uk). Oxford Circus tube. Open 5pm-1am Mon-Sat. This smart, understated little bar, tucked away below the Red Fort restaurant, offers great two-for-one cocktails during its 5-6pm happy hour.

Bar Kick
For listings see p33. An extended, if early, happy hour from 4-7pm sees selected bottled beers (Chimay Rouge, Duvel, Super Bock, Leffe and the like) at just £1.90 and cocktails for £4.50.

Moose
31 Duke Street, W1U 1LG (7644 1426). Bond Street tube. Open 4pm-2am Mon-Thur; 4pm-3am Fri, Sat.

An impressively extended happy hour (5-9pm) offers cocktails at just £3.75.

Nordic
25 Newman Street, W1T 1PN (7631 3174/www.nordicbar.com). Tottenham Court Road tube. Open noon-11pm Mon-Wed; noon-11.30pm Thur; noon-midnight Fri; 6pm-midnight Sat. There's a different happy hour offer every day at Nordic: on Monday and Tuesday, it's £10 for any bottle of wine.

Salmon & Compass
58 Penton Street, N1 9PZ (7837 3891/www.salmonandcompass.com). Angel tube. Open 4pm-2am Mon-Wed, noon-3am Thur-Sun. Selected on-tap lagers, bottled beers and wines are reduced during the weekday 3-8pm happy hour.

GOING OUT

BEAUTY

FASHION

PARTIES

FOOD

HEALTH

ECO

OUTDOORS

HOME

CHILDREN

PETS

TRANSPORT

RESOURCES

GOING OUT

BEAUTY

FASHION

PARTIES

FOOD

HEALTH

ECO

OUTDOORS

HOME

CHILDREN

PETS

TRANSPORT

RESOURCES

Fixed corkage wine bars

Avoid the hefty mark-ups levied by most bars by drinking at places that offer fixed corkage. The following wine retailers allow you to buy your vintage of choice at retail price, then add a set corkage fee so you can consume it on the premises.

Bedales
5 Bedale Street, SE1 9AL (7403 8853/ www.bedalestreet.com). London Bridge tube. Open noon-8.45pm Tue; noon-10.15pm Wed; 11.30am-10.15pm Thur; 10am-10.15pm Fri; 8.30am-6pm Sat. Corkage £8.
Browse a terrific array of wines in the ground floor shop (friendly staff are happy to advise), then head down to the cosy cellar bar.

Green & Blue ★
36-38 Lordship Lane SE22 8HJ (8693 9250/www.greenandbluewines.com). East Dulwich rail. Open 9am-11pm Mon-Thur; 9am-midnight Fri, Sat; 9am-10pm Sun. Corkage varies.
This shabby-chic wine shop and bar stocks around 150 wines. There's a small but enticing bar food menu, or for a £3 'chippage' charge you can bring your own grub.

Negozio Classica
283 Westbourne Grove, W11 2QA (7034 0005/www.negozioclassica.co.uk). Ladbroke Grove or Notting Hill Gate tube. Open 3pm-midnight Mon-Thur; noon-midnight Fri, Sun; 8.30am-midnight Sat. Corkage £6.50.
A small selection of wines is available by the glass at this Italian eaterie and wine shop, but you can also scour the shelves and choose your own bottle to take home or drink in.

Planet of the Grapes
9/10 Bulls Head Passage, Leadenhall Market, EC3V 1LU (7929 7224/www.planetofthe grapes.co.uk). Bank tube. Open 10am-10pm Mon; 10am-11pm Tue-Fri. Corkage £10.
Over 450 wines are available at this unfussy wine merchant's, where you can pre-book older bottles for decanting before you arrive.

1707 Wine Bar
181 Piccadilly, W1A 1ER (7734 8040/www. fortnumandmason.com). Piccadilly Circus tube. Open noon-11pm Mon-Sat; noon-5.30pm Sun. Corkage £10/£5 half bottle.
Buying and supping wines from Fortnum's cellar is a very civilized affair. The bar itself is deliciously chic, while snacks are based on fresh, seasonal produce from the food hall.

Wine Library
43 Trinity Square, EC3N 4DJ (7481 0415/ www.winelibrary.co.uk). Tower Hill tube. Open 11am-6pm Mon; 11am-8pm Tue-Fri. Corkage £4.50.
In its atmospheric vaulted cellars, the Wine Library offers a great range of retail wines, plus an impressive buffet lunch.

Late-night drinking

After 11pm, finding another drink can be surprisingly tricky. Here's our pick of places to try once last orders have been called; for late-night eateries, *see p91*.

CENTRAL

Another Soho late-nighter is **Akbar**, while up in Marylebone there's also **Moose Bar** (for both, *see p29*).

Ain't Nothin But… The Blues Bar
20 Kingly Street, W1B 5PZ (7287 0514/ www.aintnothinbut.co.uk). Oxford Circus tube. Open 6pm-1am Mon-Wed; 6pm-2am Thur; 5pm-2.30am Fri; 3pm-2.30am Sat; 3pm-midnight Sun. Admission £5-£7 after 9.30pm Thur & after 8.30pm Fri, Sat.
Resolutely scuffed-up and little changed in years, Ain't Nothin But… is a classic, with live blues and much toe-tapping every night.

Green Carnation
5 Greek Street, W1D 4DD (7434 3323/www. greencarnationsoho.co.uk). Tottenham Court Road tube. Open 4pm-2.30am Mon-Sat; 4pm-midnight Sun. Admission £5 after 10pm Fri, Sat.
Head up to the opulent first floor of this Soho gay bar, where green and gold lacquered walls provide a sumptuous backdrop to witty banter, arty soirées and shameless flirting.

Long Bar
Sanderson, 50 Berners Street, W1T 3NG (7300 1400/www.sandersonlondon.com). Oxford Circus or Tottenham Court Road tube. Open 11.30am-2am Mon-Wed; 11.30am-3am Thur-Sat; noon-10.30pm Sun.
Cocktails in the candlelit courtyard are a sophisticated end to an evening – and at £12 a martini, less ruinous than you might fear.

Nueva Costa Dorada
47-55 Hanway Street, W1T 1UX (7631 5117). Tottenham Court Road tube. Open 5pm-3am Tue-Sat.
This once down-at-heel basement bar has now been spruced up – though the kitsch live flamenco shows remain. Quaff rioja in the booth-lined bar or refuel with some tapas.

NORTH

Al's Café Bar
11-13 Exmouth Market, EC1R 4QD (7837 4821). Angel tube or Farringdon tube/rail. Open 8am-11pm Mon; 9am-2am Tue-Sat; 9am-10.30pm Sun.
Part all-day café, part late-night drinking mecca, Al's is an endearingly scruffy affair with a spot-on selection of beers.

Bartok
78-79 Chalk Farm Road, NW1 8AR (7916 0595/www.bartokbar.com). Chalk Farm tube. Open 3pm-3am daily. Admission £5 after 10pm Fri, Sat.

GOING OUT

BEAUTY

FASHION

PARTIES

FOOD

HEALTH

ECO

OUTDOORS

HOME

CHILDREN

PETS

TRANSPORT

RESOURCES

BEAUTY

FASHION

PARTIES

FOOD

HEALTH

ECO

OUTDOORS

HOME

CHILDREN

PETS

TRANSPORT

RESOURCES

With its red decor, arty light installations and sleek leather sofas, Bartok offers welcome respite from the chaos of Camden.

Dalston Jazz Bar ⭐

4 Bradbury Street, N16 8JN (7254 9728). Dalston Kingsland rail. Open 5pm-3am Mon-Thur; 5pm-5am Fri, Sat; 5pm-2am Sun. No credit cards.
A comfortable jumble of old sofas and books, bargain cocktails and eclectic tunes make this place a classic late-night haunt.

EAST

See also Shoreditch's **Sosho** (*p28*).

Charlie Wright's International Bar

45 Pitfield Street, N1 6DA (7490 8345). Old Street tube/rail. Open noon-1am Mon-Wed; noon-4am Thur, Fri; 5pm-4am Sat; 5pm-2am Sun. Admission £4 after 10pm Fri, Sat; £3 Sun.
This no-nonsense bar is an Old Street legend. It's all about pre-dawn debauchery and spirit-swigging – so don't expect polished surrounds (or glasses) and fancy cocktails.

Indo

133 Whitechapel Road, E1 1DT (7247 4926). Aldgate East or Whitechapel tube. Open noon-1am Mon-Thur, Sun; noon-3am Fri, Sat.
Indo's narrow, dimly-lit premises contain a joyous mishmash of art, clutter and in-the-know locals: try to bag one of the front sofas.

Mother Bar

333 Old Street, EC1V 9LE (7739 5949/www.333mother.com). Old Street tube/rail. Open 8pm-3am daily.
Plenty of rival post-pub drinking dens have sprung up round these parts, but all roads still lead, eventually, to Mother's shabby flight of stairs and red and gold rooms.

SOUTH

We're also partial to London Bridge's **Hide Bar** (*see p28*), with its seemingly endless list of wines, spirits and cocktails.

Dogstar

389 Coldharbour Lane, SW9 8LQ (7733 7515/www.antic-ltd.com). Brixton tube/rail. Open 4pm-2am Mon-Thur; 4pm-4am Fri; noon-4am Sat; noon-2am Sun. Admission £5 after 10pm Fri, Sat.
The long-running Dogstar is still going strong, with a music-savvy crowd swigging lager and dancing to hip hop and funk.

Hive

11-13 Brixton Station Road, SW9 8PA (7274 8383/www.hivebar.net). Brixton tube/rail. Open 5pm-midnight Mon-Wed; 5pm-2am Thur; 5pm-3am Fri; 11am-3am Sat; 11am-midnight Sun.
Hive's cocktail list (£6-£7) pays tribute to mixologists past and present, ranging from forgotten favourites to modern classics.

WEST

Harlem

78 Westbourne Grove, W2 5RT (7985 0900/www.harlemsoulfood.com). Bayswater or Notting Hill Gate tube. Open 5pm-2.30am Mon; noon-2.30am Tue-Fri; 10am-2.30am Sat; 10am-midnight Sun.
DJs spin electro, funk and soul in the compact basement bar; if you're peckish, all-American soul food is served until late in the diner.

Lodge Tavern

53 The Mall, W5 3TA (8567 0173/www.thelodgetavern.co.uk). Ealing Broadway tube/rail. Open noon-1am Mon-Fri; noon-2am Sat; noon-midnight Sun.
There are decent DJs at weekends and a quirky vibe, though the selection of beers is uninspired – best opt for a well-mixed cocktail.

Ruby & Sequoia

6-8 All Saints Road, W11 1HH (7243 6363/www.ruby.uk.com). Ladbroke Grove or Westbourne Park tube. Open 6pm-12.30am Mon-Thur; 6pm-2am Fri; 11am-2am Sat; 11am-12.30am Sun.
It's not the latest-opening joint in town, but this modish bar is a gem for a post-pub cosmopolitan or two. Lay claim to one of the olive leather booths, and admire the edgy art.

Pubs with games

Balham Bowls Club
7-9 Ramsden Road, SW12 8QX (8673 4700/ www.antic-ltd.com). Balham tube/rail. Open 4-11pm Mon-Thur; 4pm-midnight Fri; noon-midnight Sat; noon-11pm Sun.
Sadly the bowls club has long since disbanded and quirky memorabilia is all that remains; sporting types can, however, play snooker on two full-size tables. There's also a chess set for the more cerebrally-inclined.

Balls Brothers Hay's Galleria
Tooley Street, SE1 2HD (7407 4301/ www.ballsbrothers.co.uk). London Bridge tube/rail. Open 8am-11pm Mon-Fri.
This wine bar takes its pétanque very seriously indeed, hosting the City Pétanque Challenge. The competition aside, its outdoor pitch can be booked throughout the summer.

Bar Kick
127 Shoreditch High Street, E1 6JE (7739 8700/www.cafekick.co.uk). Liverpool Street or Old Street tube/rail. Open noon-11pm Mon-Wed, Sun; noon-midnight Thur-Sat.
A boisterous crowd gathers in this flag-bedecked bar for fast and furious table football. If you're a dab hand, tournaments are held on the last Thursday of the month.

Bricklayer's Arms
32 Waterman Street, SW15 1DD (8789 3932/www.bricklayers-arms.co.uk). Putney Bridge tube/Putney rail. Open noon-11pm Mon-Sat; noon-10.30pm Sun.
The oldest boozer in Putney offers suitably traditional diversions: bar skittles, shove ha'penny and the occasional pub quiz.

Freemasons Arms
32 Downshire Hill, Hampstead Heath, NW3 1NT (7433 6811/www.freemasonsarms. co.uk). Hampstead Heath tube. Open 11am-11pm daily.
This prize-winning gastropub features a London skittle alley in its cellar – played with a wooden 'cheese' and 21 skittles. The alley can be hired, see www.londonskittles.co.uk.

Mango Landin'
40 St Matthew's Road, SW2 1NL (7737 3044). Brixton tube/rail then 2, 3, 133, 159 bus. Open 5pm-midnight Mon-Thur; noon-3am Fri, Sat; noon-11.30pm Sun.
This tropical-inspired, late-licence cocktail bar is dotted with mates acting out grudge matches on the proliferation of chessboards.

Oakdale Arms
283 Hermitage Road, N4 1NP (8800 2013/ www.individualpubs.co.uk/oakdale). Manor House tube/Seven Sisters tube/rail. Open noon-11pm Mon-Sat; noon-10.30pm Sun.
Those of a competitive bent will be in heaven, with air hockey, board games, chess, darts, pool, table football and a Wii console; a splendid array of small brewery ales provides consolation in defeat.

Pembury Tavern
90 Amhurst Road, E8 1JH (8986 8597/ www.individualpubs.co.uk/pembury). Hackney Central or Hackney Downs rail. Open noon-11pm daily.
The decor may be on the spartan side, but there's a fine array of games (bar billiards, pool, chess, Scrabble and backgammon among them), plus quality real ales from Cambridge's Milton Brewery.

Prince of Wales
48 Cleaver Square, SE11 4EA (7735 9916/www.shepherdneame.co.uk). Kennington tube. Open noon-11pm Mon-Sat; noon-10.30pm Sun.
Head for this great pub in pretty Cleaver Square to enjoy a summer evening game of boules. Rent out a set, head for the gravelled square and you could almost be in Paris.

Warwick Arms
160 Warwick Road, W14 8PS (7603 3560/ www.warwickarmskensington.co.uk). Earl's Court or High Street Kensington tube. Open noon-midnight Mon-Sat; noon-11.30pm Sun.
A grim location hides a little gem of a pub, where Wednesday evenings bring 'Beat The Dice' nights: throw two sixes for an evening of free booze.

BEAUTY

FASHION

PARTIES

FOOD

HEALTH

ECO

OUTDOORS

HOME

CHILDREN

PETS

TRANSPORT

RESOURCES

BEAUTY

FASHION

PARTIES

FOOD

HEALTH

ECO

OUTDOORS

HOME

CHILDREN

PETS

TRANSPORT

RESOURCES

Quiz nights

Big Chill House
257-259 Pentonville Road, N1 9NL (7427 2540/www.bigchill.net). Kings Cross tube/rail. Open noon-midnight Mon-Wed, Sun; noon-1am Thur; noon-3am Fri, Sat. Quiz 7.30pm Mon. Entry £7.50.
With three floors and a lofty terrace, the Big Chill House makes it easy to do exactly what it says on the tin. The monthly Monday night quiz is a sophisticated affair (as it should be for the rather steep entry charge) called 'Sounds Familiar'. No prizes for guessing it's a music quiz.

The Bull
100 Upper Street, N1 0NP (7354 9174). Angel tube. Open noon-11pm Mon, Tue; noon-midnight Wed; noon-1am Thur-Sat; noon-10.30pm Sun. Quiz 8pm Mon. Entry £1 per person.
Always busy and buzzy, the Bull serves good quality comfort food and an impressive selection of continental beers. The new Monday night quiz here is cinematically themed, with a winning combination of high-brow and cheesy '80s film questions. Movie eggheads win cinema tickets, natch.

Crystal Palace Tavern (CPT)
193 Crystal Palace Road, SE22 9EP (8693 4968/www.cptquiz.co.uk). East Dulwich rail. Open 3-11pm Mon-Thur; noon-11.30pm Fri-Sun. Quiz 8pm Wed. Entry free.
This well-run general knowledge quiz comes highly recommended by East Dulwich locals and takes place each Wednesday. You'll be hard-pushed to beat some of the more senior regulars, mind.

The Five Bells
165-185 East End Road, N2 0LZ (8883 1714). East Finchley tube. Open 11am-11pm Mon-Thur, Sun; 11am-midnight Fri, Sat. Quiz 9pm Thur. Entry £1 per person.
They take their quizzes pretty seriously up in East Finchley. A regular attendee advises answering 'The Undertones' to any tricky music question, as the quizmaster is a big fan; same goes for 1980s cult classic *Back to the Future* when the subject is film trivia.

Mobile pub quizmaster
www.myspace.com/worldfamouspubquiz.
DJ Elliot Eastwick has been hosting his haphazard and hilarious music quiz in various pubs in north and east London since 1999. Punters come not for the prizes (ironic market tat) but the laughs and the tunes. Catchphrase? 'It will make you quizzically sick.' Check the myspace page for details of upcoming events.

The Pineapple
51 Leverton Street, NW5 2NX (7284 4631). Kentish Town tube/rail. Open noon-11pm Mon-Sat; noon-10.30pm Sun. Quiz 8.30pm Mon. Entry £1 per person.
Hidden away in a picturesque tangle of backstreets, this refurbished Kentish Town gastropub attracts a diehard band of regulars – so it's no surprise that Monday's quiz night often gets rammed. Arrive early to bag a prime table in the front bar, and sample a few real ales while you wait.

The Prince George
40 Parkholme Road, E8 3AG (7254 6060) Dalston Kingsland rail/30, 38, 56, 242, 277 bus. Open 5-11pm; 2-11pm Sat, Sun. Quiz 8.30pm Mon. Entry £1 per person.
There may not be food – this traditional boozer prides itself on that – but there is a superior jukebox, a decent selection of ales on tap (London Pride, Flowers Original, Litovel) and a friendly, locals-dominated Monday evening quiz.

Retro Bar
2 George Court, WC2N 6HH (7839 8760). Charing Cross tube/rail. Open noon-11pm Mon-Fri; 5-11pm Sat; 5-10.30pm Sun. Quiz 9pm Tue. Entry £1 per team.
With its decor and jukebox seemingly frozen in the '80s (a black-and-white photograph of Boy George hangs in pride of place), Retro Bar is one of London's most eccentric gay bars. The poptastic Tuesday night quiz is tremendous fun, sometimes inspiring impromptu singalongs to the Carpenters.

Beauty

GOING OUT

BEAUTY

FASHION

PARTIES

FOOD

HEALTH

ECO

OUTDOORS

HOME

CHILDREN

PETS

TRANSPORT

RESOURCES

Beauty

Whether you're in serious need of a massage or looking for make-up lessons that won't break the bank, here's who to call.

Bespoke beauty

Colorlab

Selfridges, 400 Oxford Street, W1A 1AB (7318 3538/www.colorlabcosmetics.com). Bond Street or Marble Arch tube. Open 9.30am-8pm Mon-Wed, Fri, Sat; 9.30am-9pm Thur; noon-6pm Sun.
Colorlab custom-blends all kinds of make-up while you wait, with prices from £18 for an eyeshadow. Colour matching discontinued make-up lines takes longer (up to a week), but prices are a steal: £40 for two lipsticks.

Cosmetics à la Carte

19B Motcomb Street, SW1X 8LB (7235 0596). Knightsbridge tube. Open 10am-6pm Mon-Sat.
'Made-to-measure' foundations are £45, while half-hour Lipstick Lovers' Lessons (£50) allow you to create your perfect colour. Staff can also precisely recreate favourite lippies, if you send a stub – though the first order costs £175.

Prescriptives

Harrods, 87-135 Brompton Road, SW1X 7XL (7730 1234/www.prescriptives.com). Knightsbridge tube. Open 10am-8pm Mon-Sat; noon-6pm Sun.
Prescriptives will custom-blend anything from concealers (£23) to foundations (£45), adding extra coverage, moisturiser, oil control, or light-reflecting particles as desired.

Boutiques

BECCA

91A Pelham Street, SW7 2NJ (7225 2501/ www.beccacosmetics.com). South Kensington tube. Open 10am-6pm Mon-Sat.

Products from make-up artist favourite Becca are great for dewy, radiant skin. Barely-there foundations cost from £30, while concealers come in a remarkable 34 shades.

HQ hair & beautystore

2 New Burlington Street, W1S 2JE (0871 220 4141/www.hqhair.com). Oxford Circus tube. Open 10am-6pm Mon, Sat; 10am-7pm Tue, Fri; 10am-8pm Wed, Thur.
A beauty junkie's dream, HQ is crammed with stellar products, from Bare Escentuals' mineral-based foundations to Terax's hair range – a firm favourite with the A-list.

Korres

124 King's Road, SW3 4TR (7581 6455/ www.korres.com). Sloane Square tube. Open 10am-7pm Mon-Sat; noon-6pm Sun.
Based on natural ingredients (so no mineral oils, silicones or propylene glycol), Korres' hair and skincare products smell good enough to eat. We love the fig body butter (£11.50).

Liz Earle Naturally Active Skincare

53 Duke of York Square, King's Road, SW3 4LY (7730 9191/www.lizearle.com). Sloane Square tube. Open 10am-7pm Mon-Sat; 11am-5pm Sun.
Packed with botanical ingredients, this streamlined range encourages a no-fuss regime of cleansing, toning and moisturising. Despite the quality, it's relatively inexpensive.

Lost in Beauty

117 Regents Park Road, NW1 8UR (7586 4411/www.lostinbeauty.com). Open 10.30am-7pm Mon-Fri; 10.30am-6.30pm Sat; noon-5.30pm Sun.
Kitted out with vintage shop fittings, this chic boutique stocks a well-edited array of beauty brands, including Phyto, Rodial and REN.

GOING OUT

BEAUTY

FASHION

PARTIES

FOOD

HEALTH

ECO

OUTDOORS

HOME

CHILDREN

PETS

TRANSPORT

RESOURCES

MAKE-UP LESSONS

BECCA
For listings, see left.
A pre-booked lesson costs £90, £45 of which is redeemable against purchases. Over a glass of champagne, you'll be shown how to create flawless skin and a polished day-to-evening look.

Cosmetics à la Carte
For listings, see left.
A huge range of lessons are on offer at the Knightsbridge store, from ten-minute make-up recharge sessions (£14) or half-hour make-up MOTs (£40) to longer, more in-depth lessons.

Lost in Beauty
For listings, see left.
Make-up artist Georgie Hamed (a regular on glossy fashion shoots) offers lessons and parties in an airy private room. Prices start from £60 for a mini-makeover.

MAC
109 King's Road, SW3 4PA (7349 0022/www.mac cosmetics.com). Sloane Square tube. Open 10am-6.30pm Mon-Sat; noon-5.30pm Sun.
Expert staff offer hour-long lessons on glamorous going out looks (£25), or more hands-on 90-minute tutorials (£50) – both fully redeemable against any purchases. A professional lash application is a steal at £7.50, false lashes included.

Pixi
For listings, see below.
Pop in for a quick 'little black dress' day-to-evening makeover (£20), or bring your make-up bag for the 90-minute masterclass (£60): staff will advise on what to clear out, as well as going through colours and techniques. After-hours parties are a bargain: for £15 a head, you get the shop to yourselves, a glass of bubbly and the services of two make-up artists.

Shu Uemura
24 Neal Street, WC2H 9QU (7240 7635). Covent Garden tube. Open 10.30am-7pm Mon-Sat; noon-5pm Sun.
Shu Uemera offers all kinds of lessons, from one-to-one 90-minute classes (£40) to two-hour masterclasses; alternatively, staff will do your eye make-up for £10.

Pixi
22A Foubert's Place, W1F 7PW (7287 7211/www.pixibeauty.com). Oxford Circus tube. Open 11am-7pm Mon-Sat; noon-5pm Sun.
Pixi's goodies range from candy-hued glosses and blushers to light, sheer foundations and credit-card slim eyecolour kits (£26), packed with subtle, deliciously easy to wear shades.

Space NK
8-10 Broadwick Street, W1F 8HW (7734 3734/www.spacenk.com). Oxford Circus or Tottenham Court Road tube. Open 10am-7pm Mon-Wed, Fri, Sat; 10am-8pm Thur.

Attentive assistants are a blessing for those needing advice, while the constantly updated product range keeps beauty mavens hooked. **Other locations** *across the city.*

This Works
18 Cale Street, SW3 3QU (7584 1887/www.thisworks.com). South Kensington tube. Open 10am-5pm Mon-Sat.
This lovely aromatherapy-based body and skincare range uses unusually high levels of cold-pressed plant oils, and is free from parabens, sulphates and synthetic fragrances. Try the Deep Calm Bath and Shower Oil (£32).

TONI&GUY ACADEMY
HAIRDRESSING MODELS
REQUIRED
FOR BEAUTIFUL CLASSIC CUTS TO COOL FASHIONABLE LOOKS

New Oxford Street Academy
MONDAY-FRIDAY
APPOINTMENTS
CUT & BLOW-DRY
A great cut available at 9.30am & 1.45pm.

Terms & Conditions:
Offer applies when you produce this flyer, otherwise a £5 booking fee is charged.

COLOUR
Highlights, colour correction, full head colour/bleach, perming & relaxing available at 9.15am & 1.45pm.

Terms & Conditions: Please note:
Highlights are charged at £20
Colour Correction at £20
Tint at £15 & Perming at £15

**For bookings & further information contact:
71-75 New Oxford Street,
London WC1A 1DG
T: 020 7836 0606
F: 020 7240 5301
www.toniandguy.com**

18 YEARS AND OVER!

Services

EYEBROW THREADING

For the uninitiated, threading is an Indian hair removal technique whereby the therapist twists a length of thread around stray hairs, whipping brows into shape at lightning-quick speed. In addition to the companies listed below, waxing queen **Arezzoo Kaviani** (*see p43*) also offers threading for £35, while the highly experienced **Rekha Joshi** offers Saturday appointments at Lost in Beauty (*see p36*) for £17.

Apsara Herbal
249 Whitechapel Road, E1 1DB (7377 2004/ www.apsaraherbal.co.uk). Whitechapel tube. Open 9.30am-7.30pm Mon-Sat; 11am-6pm Sun. No credit cards.
Threading costs just £5 to £6 and takes five to ten minutes at this no-nonsense East End beauty salon; they can generally fit you in without an appointment.

Blink Eyebrow Bar
Fenwick, 63 New Bond Street, W1A 3BS (7408 0689/www.blinkbrowbar.com). Bond Street tube. Open 10am-6.30pm Mon-Wed, Fri, Sat; 10am-8pm Thur.
Blink's innovative threading bars offer a speedy walk-in service, though appointments can be booked in advance. Eyebrows take 15 minutes and cost £17; the majority of therapists here were trained in India.
Other locations Selfridges, 400 Oxford Street, W1A 1AB (7318 2462); Harvey Nichols, 109-125 Knightsbridge, SW1X 7RJ (7235 5000).

Kamini Salon ★
14-16 Lancer Square, off Kensington Church Street, W8 4EP (7937 2411/www. kaminibeauty.com). High Street Kensington tube. Open 10am-7.30pm Tue-Fri; 10am-6pm Sat.
With over 25 years' experience, eyebrow obsessive and celebrity favourite Kamini Vaghela delivers a fast, relatively painless service and long-lasting results. She has an infallible eye for what arch will best suit your face shape, and charges £45 per session.

Malika
Toni & Guy, Canada Place, E14 5AH (7531 2375/www.malika.co.uk). Canary Wharf tube. Open 11am-7pm Mon; 10am-7pm Tue, Wed; 9am-8pm Thur; 9am-7pm Fri; 10am-5pm Sat; noon-6pm Sun.
Eyebrow shaping costs £15; we've had great results with Ritu, the company's founder. Other services include inexpensive Indian head massage, eyelash tinting and manicures.
Other locations Toni & Guy, 49 Sloane Square, SW1W 8AX (7730 8113).

Vaishaly
51 Paddington Street, W1U 4HR (7224 6088/www.vaishaly.com). Baker Street tube. Open 9am-6pm Mon-Sat.
Threading with facials guru Vaishaly Patel costs £70 for an initial consultation, then £45 thereafter. Aficionados swear by her perfect results; if she's out of your price range, ask for one of her three assistants (£30).

MANICURES

There's nothing like a quick manicure to leave you looking perfectly groomed: if you can't make time to go to a nail bar, call **Sophy Robson** or another at-home beauty therapist (*see p40*).

Marian Newman (*see p44*) and her team are also highly recommended, charging from £13 for a file and polish.

Finally, **Float** (*see p46*) offer manicures using Butter London's non-toxic nail lacquers, which are free from toluene and other chemical nasties.

Amazing Nails
Mane Line Hair Salon, 22 Weighhouse Street, W1K 5LZ (07775 780744). Bond Street tube. Open Mon-Sat 10am-6pm by - appointment only.
Handily central, Amazing Nails offers good, solid manicures and pedicures that won't break the bank. A half-hour manicure here costs £28, while a 45-minute pedi is £28.50.

GOING OUT
BEAUTY
FASHION
PARTIES
FOOD
HEALTH
ECO
OUTDOORS
HOME
CHILDREN
PETS
TRANSPORT
RESOURCES

GOING OUT

BEAUTY

FASHION

PARTIES

FOOD

HEALTH

ECO

OUTDOORS

HOME

CHILDREN

PETS

TRANSPORT

RESOURCES

California Nail Bar
*78 Heath Street, NW3 1DN (7431 8988/
www.california-nail-bar.co.uk). Hampstead
tube. Open 10am-7pm Mon-Sat; 11am-
6pm Sun.*
This reliable nail bar charges £15 for a simple
manicure with polish; if you're faking it, a full
set of gel nails costs £35.
Other location *219D Finchley Road,
NW3 6LP (7625 1188).*

Hawkeye
*5 Silver Place, off Beak Street, W1F 0JR
(7287 1847/www.hawkeyehair.com). Oxford
Circus tube. Open 10am-8pm Tue-Sat.*
Taking a different approach to express nail
bars, the therapists here make sure you relax
with a complimentary glass of wine. The
hour-long 'Pure Indulgence Experience' (£34)
includes a manicure and full arm massage,
though you can just pop in for a speedy shape
and paint (£13).

Iris Chapple ✈
*3 Spanish Place, W1U 3HX (07956
307392). Baker Street or Bond Street tube.
Open by appointment 8am-5pm Tue-Sat.
No credit cards.*
Ever-popular with glossy beauty editors,
Chapple is warm and friendly whoever you
are. Forget express treatments: this expert
takes a good hour to file and polish nails to
her trademark 'square with a bevelled edge'
perfection. It costs £35 – but you'd pay as
much for less in many a nail bar. Pedicures
are equally miraculous.

AT-HOME TREATMENTS

After a relaxing massage or facial,
the last thing you want to do is trek
home. The answer is a mobile beauty
therapist, who'll come to your home
and leave you perfectly pampered.

InParlour
*7736 7713/www.inparlour.co.uk.
Open appointments line 9am-7pm
Mon-Fri.*
On-call experts range from beauticians
and yoga teachers to stylists and
wardrobe experts, with a minimum fee
of £60 per visit. The popular Heavenly
Bodies fake tan (£65) is artfully applied
with pashmina brushes, with darker
areas on your shoulders and
décolletage to mimic the real thing.

Perfectly at Home
*7610 8000/www.perfectlyathome.
com. Open appointments line 10am-
6.30pm Mon-Fri; 10am-5pm Sat.*
This celebrity-set favourite offers
everything from haircuts to reflexology,
with a particularly broad range of fake
tans and facials. Its 50 hand-picked
therapists are available from 10am to
10pm seven days a week; most hour-
long treatments cost £75.

Return to Glory
*7993 8063/www.returntoglory.
co.uk. Open appointments line
9.30am-5.30pm Mon-Sat.*
Whatever the service (from Swedish
massage to manicures), you'll pay a
flat rate of £55 an hour, £70 for 90
minutes or £90 for two hours. On the
website, click on profiles of experts in
your area to check their qualifications,
customer feedback and availability.

Sophy Robson
*07956 599050. Open appointments
line 9am-7pm Mon-Sat. No credit cards.*
Manicurist Sophy Robson's speciality
is the 'medi-pedi' – a chiropody-style
overhaul of your feet that banishes
hard skin and includes a massage,
exfoliation and polish. Prices depend
on where you live, but expect to pay
around £50-£60 for a pedicure, £30-
£40 for a manicure, or £80 for both.

Leighton Denny
Urban Retreat, 5th Floor, Harrods, 87-135 Brompton Road, SW1X 7XL (7893 8333/ www.harrods.com). Knightsbridge tube. Open 10am-8pm Mon-Sat; noon-6pm Sun.
An expert when it comes to the perfectly shaped nail, the ebullient Leighton Denny and his crack team of manicurists can be found at Harrods' Urban Retreat. Using his long-lasting polishes a mani costs £35, a pedi £45.

MASSAGE

City Beach
10 Lamb Street, E1 6EA (7247 7878). Liverpool Street tube/rail. Open 10am-7pm Mon-Wed; 10am-8pm Thur; 10am-6pm Fri-Sun. No credit cards.

Tranquillity
07850 426387/www.tranquil-beauty.co.uk. Open appointments line 9am-7pm Mon-Sat.
Operating in north and east London, mobile beauty therapist Tracy offers everything from basic beauty maintenance (manicures, waxing) to luxurious massages, body wraps and Elemis facials. You could have an hour-long Swedish massage for £37, for example, or a bikini wax for £10.

Unlisted London
0845 225 5505/www.unlisted london.com. Open appointments line 9am-9pm Mon-Sat; 10am-6pm Sun.
Aimed at stressed-out high-flyers, Unlisted offers a huge menu of treatments and a team of therapists that work 'pretty much 24/7' and cover the whole of London. Facials, at £75 per hour, include REN, Rodial and Karin Herzog; the minimum call-out charge is £75.

The massages at this Spitalfields salon come recommended and are great value: a full body massage (for women only) costs £30, while a half-hour back, neck and shoulder rub is £20.

Human Nature
13 Malvern Road, NW6 5PS (7328 5452/ www.thismassageworks.co.uk). Kilburn Park or Maida Vale tube. Open 9am-6.30pm Mon-Sat.
In a modest basement beneath a health food shop, expert therapist Nari is waiting to pummel you into submission. His massages are intense – not for the faint-hearted, but deeply effective. Starting with a skin brush, the full body massage is £80 for an hour. Nari can also visit your home (from £130).

Lavender Hill Siam Beauty
119 Lavender Hill, SW11 5QL (7585 1222/ www.siambeauty.co.uk). Clapham Junction rail. Open 9.30am-11pm daily. Massage 11am-11pm daily.
We salute this no-frills gem for its long opening hours and amazing value for money. Thai or Swedish massage costs a mere £30 for an hour, while other treatments are equally cheap: a brow shape is yours for a paltry fiver, while hour-long Decleor or Dermalogica facials cost from £25.
Other location *12 Lavender Hill, SW11 5RW (7924 1695).*

Michelle Roques-O'Neill
Sarah Chapman Skinesis Clinic, 106 Draycott Avenue, SW3 3AE (massages 07890 265802/salon 7589 9585/www. sarahchapman.net). South Kensington tube. Open Fri, Sat times vary. No credit cards.
Michelle Roques-O'Neill is famed for her aromatherapy massages which, in her own words, lead to a level of 'emotional healing'. Now operating out of the Sarah Chapman Skinesis Clinic in Chelsea, she's still working her magic, from £150 for 90mins.

Pure Massage
3-5 Vanston Place, SW6 1AY (7381 8100/ www.puremassage.com). Fulham Broadway tube. Open 11am-9pm Mon-Fri; 10am-9pm Sat; 11am-6pm Sun.

GOING OUT

BEAUTY

FASHION

PARTIES

FOOD

HEALTH

ECO

OUTDOORS

HOME

CHILDREN

PETS

TRANSPORT

RESOURCES

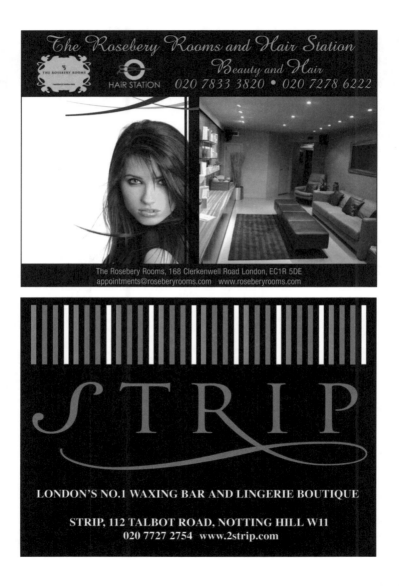

Pure offers a wide range of massages in tranquil surroundings. Drop in for a 15-minute, fully clothed 'chair' massage (£15), or indulge in 90 dreamy minutes with the Body Pure Massage (£97), combining deep tissue, Thai, Swedish and acupressure techniques. **Other locations** *Fenwick, 63 New Bond Street, W1A 3BS (0800 083 2520); 226 Upper Richmond Road, SW15 6TG (0800 083 2520).*

Shine Holistic

52 Stoke Newington Church Street, N16 0NB (7241 5033/www.shineholistic.co.uk). 73, 476 bus. Open 10am-9.15pm Mon-Fri; 10am-6pm Sat; 11am-5pm Sun.
Practitioners at this friendly holistic health centre offer all manner of massage specialisms, from Thai to deep tissue, in the spacious, stylishly understated treatment rooms. Aromatherapy massages with Florentina (£50/hr) are blissful, easing out every tension with a bespoke blend of oils that's tailored to each client's needs.

WAXING

Hair removal expert **Kamini** (*see p39*) also offers waxing. Using aromatherapy wax, she promises silky-smooth results and no ingrown hairs.

For a waxing session in the comfort of your own home, *see p40*.

Arezoo Kaviani

Hans Crescent, Knightsbridge (7584 6868/ www.arezoo.co.uk). Knightsbridge tube. Open 9am-9pm daily. No credit cards.
Celebrity favourite Arezoo Kaviani charges £35 for a bikini wax, £70 for a Playboy. Specify if you'd like to be waxed by Arezoo herself, and book well ahead.

Katie Young's

Unit 12, Hoxton Walk, Hoxton Street, N1 6RA (7739 9271). Old Street tube. Open 10am-5 pm Mon; 10am-6pm Tue, Wed; 10am-7pm Thur, Fri; 9am-6pm Sat.
This cheap-and-cheerful Hoxton salon provides good quality waxing at bargain rates, charging from £12 for a half-leg wax.

Ki Mantra Urban Life Spa

5 Camden Passage, N1 8EU (7226 8860/ www.kimantra.co.uk). Angel tube. Open 11am-8pm Mon; 10am-8pm Tue-Sat; 11am-6pm Sun.
Waxing prices are surprisingly reasonable at this Islington salon, located just off Upper Street: a half leg wax is £15, a bikini £10, and a full leg and bikini £25. Weekends tend to be busy, so try to book ahead.

Otylia Roberts

Greenhouse, 142 Wigmore Street, W1U 3SH (7486 5537/www.otyliaroberts.co.uk). Bond Street tube. Open 10am-6pm Mon; 10am-7pm Tue-Thur; 10am-5.30pm Fri; 9.30am-4.30pm Sat.
Queen of the Brazilian, Polish-born Otylia Roberts uses beeswax-based hot wax instead of strips. Less painful, and with better results, it is pricier: from £34 for a half leg (the Brazilian is £49, while a Hollywood is £51).

Strip

112 Talbot Road, W11 1JR (7727 2754/ www.2strip.com). Westbourne Park tube. Open 10am-8pm Mon-Thur; 10am-6pm Fri, Sat; noon-5pm Sun.
The therapists at Strip use Lycon wax, which promises – and, say our sources, delivers – a less painful wax; treatment rooms also feature distracting plasma screen TVs. Prices aren't too steep, with a bikini costing from £22. The lengthy menu also has plenty of options for men, from back waxes to 'Male Brazilians'.

City Secret

For the cheapest beauty treatments in town, make tracks to the student-run **London School of Beauty** (48 Margaret Street, W1W 8SE, 7580 0355). Here, supervised students will beautify you for a fraction of the cost: an hour-long French manicure will set you back £7.50, for instance, while a stress-busting 90-minute aromatherapy massage costs just £25.

GOING OUT

BEAUTY

FASHION

PARTIES

FOOD

HEALTH

ECO

OUTDOORS

HOME

CHILDREN

PETS

TRANSPORT

RESOURCES

GOING OUT
BEAUTY
FASHION
PARTIES
FOOD
HEALTH
ECO
OUTDOORS
HOME
CHILDREN
PETS
TRANSPORT
RESOURCES

Address Book Secrets
Kathy Phillips

International beauty director for Vogue Asia and founder of This Works

There are lots of hairdressers who can do fancy haircuts that will look good in pictures, but to me the art of a good cutter is someone who can look at a client and do something that is really right for them and will fit their everyday lifestyle. Cutters like that don't come along very often, believe me, but **Luke Hersheson** at Daniel Hersheson (45 Conduit Street, W1S 2YN, 7434 1747, www.danielhersheson.com) is one of them. No amount of beauty treatments, make-up or cosmetic surgery will make as much difference as a really good cut.

In terms of colourists, **Josh Wood** (Real Hair, 6-8 Cale Street, SW3 3QU, 7589 0877, www.realhair.co.uk) is the top man in the world at the moment. He gets flown all over the globe to do people's hair, and does everyone from Elle Macpherson to Kylie. But he also trains other people, and even if you can't afford the top colourist it's still worth going to the salon. The people there will still have all the latest knowledge, but are a bit more affordable.

The manicurist who is the doyenne of the fashion world is **Marian Newman**. She works with brands like Dior on all their big advertising campaigns, and she's trained a team of nail technicians in her technique at Charles Worthington's salon (7 Percy Street, W1T 1DH, 7631 1370, www.cwlondon.com). Her team can do a customised manicure with special products geared towards the condition of your nails, and you're given a personalised hand cream to take away, with added ingredients to pep up your particular skin type.

I really rate facials with **Sarah Chapman** (Sarah Chapman Skinesis Clinic, 106 Draycott Avenue, SW3 3AE, 7589 9585, www.sarahchapman.net). She's a very experienced facialist, who works with the Environ range of products. They're developed by a well-known South African dermatologist who specialises in sun damage, and are great for treating anything from brown spots to dry and difficult skin.

Sophie Thorpe, also based at the Sarah Chapman Clinic (*see above*) is the queen of semi-permanent make-up. She rectifies and shapes eyebrows using a safe tattoo method which is great for blondes, people with alopecia and anyone who has lost their eyebrows. She's a genius at making them look absolutely natural.

I love the **Elemis Day Spa** (2-3 Lancashire Court, W1S 1EX, 7499 4995, www.elemis.com). It's small and surprisingly quiet and peaceful, considering it's so central – a little oasis in the city. The therapists do delicious massages and wonderful oriental mud treatments that help with things like slimming, detoxing and moisturising. You sit in a hot steam room to bake for a while, then you get showered off at the end. It's a wonderful thing to do on your own, or with a boyfriend or friend.

Spas

Best for...
Amazing facials

Adamina Day Spa
276-280 Kensington High Street, W8 6ND (7751 1611/www.adaminaspa.com). High Street Kensington tube. Open 10am-8pm Mon-Sat; 11am-5pm Sun.
Adamina offers superlative facials using rarely-seen Yon-ka products – beloved of facialists and A-listers across the pond. The collagen-boosting 'Adamina Glow' is a good place to start: £100 for 90 blissful minutes.

Angel Therapy Rooms
16B Essex Road, N1 8LN (7226 1188/www.angeltherapyrooms.com). Angel tube. Open noon-8pm Wed, Thur; 11am-7pm Fri; 11am-6pm Sat; 11am-5pm Sun.
Set in a lovely Victorian townhouse, Angel Therapy Rooms offers a range of organic treatments. The superb signature Holistic Facial blends reiki, reflexology and intense massage techniques (£95/75mins).

Eve Lom
2 Spanish Place, W1U 3HU (7935 9988/www.evelom.co.uk). Bond Street tube. Open 9am-5pm Tue-Sat. No credit cards.
The signature facial (£140/90mins) involves a thorough cleanse, a pore-opening paraffin wax mask, lymphatic drainage and an acupressure massage; afterwards, even spa cynics have admitted to seeing a visible difference. To see Lom herself (£250), book a couple of months ahead.

Fresh
92 Marylebone High Street, W1U 4RD (7486 4100/www.fresh.com). Baker Street tube. Open 10am-7pm Mon-Wed, Fri, Sat; 10am-8pm Thur; 11am-5pm Sun.
In an elegant treatment room, hidden away at the back of this friendly shop, customised facials take an hour (£65). While a face mask works its magic, enjoy a neck, shoulder and hand massage. Afterwards, therapists are happy to apply a touch of Fresh make-up.

Best for...
Budget pampering

Ironmonger Row Turkish Baths
1-11 Ironmonger Row, EC1V 3QF (7253 4011/www.aquaterra.org/Islington/IRB). Angel tube or Old Street tube/rail. Open Men only 9am-9.30pm Tue, Thur; 9am-6.30pm Sat. Women-only 9am-9.30pm Wed, Fri; 10am-6.30pm Sun. Mixed 2-9.30pm Mon.
Admission to these Grade II-listed baths is a bargain at £7.70 on weekday mornings, or £12.80 for afternoon or weekend sessions. That buys you up to three hours in the Turkish hot rooms, steam room, plunge pool and relaxation areas. Sprawl on a marble slab for an olive oil soap scrub (from £8) or invest in a massage (from £24/30mins).

Porchester Spa
The Porchester Centre, Queensway, W2 5HS (7792 3980/www.westminster.gov.uk/leisureandculture/sports/porchesterspa.cfm). Bayswater tube. Open women only 10am-10pm Tue, Thur, Fri; 10am-4pm Sun. Men only 10am-10pm Mon, Wed, Sat. Mixed couples 4-10pm Sun. Last admission 2hrs before closing.
The Grade II-listed Porchester's marble and green-tiled relaxation room is an art deco delight, while downstairs lies a warren of hot rooms, steam rooms and a sauna. Treatments include shmeise massages (£25), performed with a soapy raffia brush, and must be booked ahead. Admission is £20.35 for non-members, or £28.25 per couple on Sundays.

Spa London
York Hall Leisure Centre, Old Ford Road, E2 9PJ (8709 5845/www.spa-london.org). Bethnal Green tube. Open women only 10am-9.30pm Tue, Fri; 10am-4.30pm Wed; 9am-7.30pm Sat. Men only 11am-9.30pm Mon; 10am-9.30pm Thur. Mixed 5-9.30pm Wed; 9am-7.30pm Sun.
We didn't like losing the Turkish baths that made way for Spa London, but there's no denying it's good value for money – and rather slick to boot. After paying admission (£21 for non-members) you can relax in the steam rooms, Turkish hot rooms, sauna,

GOING OUT

BEAUTY

FASHION

PARTIES

FOOD

HEALTH

ECO

OUTDOORS

HOME

CHILDREN

PETS

TRANSPORT

RESOURCES

GOING OUT

BEAUTY

FASHION

PARTIES

FOOD

HEALTH

ECO

OUTDOORS

HOME

CHILDREN

PETS

TRANSPORT

RESOURCES

monsoon showers and relaxation room, or book in for one of the reasonably priced treatments or massages.

Best for...
Serious relaxation

Berkeley Spa ★
The Berkeley Hotel, Wilton Place, SW1X 7RL (7201 1699/www.the-berkeley.com). Knightsbridge tube. Open 8am-9pm Mon-Fri; 9am-7.30pm Sat, Sun.
If one were hopelessly rich, one just might move into the Berkeley and become a fixture at the spa. The facials, using dermatologist's favourite DDF products, are excellent, eliminating every molecule of dirty city air (from £85/hr). To seriously unwind, take a dip in the ultra-glamorous rooftop pool afterwards – it's like being briefly but blissfully transported to a Cote d'Azur villa.

Body Experience
50 Hill Rise, Richmond, Surrey TW10 6UB (8334 9999/www.bodyexperience.co.uk). Richmond tube/rail. Open 9am-8.30pm Mon-Thur; 9am-7.30pm Fri, Sat; 9am-5.30pm Sun.
The robes at Body Experience are the cosiest in London, and there's a wonderfully peaceful relaxation room and outdoor terrace where you can curl up with a complimentary post-treatment herbal tea and fresh fruit salad. For an unbelievably good massage ask for Maggie, whose blend of techniques and judiciously-applied pressure works miracles on hunched backs and stressed muscles.

Float
2A Bridstow Place, W2 5AE (7727 7133/ www.float.co.uk). Notting Hill Gate tube. Open 9am-9pm Mon-Sat; 10am-6pm Sun.
Floatation therapy involves lying in a dark, warm salt-water filled pod: the salt keeps you from sinking, while the watery suspension slowly unknots bad postural habits. After an hour-long session (£30 off-peak), book a massage or Living Nature facial afterwards (£60/hr). The latter is sheer bliss, as the therapist gently applies a mask of warm manuka honey to your face.

Best for...
A quick fix

Bliss
60 Sloane Avenue, SW3 3DD (7590 6146/ www.blisslondon.co.uk). Sloane Square or South Kensington tube. Open 9.30am-8pm Mon-Fri; 9.30am-6.30pm Sat; noon-6pm Sun.
New York import Bliss shows the competition that speedy can also be special. Mani- and pedicures are the speciality and last for weeks. It's great for unchatty Londoners, as you can don headphones and watch sitcoms as your tootsies are shaped, buffed and polished (from £30/30mins).

Cucumba
12 Poland Street, W1F 8QB (7734 2020/ www.cucumba.co.uk). Oxford Circus tube. Open 10am-8pm Mon-Fri; 11am-7pm Sat; by appointment Sun.
Ten minutes is enough for a nifty head massage, threading or a foot spa (all £12.50) – and if it's just too good to call a halt to, a cheeky five minutes more is £3.50. Twenty-minute sessions, meanwhile, are £20.

Groom
49 Beauchamp Place, SW3 1NY (7581 1248/www.groomlondon.com). Knightsbridge tube. Open 9.30am-8pm Mon-Wed, Fri, Sat; 9.30am-9pm Thur; 11.30am-6pm Sun.
With two therapists working on you at once, Groom delivers fast results. Nippiest of all are the half-hour packages: the Zoom Groom (£65) incorporates a mini-facial and manicure or pedicure, while the Wax Works package (£60) includes a lightning-speed half leg, bikini and underarm wax.

Best for...
Men

Nickel Spa
27 Shorts Gardens, WC2H 9AP (7240 4048/www.nickelspalondon.co.uk). Covent Garden tube. Open noon-6pm Mon; 10am-7pm Tue, Wed, Sat; 10am-8pm Thur, Fri; noon-5pm Sun.

GOING OUT

BEAUTY

FASHION

PARTIES

FOOD

HEALTH

ECO

OUTDOORS

HOME

CHILDREN

PETS

TRANSPORT

RESOURCES

Gentlemen's club melds with contemporary spa at this reliable men-only venue. An hour-long sports therapy massage is suitably manly (£90), while traditional wet shaves are £40. For the office-bound chap, a (fake) sun-kissed face is £25.

Best for...
Sheer luxury

Spa at Brown's

Brown's Hotel, Albemarle Street, W1S 4BP (7518 4009/www.brownshotel.com). Green Park tube. Open 9.30am-8pm daily.
With lots of dark wood, low lighting and expensive fixtures, Brown's plush spa is a delight. Treatment rooms are sumptuously kitted out for treats such as Mama Mio's pampering pregnancy massages (from £60/45mins) and slimming wraps using Carita and Natura Bisse wonder products (from £90).

Spa InterContinental

InterContinental Park Lane, 1 Hamilton Place, W1J 7QY (7318 8691/www.spa intercontinental.com). Hyde Park Corner tube. Open 9am-9pm Mon-Sat; 10am-6pm Sun.
In a spa where you find Elemis and La Thérapie's gorgeous, hard-working products, you can be assured of a top-notch treatment in soothing, luxurious surroundings. An extensive menu of 15-minute booster treatments (£22.50), which can be added on to longer massages, facials or floats, are great for the time-poor.

Spa at Mandarin Oriental

Mandarin Oriental Hyde Park, 66 Knightsbridge, SW1X 7LA (7838 9888/www.mandarinoriental.com). Knightsbridge tube. Open 7am-10pm daily.
Arrive early to wind down in the wet rooms and relaxation areas of this most opulent of hotel spas, with its sleek, Eastern-inspired decor and 'Amethyst Crystal' steam room. If money's no object, the shiatsu-inspired ginger ritual offers two hours of heavenly massage, with two therapists working in unison (£250).

With fantastic, male-specific grooming products upstairs, the treatments happen downstairs, where the decor is New York boxing gym meets submarine. Hour-long massages can be teeth-grittingly hard if you wish, but the aesthetic side is not overlooked – an eye-watering 'back, sack and crack' wax can be yours for £60.

Refinery

60 Brook Street, W1K 5DU (7409 2001/www.the-refinery.com). Bond Street tube. Open 10am-7pm Mon, Tue; 10am-9pm Wed-Fri; 9am-6pm Sat; 11am-5pm Sun.

GOING OUT

BEAUTY

FASHION

PARTIES

FOOD

HEALTH

ECO

OUTDOORS

HOME

CHILDREN

PETS

TRANSPORT

RESOURCES

Hair

Our pick of the city's hairdressers and services caters for all budgets, with everything from trainee cuts to no-expense-spared Mayfair salons.

Blow-dry bars & lessons

Most salons worth their salt will do just a blow-dry – simply pop in and ask. Prices vary considerably, depending on how swish the salon is and how senior the stylist: we've come across anything from £15 to £40. The following offer blow-dry lessons, or a particularly special service.

Aveda Institute

174 High Holborn, WC1V 7AA (7759 7355/ www.aveda.co.uk). Holborn tube. Open 9am-7pm Mon-Wed; 8am-8pm Thur-Fri; 9am-6.30pm Sat; 11am-5pm Sun.
Blow-dries range from £25 with an assistant to £64 with an artistic director, and are best booked a week in advance. One-on-one 75-minute lessons with Olivier are offered on Thursdays, Fridays and Saturdays.

Hersheson's Blow Dry Bar

Topshop, 214 Oxford Street, W1W 8LG (7927 7888/www.hershesonsblowdrybar. com). Oxford Circus tube. Open 9am-9pm Mon-Sat; 11.30am-6pm Sun.
Down in the bowels of Topshop's lower ground floor, a pink-and-white pod contains three blow-dry stations, with one reserved for walk-ins. Choose from eight catwalk-inspired styles, from the tousled Bardot up-do to the sleek Super Straight for £21: appointments last half an hour.

Headmasters Blo Out Bar

Fenwick, 63 New Bond Street, W1A 3BS (7629 9161/www.hmhair.co.uk). Bond Street tube. Open 10am-6.30pm Mon-Wed, Fri, Sat; 10am-8pm Thur.

Choose from a menu of six styles (£22), in this glassed-off area in the beauty hall. For added gloss, conditioning treatments are £7.50.

Michaeljohn

25 Albemarle Street, W1S 4HU (7629 6969/www.michaeljohn.co.uk). Green Park tube. Open 9am-6.30pm Mon-Wed, Fri; 9am-8pm Thur; 9am-7.30pm Sat.
For a flat rate of £80, Michaeljohn offer hour-long tutorials in anything you fancy – from mastering an up-do to achieving the perfect blow-dry. If you'd like to book a series of tutorials or go with a friend, staff may be able to arrange a special rate; call for details.

Pimps and Pin-ups ★

14 Lamb Street, E1 6EA (7426 2121/ www.pimpsandpinups.com). Liverpool Street tube/rail. Open 10am-8pm Mon-Fri; 10am-6pm Sat, Sun.
To really look the part at a '30s-style tea-dance or rockabilly night, use Pimps and Pin-ups' unique styling service. Bring in a picture of your favourite bygone starlet and your consultant will emulate their look – whether it's sleek, Veronica Lake-style bangs or Greta Garbo waves. Drop in for a consultation to find out if your chosen style involves a set (£60) or simply a blow-dry (£40). If a stylist's free, they'll do gent's quiffs for around £15.

Scissors Palace

122 Holland Park Avenue, W11 4UA (7221 4004). Holland Park tube. Open 9am-6pm Mon, Tue, Sat; 9am-7pm Wed; 9am-8pm Thur; 9am-7.30pm Fri; 11am-6pm Sun.
At £15 for an express blow dry, including a heavenly head massage, this West London walk-in service is a steal. After half an hour in the hands of an expert stylist, we walked out with smooth, gleaming tresses.

Hairdressers

BUDGET

Clipso

35 Windmill Street, W1T 2JS (7580 3449/
www.clipso.co.uk). Tottenham Court Road
tube. Open 10am-7pm Mon, Tues, Fri;
10am-9pm Wed, Thurs; 9.30am-6pm Sat.
Regulars praise the friendly service and in-
depth consultations about cuts and upkeep –
plus you get a complimentary glass of wine.
Prices for women's cuts range from £35-£90:
Jack (£35) is highly recommended – 'the best
cuts I've ever had', says one devotee.

Cuts

39 Frith Street, W1D 5LL (7734 2171).
Tottenham Court Road tube. Open 11am-
7pm Mon-Fri; 10am-6pm Sat; noon-5pm
Sun. No credit cards.
This no-frills salon in central Soho is
particularly highly thought of by male
acquaintances, and charges from £28.50-
£32.50 for cuts (£35-£40 for women).

Stamp Hair

139 Bethnal Green Road, E2 7DG (7613
3097/www.stamphair.com). Liverpool Street
tube/rail. Open 11am-8pm Mon-Wed, Fri;
11am-9pm Thur; 11am-6pm Sat; 11am-
5pm Sun.
Thanks to Sicilian owner Vince's sharp,
consummately stylish cuts, this easygoing
salon is a mecca for local fashion kids.
Artwork by emerging local talent occupies
one wall, while the vibe is über-friendly.
Men's cuts cost £25, ladies' from £37.

Vision Hairdressers

8 Dray Walk, The Old Truman Brewery, 91
Brick Lane, E1 6QL (7247 6842/www.vision
hair.co.uk). Liverpool Street tube/rail. Open
10am-7pm Mon-Wed, Sat; 11am-9pm
Thur, Fri; 11am-6pm Sun.
Beloved of fashionable East Londoners,
Vision offers sleek cuts and colour in slick

CUT PRICE

The cheapest way to get your tresses
trimmed is to become a hairdressing
model. Trainees' work is checked by a
qualified supervisor, though that does
mean it takes time – generally two to
three hours for a cut. All of the salons
listed below need models on a regular
basis, though you need to call ahead.

The classic place for a bargain cut
is the **Toni & Guy Training Academy**
(71-75 New Oxford Street, WC1A 1DG,
7836 0606). Cuts cost a fiver (or free
with a newspaper ad) and are closely
supervised, with five to six students to
one art director. Highlights are £20,
tints £15 – but more extreme, fashion-
led cuts and colour are free. **Vidal
Sassoon Creative Academy** (56
Davies Mews, W1K 5AA, 7318 5205)
is equally well-established, offering
weekday appointments between 10am

and 2pm. Cuts cost £11 (£4.50 for
students) while highlights are £35,
and there's a maximum student-
teacher ratio of 13 to one.

Soho's **Fish Hairdressing** (see p50)
offers Monday morning appointments
as in-house training for salon juniors.
There's close supervision from the
stylists, and a some flexibility over
styles. Cuts are £5, colour from £15.
Mahogany Academy (22 Dering Street,
W1S 1AN, 7629 4078, www.mahogany
hair.co.uk), meanwhile, doesn't
charge a penny. Participants are
qualified hairdressers looking to learn
new techniques, so you're in safe
hands. Finally, the **Aveda Academy**
(0870 428 6384, see p48) holds a
host of colour and cutting workshops
and classes, and frequently needs
models; call to find out what's on.

GOING OUT

BEAUTY

FASHION

PARTIES

FOOD

HEALTH

ECO

OUTDOORS

HOME

CHILDREN

PETS

TRANSPORT

RESOURCES

surrounds. Free drinks and Japanese head massages are a bonus at these prices: ladies' cuts cost from £33, gents' from £28.

MODERATE

Fish

30 D'Arblay Street, W1F 8ER (7494 2398/ www.fishweb.co.uk). Oxford Circus tube. Open 10am-7pm Mon-Wed, Fri; 10am-8pm Thur; 10am-5pm Sat.
Housed in a blue-tiled former fishmongers, Fish is part hip hairdresser, part laid-back barbershop. Gent's cuts cost from £34, women's from £41: Donna is a dab hand.

Taylor Taylor

137 Commercial Street, E1 6BJ (7377 2737/ www.taylortaylorlondon.com). Liverpool Street tube/rail. Open 10am-8pm Mon-Wed; 10am-9pm Thur; 10am-7pm Fri; 10am-6pm Sat, Sun.
Opulent decor (chandeliers, birdcages and gold tiling) and complimentary cocktails make a cut here blissfully pampering. Prices start from £49 for women, but it's worth spending a bit extra for the art director-level stylists: Drew does great cuts (£60), while Nadia's fantastic for colour (£112.50 full head).
Other locations *12 Cheshire Street, E2 6EH (7033 0330).*

Unruly Studio

100 Westbourne Studios, 242 Acklam Road, W10 5JJ (8964 9200/www.unrulystudio. co.uk). Ladbroke Grove or Westbourne Park tube. Open 10am-10pm Mon-Fri; 10am-6pm Sat.
Unruly's director Michael specialises in curly hair, achieving miraculous results (from £50). Open until late, the salon has great customer service: free fringe trims are offered between cuts, PlayStations and Wi-Fi supplement the usual magazines, and if you spend over £60 the salon will pay your congestion charge.

Zoo N1

267 Upper Street, N1 0NY (7226 1865). Angel tube. Open 10am-6.15pm Mon-Wed; 10am-7pm Thur, Fri; 10am-5.30pm Sat; 11am-5pm Sun.
This busy Islington salon offers ladies' cuts and restyles at £44 from a switched-on team of senior stylists, many of whom work on magazine shoots and catwalk styling on the side. Our fashionista friends' favourite is Japanese stylist Taka.

EXPENSIVE

For colour, Josh Wood at **Real Hair** *(see p44)* is also highly recommended.

Daniel Hersheson

Harvey Nichols, 109-125 Knightsbridge, SW1X 7RJ (7201 8797/www.daniel hersheson.com). Knightsbridge tube. Open 10am-8pm Mon-Sat; noon-6pm Sun.
For perfect highlights book an appointment with head colourist Sibi Bolan, who's one of the best in London; a half-head with her costs £170. Cuts start at £55 (men's from £45), though you'll pay £250 to see Daniel himself: both branches also offer afro hair services.
Other locations *45 Conduit Street, W1S 2YN (7434 1747).*

Errol Douglas

18 Motcomb Street, SW1X 8LB (7235 0110/ www.erroldouglas.com). Knightsbridge tube. Open 9am-6pm Mon; 9am-7pm Tue-Sat.
Converts rave about the salon's relaxed atmosphere and beautifully sleek cuts and blow-dries. Its eponymous owner is charm itself: down to earth, and good at listening to what you want. A cut with him costs £185 for women and £85 for men, although prices drop considerably if you see another member of the team.

Jo Hansford

19 Mount Street, W1K 2RN (7495 7774/ www.johansford.com). Bond Street or Green Park tube. Open 8.30am-6pm Tue-Sat.
Fashion editors' favourite Hansford is probably the best-known colourist in London – and much in demand for perfectly blended highlights or colour correction emergencies. A half-head costs from £140 to £400, tints from £85 to £150; if you're in a hurry, the aptly named Flying Colours – colours applied by comb – takes half an hour (from £75).

Fashion

GOING OUT
BEAUTY
FASHION
PARTIES
FOOD
HEALTH
ECO
OUTDOORS
HOME
CHILDREN
PETS
TRANSPORT
RESOURCES

Accessories

We've focused on smaller boutiques and independent labels rather than well-known high street names and department stores (unless they offer a particular speciality). For the complete low-down on London's shopping scene, invest in a copy of Time Out's *Shops & Services* guide.

Bags

Ally Capellino
9 Calvert Avenue, E2 7JP (7613 3073/ www.allycapellino.co.uk). Liverpool Street tube/rail. Open noon-6pm Wed-Fri; 10am-6pm Sat; 1-4pm Sun.
Ally Capellino's cult accessories empire has been quietly bubbling away since 1980; her beautifully made, unisex leather, cotton and canvas bags, from £55, are fashion classics.

Doors by Jas MB
8 Ganton Street, W1F 7QP (7494 2288/ www.doorsbyjasmb.com). Oxford Circus tube. Open 11am-7pm Mon-Sat; 1-5pm Sun.
Chaps can't go wrong with these Italian leather shoulder bags and holdalls. Jas Sehmbi's career has seen him go from designing record bags in Soho to working with the likes of Louis Vuitton – and his bags are the kind of stylish wardrobe staples that'll last for years.

Jigsaw Accessories
49 South Molton Street, W1K 5LH (7499 3385/www.jigsaw-online.com). Bond Street tube. Open 10am-6.30pm Mon-Wed, Fri, Sat; 10am-7.30pm Thur; noon-6pm Sun.
Check out Jigsaw's super-soft leather bags (made in the same factory as Prada's), which cost from £245, along with its lovely collection of belts, jewellery and shoes.

Mimi ★
40 Cheshire Street, E2 6EH (7729 6699/ www.mimimika.com). Liverpool Street tube/rail. Open 10.30am-6pm Wed-Sat; 11am-6pm Sun.
Central St Martin's graduate Mimi Berry designs simple, elegant leather bags and purses in beautiful hues. The satchel-style Elsie (£200) is a classic, while leather Oyster card holders are a mere £20.

Ollie & Nic
20 Foubert's Place, Carnaby Street, W1 7PL (7494 4214/www.ollieandnic.com). Oxford Circus tube. Open 10am-7pm Mon-Wed, Fri, Sat; 10am-8pm Thur; noon-6pm Sun.
Refreshingly inexpensive, Ollie & Nic's sparkling new Carnaby Street flagship is ideal for credit-crunched style lovers. Designs are unique (rather than poor It-bag copies), with cute shoulder bags, clutches and retro-floral cotton shoppers.

Pickett
32-33 & 41 Burlington Arcade, W1J 0PZ (7493 8939/www.pickett.co.uk). Green Park tube. Open 9am-6pm Mon-Fri; 10am-6pm Sat.
There's nothing too quirky at Pickett – it's the deliciously conservative styles that excite. Check out the men's attaché cases and A-lister-worthy leather and canvas holdalls.

Poppy Valentine
Unit 16, Portobello Green Arcade, 281 Portobello Road, W10 5TZ (www.poppyvalentine.com). Ladbroke Grove tube. Open 10am-5.30pm Tue-Sat.
Using vintage fabric remnants, Claire Read creates boho bags (and dresses) that are quite unlike any you'll find on the high street. Bag a sweet 'Molly' for £49, with pleated fabric and amber-effect handles – or bring your own material for a bespoke bag, at no extra cost.

Glasses & sunglasses

Cutler & Gross
16 Knightsbridge Green, SW1X 7QL (7581 2250/www.cutlerandgross.com). Knightsbridge tube. Open 9.30am-7pm Mon-Sat; noon-4pm Sun.
Established for three decades, this renowned opticians has over 600 frame styles in its archive (book a viewing appointment), plus a regularly renewed selection of sunglasses. Styles vary hugely, but include a mixture of modern and retro shapes. Unique vintage frames are on sale in the sister shop at no.7. **Other locations** *7 Knightsbridge Green, SW1X 7QL (7590 9995).*

David Clulow at Selfridges
400 Oxford Street, W1A 1AB (0800 123400/www.selfridges.com). Bond Street or Marble Arch tube. Open 9.30am-8pm Mon-Wed, Fri, Sat; 9.30am-9pm Thur; noon-6pm Sun.
The large sunglasses-only concession on the ground floor Wonder Room at Selfridges stocks all the big, blingy fashion names, from Prada and Robert Cavalli to Tom Ford and Oliver Peoples. Prices go from £99 to £2,000.

Kirk Originals
29 Floral Street, WC2E 9DP (7240 5055/www.kirkoriginals.com). Covent Garden tube. Open 11am-7pm Mon-Sat; noon-5pm Sun.
Bright and über-trendy, Jason Kirk's appealing premises display contemporary art alongside a host of elegant frames. Kirk's own designs cost from £165, and are mixed up with a handful of other hip brands.

Linda Farrow at Harrods
87-135 Brompton Road, SW1X 7XL (7730 1234/www.harrods.com). Knightsbridge tube. Open 10am-8pm Mon-Sat; noon-6pm Sun.
Linda Farrow's vintage sunglasses, beloved of fashionistas, have their own gallery at Harrods. Farrow's 1970s and '80s gems were rediscovered in a factory by her son in 2003, and the business swiftly relaunched. In addition to vintage specs, you'll also find new designer collaborations; prices start at £150.

Mallon & Taub
35D Marylebone High Street, W1U 4QB (7935 8200/www.mallonandtaub.com). Baker Street or Regent's Park tube. Open 10am-6.30pm Mon-Wed, Fri, Sat; 10am-7pm Thur; noon-5pm Sun.
The high-tech premises impress, while friendly opticians take time to talk to each customer. A fab range of brands includes Miu Miu, Oliver Peoples and Rayban; prices go stratospheric, but start at a palatable £120.

Spex in the City
1 Shorts Gardens, WC2H 9AT (7240 0243/www.spexinthecity.com). Covent Garden or Leicester Square tube. Open 11am-6.30pm Mon-Fri; 11am-6pm Sat; 1-5pm Sun.
Expect a well-chosen range of European and British frames, including Orgreen, Alain Mikli and Oliver Goldsmith. Prices start at £80, rising to around £280.

36 Opticians
36 Beauchamp Place, SW3 1NU (7581 6336/www.36opticians.co.uk). South Kensington or Knightsbridge tube. Open 10am-6pm Mon-Sat.
Prices at this relaxed but expert opticians start at an affordable £45 for no-frills, classic frames. Trendies may prefer pricier styles by the likes of Tom Ford and Barton Perreira.

City Secret

Sat on a pair of treasured frames once too often? Take the sacred remains down to **Opera Opera** (98 Long Acre, WC2E 9NR, 7836 9246, www.operaopera.net), a tiny, family-run opticians in Covent Garden. Copies of vintage frames are a speciality here, along with all manner of bespoke designs; the service costs from £275. The shop also sells its own Harpers eyewear brand, which ranges from appealingly chunky NHS-inspired frames to glamorous aviator and cat's-eye shapes.

GOING OUT

BEAUTY

FASHION

PARTIES

FOOD

HEALTH

ECO

OUTDOORS

HOME

CHILDREN

PETS

TRANSPORT

RESOURCES

GOING OUT

BEAUTY

FASHION

PARTIES

FOOD

HEALTH

ECO

OUTDOORS

HOME

CHILDREN

PETS

TRANSPORT

RESOURCES

Address Book Secrets
Brix Smith
Owner, Start London

One of my favourite designer labels at the moment is **Lungta de Fancy** (2nd Floor, 3-4A Little Poland Street, W1W 7BD, 7437 5555, www.lungtadefancy. com, by appointment only), which we stock at Start (*see p60*). It's a collaboration between five Japanese designers, who make very fresh, edgy garments in waxed cottons. The designs are wonderfully theatrical, and a bit like a younger Vivienne Westwood.

For shoes, I make a beeline for the newly-opened **Christian Louboutin** store (17 Mount Street, W1K 2RJ, 7491 0033). The shoes are a really great balance between comfortable and sexy. There's a particular shoe he does with a huge bow on the side that's practically dragging along the floor – I call it the drunken bow. It comes in black, fuschia and blue, and I love it in every shade.

The best thing about London is its markets. I have different hunting grounds for different things. For example, if I'm after furniture I'll go somewhere like **Alfie's Antique Market**, near Marylebone (13-25 Church Street, NW8 8DT, 7723 6066, www.alfiesantiques.com, closed Mon, Sun). They specialise in 1940s, '50s and '60s Italian design, which I adore. Both my husband and I have a bit of an obsession with quirky furniture, particularly chandeliers and glass.

For food, we visit the **Marylebone Farmers' Market** (*see p99*). We go there every Sunday morning and get all our food for the week: beautiful fruit, fresh vegetables and organic breads. It's the hippest market I know – whenever you go there you see fabulous people like Erin O'Connor, looking all bleary-eyed and dressed down in their Sunday gear.

Another Sunday tradition of ours is going to **Fifteen** (15 Westland Place, N1 7LP, 0871 330 1515, www. fifteen.net) – it serves the best breakfasts in London. We usually have two poached eggs and bubble and squeak. It also has homemade muesli and Bloody Marys, plus the hugest bacon sarnies you've ever seen.

I love to trawl the art galleries in Shoreditch. Every month, for the **First Thursdays** event (www.firstthursdays. co.uk) they all open their doors until late and you can spend hours walking from one to another, and bumping into people you know. I particularly like the **Maureen Paley Gallery** (21 Herald Street, E2 6JT, 7729 4112, www. maureenpaley.com) and the **Trolley Gallery** (73A Redchurch Street, E2 7DJ, 7729 6591).

After we've been there, my husband and I visit our favourite restaurant in Shoreditch – **Saf** (152-154 Curtain Road, EC2A 3AT, 7613 0007). It's a vegan gourmet place that opened recently. All the cheese is made from nuts: you can have almond nut cheese, macadamia nut cheese and even ice-cream made from nuts. It has really lovely decor – very clean and modern, with a lofty, New York feel, and everything is beautifully presented.

Jewellery

For more playful, quirky lines, we love online retailer **Hannah Zakari** (www.hannahzakari.co.uk). A showcase for independent designers and crafty types, it stocks a bewildering array of goodies, with prices as low as £4 for brooches. If you're prepared to pay for shipping, US crafts collective **Etsy** (www.etsy.com) is an unrivalled source of handmade pieces.

Berganza
88-90 Hatton Garden (entrance on Greville Street), EC1N 8PN (7404 2336/www.berganza.com). Chancery Lane tube/Farringdon tube/rail. Open 10am-5pm Mon-Sat.
Specialising in antique rings, which come in beautifully tattered velvet boxes and with handwritten provenance labels, Berganza offers a gorgeous range of sparklers, many of them Victorian, with the odd Art Deco gem.

Claire Aristides
2.11 Kingly Court, W1B 5PW (7434 2161/www.clairearistides.com). Oxford Circus tube. Open 11am-7pm Mon-Sat; noon 6pm Sun.
This style magazine staple is the twinkling gem of Kingly Court, with its delicate, vintage-looking pieces. You can buy make-your-own kits packed with crystal beads or charms (from £20), along with jewellery-making tools.

ec one
41 Exmouth Market, EC1R 4QL (7713 6185/www.econe.co.uk). Farringdon tube/rail. Open 10am-6pm Mon-Wed, Fri; 11am-7pm Thur; 10.30am-6pm Sat.
Co-owner Jos Skeates' designs are for the bold (and affluent), but there are plenty of more modestly priced pieces, such as Alex Monroe's delicate silver buttercup rings (£90). New designers are introduced all the time, so there's always fresh temptation.

Electrum Gallery
21 South Molton Street, W1K 5QZ (7629 6325). Bond Street tube. Open 10am-6pm Mon-Sat.
Exclusive pieces available in this gallery-cum-shop include work by recent graduate Lina Petersen and more than a hundred other contemporary designers.

French's Dairy
13 Rugby Street, WC1N 3QT (7404 7070/www.frenchsdairy.com). Holborn or Russell Square tube. Open 11am-6pm Mon-Fri; 11am-4pm Sat.
With prices ranging from £20 to £2,000, this sweet little shop, housed in a former dairy, has something for all budgets. Pretty necklaces from Les Néréides are at the lower end of the price spectrum, while Phillipe Ferrandis' opulent handmade pieces are guaranteed show-stoppers.

Kabiri
37 Marylebone High Street, W1U 4QE (7224 1808/www.kabiri.co.uk). Baker Street tube. Open 10am-6.30pm Mon-Sat; noon-5pm Sun.
Stocking around 100 wildly differing designers, the often-changing wares range from the fun (Tatty Devine's colourful, quirky pieces; Giles and Brother's playful pendants) to the decadent (Rajiv Arora's gemstones and pearls). Prices vary accordingly.

Lara Bohinc 107
49F Sloane Street, SW1X 9BZ (7730 8194/www.larabohinc107.co.uk). Sloane Square tube. Open 10am-6pm Mon, Tue, Thur-Sat; 10am-7pm Wed; noon-5pm Sun.
Glamorous, Slovenian-born Bohinc is best known for her intricate, laser-cut designs, but recent forays into heavy, Egyptian-inspired jewellery are just as striking.

Lesley Craze Gallery
33-35A Clerkenwell Green, EC1R 0DU (7608 0393/www.lesleycrazegallery.co.uk). Farringdon tube/rail. Open 10am-5.30pm Tue-Sat.
Hidden away in Clerkenwell, this gallery houses the work of over 100 international jewellers, metalsmiths and textile designers. Its contemporary skew ensures a healthy dollop of emerging talent; perfect for one-off gifts for creative types.

GOING OUT
BEAUTY
FASHION
PARTIES
FOOD
HEALTH
ECO
OUTDOORS
HOME
CHILDREN
PETS
TRANSPORT
RESOURCES

GOING OUT

BEAUTY

FASHION

PARTIES

FOOD

HEALTH

ECO

OUTDOORS

HOME

CHILDREN

PETS

TRANSPORT

RESOURCES

Shoes & trainers

Adidas Originals Store
9 Earlham Street, WC2H 9LL (7379 4042/ www.adidas.com). Covent Garden tube. Open 10.30am-7pm Mon-Sat; noon-6pm Sun.
Among the updated classics here is the Superstar Vintage basketball shoe, with its distinctive shell-toe (£90), whose first incarnation was introduced in 1970. Other timeless old-timers include the iconic green and white colourway (£100).

Black Truffle
52 Warren Street, W1T 5NJ (7388 4547/ www.blacktruffle.com). Warren Street tube. Open 11am-6.30pm Mon-Sat.
This sleek boutique is full of wearable but individual shoes, with footwear from Eley Kishimoto, Repetto and Jocomonda – plus Paul & Joe and F Troupe for men. A fetching pair of dove grey Chie Mihara t-bars are £159.

Georgina Goodman
44 Old Bond Street W1S 4GB (7493 7673/ www.georginagoodman.com). Green Park tube. Open 10am-6pm Mon-Wed, Fri, Sat; 10am-7pm Thur.
Even Manolo Blahnik's a fan of Goodman's exquisitely-made statement heels (from £300). They're surprisingly comfortable too – you can even run for a bus in them. Leather-soled ballet flats (from £165) are also a big seller.

Gloria's ✈
6 Dray Walk, E1 6QL (7770 6222/www. superdeluxe.net). Liverpool Street tube/rail. Open 10am-7pm daily.
Gloria's (Gloria Gaynor – trainer, geddit?) is sneakerfreak heaven, with stock hailing from Hong Kong, Japan, Europe and New York. There's precious little attitude if you're a collecting novice, though you'll have to get past the hordes of drooling collectors first.

Kazmattazz
39 Hoxton Square, N1 6NN (7739 4133/ www.kazmattazz.com). Old Street tube/rail. Open 10.30am-6.30pm Mon-Thur; 10.30am-10pm Fri-Sun.

Nike, Adidas and Etnies are just some of the brands on sale at this lively, no-frills sneaker shop. Lesser-seen names include Ballerr, Ecco and Fila, and prices range from £30-£60.

Lollipop London
114 Islington High Street, N1 8EG (7226 4005/www.lollipoplondon.com). Angel tube. Open 11am-6pm Mon-Wed; 11am-7pm Thur-Sat; noon-5pm Sun.
Ignore the cutesy name: a fabulous display of shoes is guaranteed at this small boutique, where owner Laura Alnatt sources a rich array of hard-to-find designers. Flatties are from £40; heels around the £150 mark.

Oliver Sweeney
66 New Bond Street W1S 1RW (7355 0387/ www.oliversweeney.com). Bond Street tube. Open 10am-7pm Mon-Sat; noon-6pm Sun.
Sweeney makes some of the best-looking, most comfortable men's shoes around, and is a fashion-editors' favourite. The classic Kamanchi loafer is £225, while a pair of daring stingray-skin Bells, made to order, costs £750. **Other location** *133 Middlesex Street, E1 7JS (7626 4466).*

Size?
33-34 Carnaby Street, W1F 7DW (7287 4016/www.size-online.co.uk). Oxford Circus tube. Open 10am-7.30pm Mon-Wed, Fri, Sat; 10am-8pm Thur; noon-6pm Sun.
Size? is a seemingly obvious inclusion on this list – but it remains a constant favourite with the sneak-obsessed. Lakai and DVS are some of the leftfield labels stocked alongside more common brands (Puma, Reebok, Nike et al). **Other locations** *across the city.*

Sniff
1 Great Titchfield Street, W1W 8AU (7299 3560/www.sniff.co.uk). Oxford Circus tube. Open 10am-7pm Mon-Fri; 10am-6.30pm Sat; noon-6pm Sun.
Sniff sells shoes for every occasion, from Converse to stacked wedges and glamour-puss heels from Paco Gil and Miss L Fire. The in-house brand is well worth a look, with heels from around £70, and there's a decent selection of footwear for chaps.

Bespoke

The best way to get a truly individual look and a perfect fit?
Simple: go bespoke.

Bikinis & underwear

Biondi
55B Old Church Street, SW3 5BS (7349 1111/www.biondicouture.com). Sloane Square tube. Open 10.30am-6.30pm Mon-Sat.
This luxury bikini boutique also offers a great bespoke service. With made-to-measure (from £250), staff work from existing shapes and materials; with couture (£350-£400), they'll create your dream two-piece from scratch.

Buttress & Snatch
7502 3139/www.buttressandsnatch.co.uk. Open by appointment only.
'Handmade in Hackney by honest hard-working girls' is the company motto; sure enough, prices are good and the quality's great. Fully bespoke bikinis and lingerie cost from £200 and take up to four weeks to make.

Outland Boutique
97-99 Cheshire Street, E1 6HR (07961 902145/www.ilovehats.com). Liverpool Street tube/rail. Open by appointment only.
This seductive little boudoir creates exquisite bespoke lingerie from luxurious silks and satins – perfect for special occasions.

Jeans

Bodymetrics at Selfridges
400 Oxford Street, W1A 1AB (0800 123400/ www.selfridges.com). Bond Street or Marble Arch tube. Open 9.30am-8pm Mon-Wed, Fri, Sat; 9.30am-9pm Thur; noon-6pm Sun.
Bodymetrics' 3D scanner promises a perfect fit; once your measurements have been taken, choose your ideal fabric, fit and cut. The only downside is the price tag – from £450.

Shirts

In addition to the following shirtmakers, trusty **Marks & Spencer** (0845 609 0200, www.marksandspencer.com) now offers an online made-to-measure service. Choose your fit, detailing, monogram and material, and the finished shirt will be sent to you within 21 days (from £30).

Charlie Allen
1 Coopers Yard, 181 Upper Street, N1 1RQ (7359 0883/www.charlieallen.co.uk). Angel tube/Highbury & Islington tube/rail. Open by appointment 10am-7pm Mon-Sat.
The made-to-measure shirt service, which gives you the choice of over 500 fabrics, takes three to six weeks and costs from £150.

Ede & Ravenscroft
8 Burlington Gardens, W1X 1LG (7734 5450/www.edeandravenscroft.co.uk). Green Park tube. Open 9am-6pm Mon-Fri; 10am-6pm Sat.
A bespoke shirt from Ede & Ravenscroft makes a stylish gift. Your chosen length of material is boxed up for the lucky recipient, who then visits the shop to be measured up and pick his collar and cuffs (from £110). **Other locations** *across the city.*

New & Lingwood
53 Jermyn Street, SW1Y 6LX (7493 9621/www.newandlingwood.com). Piccadilly Circus tube. Open 9am-6pm Mon-Fri; 10am-6pm Sat.
For seriously smart gents (and Eton pupils: official supplier status was granted in 1865), New & Lingwood offer more than 700 fabrics, plus optional embroidery. There's a minimum order of four shirts (from £165 each).

GOING OUT

BEAUTY

FASHION

PARTIES

FOOD

HEALTH

ECO

OUTDOORS

HOME

CHILDREN

PETS

TRANSPORT

RESOURCES

Shoes & trainers

John Lobb
9 St James's Street, SW1A 1EF (7930 3664). Green Park tube. Open 9am-5.30pm Mon-Fri; 9am-4.30pm Sat.
One of the finest shoemakers in the world, the eponymous Mr Lobb was cobbler to King Edward VII. At £2,300, made-to-measure shoes might cost nigh-on a king's ransom, but will be the finest footwear you'll ever buy.

NIKEiD Studio London
NikeTown, 236 Oxford Street, W1W 8LG (7612 0990/www.nikeid.nike.com). Oxford Circus tube. Open 10am-7pm Mon-Wed; 10am-8pm Thur-Sat; noon-6pm Sun.
Book a one-on-one session with a design consultant to create your dream pair of trainers; the service costs from £65 to £160.

Selve
First Floor, 93 Jermyn Street, SW1Y 6JE (7321 0200/www.selve.co.uk). Open by appointment 9am-5pm Mon-Fri.
A godsend for those with unusually sized feet, Selve's 3D measuring scanner ensures a perfect fit. Each season, 20 designs are offered in sizes 1-11 (in three widths). It costs from £250 and takes from five to six weeks.

Terry de Havilland
336 Kingsland Road, E8 4DA (7254 4445/ www.terrydehavilland.net). Liverpool Street tube/rail or Old Street tube/rail then 149 bus. Open by appointment only.
This shoemaker extraordinaire began making his gorgeous, vertigo-inducing wedge heels and platform shoes back in the '60s. Bespoke show-stoppers can be created in two to three weeks and cost from £250-£450.

Suits

Chris Kerr
52 Berwick Street, W1F 8SL (7437 3727/ www.eddiekerr.co.uk). Oxford Circus tube. Open 8am-5.30pm Mon-Fri; 8.30am-1pm Sat.

Eddie Kerr has been making suits for celebs since the '60s. Now semi-retired, he's handed over the reins to son Chris, and they're still creating sharp bespoke suits, shirts and ties in their friendly, unostentatious shop. With full suits starting at around £1,100, it's an affordable way to indulge in real tailoring.

Gieves & Hawkes
1 Savile Row, W1S 3JR (7434 2001/ www.gievesandhawkes.com). Green Park or Piccadilly Circus tube. Open 9.30am-6.30pm Mon-Thur; 9am-6pm Fri; 10am-6pm Sat.
Despite four centuries of bespoke supremacy, Gieves and Hawkes' approach to style can be surprisingly contemporary. Bespoke suits take about three fittings and cost from £3,000, while a made-to-measure suit will set you back around £695.

Imtaz
7 the Walk, Independent Place, Shacklewell Lane, E8 2HE (7503 3537/www.imtaz.com). Dalston Kingsland rail. Open 9.30am-5.30pm Mon-Fri; by appointment only Sat & weekday evenings. No credit cards.
London College of Fashion-trained Imtaz Khaliq has built up a loyal following with businessmen and women alike, with a bespoke service starting from £700.

Kilgour
8 Savile Row, W1S 3PE (7734 6905/www. kilgour.com). Green Park or Piccadilly Circus tube. Open 9am-6pm Mon-Wed, Fri; 9am-7pm Thur; 10.30am-6pm Sat.
Kilgour's sleek, modern store reflects its new design direction. A perfectly-tailored bespoke suit costs upwards of £2,900, but prices are half that for 'entry level' suits (fitted and cut on Savile Row, but basted externally).

Mr Start
40 Rivington Street, EC2A 3BN (7729 6272/www.start-london.com) Old Street tube/rail. Open 10.30am-6.30pm Mon-Fri; 11am-6pm Sat, 1-5pm Sun.
Made-to-measure suits at this Rivington Street boutique cost from £750. The laid-back atmosphere and friendly staff will soon put nervous novice suit-buyers at their ease.

Clothes

Fashion's thorniest problems solved – including where to find the perfect pair of jeans.

Boutiques

Another boutique well worth checking out is **Start** (*see p60*), which mixes international superbrands with newer (and cheaper) names to great effect.

Aimé
32 Ledbury Road, W11 2AB (7221 7070/ www.aimelondon.com). Notting Hill Gate tube. Open 10am-6.30pm Mon-Sat.
Aimé showcases the pick of Francophile fashion, stocking labels such as APC, Isabel Marant and Antik Batik (*see also p179*).

Browns
23-27 South Molton Street, W1K 5RD (7514 0000/www.brownsfashion.com). Bond Street tube. Open 10am-6.30pm Mon-Wed, Fri, Sat; 10am-7pm Thur.
Famed as it is, we couldn't omit the *grande dame* of London's boutiques. Browns stocks a heady mix of established names and edgy new talent; Erin Mullaney, formerly of Selfridges, is the new buyer casting her expert eye over the international collections.

Feather & Stitch
54 Hill Street, TW9 1TW (8332 2717/www. featherandstitch.com). Richmond tube/rail. Open 10am-6pm Mon-Fri; noon-6pm Sun.
Run by two London College of Fashion graduates, this Richmond boutique is packed with leftfield designers. Look out for Rebecca Taylor, and Philip Lim protégé Grace Sun.

Hub
49 & 88 Stoke Newington Church Street, N16 0AR (7254 4494/www.hubshop.co.uk) Angel tube or Bus 73. Open 10.30am-6.30pm Mon-Sat; noon-5pm Sun.

Hub showcases perfectly picked pieces from mid-range labels such as See by Chloé and Sonia Rykiel; don't miss the cotton summer dresses, designed by co-owner Beth Graham.

KJ's Laundry ★
74 Marylebone Lane, W1U 2PW (7486 7855/www.kjslaundry.com). Bond Street tube. Open 10am-7pm Mon-Wed, Fri, Sat; 10am-8pm Thur; 11am-5pm Sun.
Expect interesting, lesser-known designers at this über-chic store, where nothing costs over £350. Covetable pieces include slinky, stripy halternecks from Richard Ruiz.

Labour of Love
193 Upper Street, N1 1RQ (7354 9333/ www.labour-of-love.co.uk). Highbury & Islington tube/rail. Open 11am-6.30pm Mon-Sat; noon-5.30pm Sun.
Owner Francesca Forcolini combines her own Labour of Love label with a host of quirky smaller labels, plus shoes and accessories, temptingly arrayed in antique cabinets.

No-one
1 Kingsland Road, E2 8AA (7613 5314/ www.no-one.co.uk). Old Street tube/rail. Open 11am-7pm Mon-Sat; noon-6pm Sun.
This criminally cool Shoreditch boutique is surprisingly friendly, stocking hip labels like Henrik Vibskov, Mala Brajkovic and even Cheap Monday (it was the first UK stockist).

Shop at Maison Bertaux
Basement, 27 Greek Street, W1D 5DF (05601 151584/www.shopatmaisonb.com). Open 11am-6.30pm Tue-Sat.
Buried beneath the croissants and cakes of London's oldest pâtisserie is the super cute Shop, a tiny, secret, Soho purveyor of Eley Kishimoto, Sonia Rykiel, APC and Obey.

GOING OUT
BEAUTY
FASHION
PARTIES
FOOD
HEALTH
ECO
OUTDOORS
HOME
CHILDREN
PETS
TRANSPORT
RESOURCES

Charity shops

British Red Cross
85 Ebury Street, SW1W 9QU (7730 2235/
www.redcross.org.uk). Victoria tube/rail.
Open 10am-5.30pm Mon-Sat.
Designer labels abound, thanks to moneyed
locals: you could snap up a pair of Manolo
Blahniks or a smart Armani skirt, and there
are puffy '80s ballgowns galore. The Chelsea
branch (67 Old Church Street, SW3 5BS, 7351
3206) is equally good.

Crusaid
Crusaid, 19 Churton Street, SW1V 2LY
(7233 8736/www.crusadeshop.co.uk).
Victoria tube/rail. Open 10am-6pm Mon-
Sat; 11am-3pm Sun.
An excellent all-rounder, Crusaid offers rich
pickings among its vinyl, CDs, books and
clothes: Nicole Farhi gems are often to be
found on its crowded rails.

Oxfam Hampstead
61 Gayton Road, NW3 1TU (7794 4474/
www.oxfam.co.uk). Hampstead tube. Open
10am-5pm Mon-Sat.
Once again, charity shopping in a well-heeled
neighbourhood pays dividends: expect
quality separates, frocks, knits, shoes and
accessories, along with a great books section.

Salvation Army
Princes Street, W1 2LQ (7495 3958)
Oxford Circus tube. Open 10am-6pm
Mon-Sat.
This two-floor space stocks an eclectic array
of clothes, from sparkly platforms to wool
military jackets. It's popular with eagle-eyed
London College of Fashion students, so arrive
early to nab the bargains.

Traid
61 Westbourne Grove, W2 4UA (7221
2421/www.traid.org.uk). Royal Oak tube.
Open 10am-6pm Mon-Sat; 11am-5pm Sun.
Follow the fashion stylists and journalists to
Traid, with its small, boutiquey feel, superior
labels and award-winning in-house recycled
fashion label, TRAIDremade.

Jeans

Not only does **Selfridges** (*see p53*) offer
a bespoke jeans service, it also has one of
the best denim departments in town.

Donna Ida
106 Draycott Avenue, SW3 3AE (7225 3816/
www.donnaida.com). South Kensington tube.
Open 10am-7pm Mon-Fri; 10am-6.30pm
Sat; 1-6pm Sun.
This smart boutique showcases a changing
array of hot labels (currently including Ditto's,
Rock & Republic and Siwy), while staff have
a keen eye for which styles will best achieve
a leggy, pert-of-bottom look. You can even
call ahead to book a one-on-one consultation.

Harvey Nichols
109-125 Knightsbridge, SW1X 7RJ
(7235 5000/www.harveynichols.com).
Knightsbridge tube. Open 10am-8pm
Mon-Sat; noon-6pm Sun.
Sleek, slim-fitting beauties from Goldsign,
fair-trade jeans from Edun and classics from
J Brand are among the multitude of hip labels
in Harvey Nichols' expansive jeans section.

Start ★
42 Rivington Street, EC2A 3BN (7729
3334/www.start-london.com). Old Street
tube/rail. Open 10.30am-6.30pm Mon-Fri;
11am-6pm Sat; 1-5pm Sun.
Owner Brix Smith has an unerring eye when
it comes to finding your perfect fit from a
stellar selection of brands: Superfine, Earnest
Sewn, Acne, J Brand… We could go on.

Trilogy
33 Duke of York's Square, King's Road,
SW3 4LY (7730 6515/www.trilogystores.
co.uk). Sloane Square tube. Open 10am-7pm
Mon-Sat; noon-6pm Sun.
A veritable temple to cult denim brands,
Trilogy's stock includes better-known labels
(James Jeans, Hudson, True Religion) and
lesser-known finds such as Anlo's lovely,
perfectly-tailored trews.
Other location *63 Weymouth Street,*
W1G 8NU (7486 8085).

Lingerie & swimwear

The ultimate indulgence is bespoke undies and bikinis (*see p57*) – a delicious extravagance. We're also smitten with the bow-bedecked silk knickers available at **Sugarlesque** (www.sugarlesque.com), which also does a lovely line in burlesque nipple tassels and ostrich-feather fans.

Agent Provocateur
6 Broadwick Street, W1V 1FH (7439 0229/ www.agentprovocateur.com). Tottenham Court Road tube. Open 11am-7pm Mon-Wed, Fri, Sat; 11am-8pm Thur; noon-5pm Sun.
Incredibly sexy cuts, gorgeous fabrics and friendly assistants make this place lingerie shopping heaven; bras cost from around £55. **Other locations** *across the city.*

Bordello
55 Great Eastern Street, EC2A 3HP (7503 3334/www.bordello-london.com). Old Street tube. Open noon-7pm Tue, Wed; 12.30-7.30pm Thur-Sat.
This decadent boutique stocks seductive corsets by Miss Katie, plus silky, frothy lingerie from the likes of Myla, Ayten Gasson, Ell & Cee and Mimi Holliday.

Heidi Klein
174 Westbourne Grove, W11 2RW (7243 5665/www.heidiklein.com). Notting Hill Gate tube. Open 10am-6pm Mon-Sat; noon-5pm Sun.
Head here for impeccably cut swimsuits, men's trunks and bikinis (from around £120). **Other location** *257 Pavillion Road, SW1X 0BP (7259 9418).*

Myla
74 Duke of York Square, King's Road, SW3 4LY (7730 0700/www.myla.com). Sloane Square tube. Open 10am-6.30pm Mon-Sat; noon-5pm Sun.
Myla's sumptuous silk, satin and lace designs are sexy but never tawdry, with bras from £60. **Other locations** *across the city.*

Odabash
48B Ledbury Road, W11 2AJ (7229 4299/ www.odabash.com). Notting Hill Gate tube. Open 10am-6pm Mon-Sat; noon-5pm Sun.
Expect sleek designs and a subtle colour palette at Melissa Odabash's swimwear boutique; most bikinis cost around £124.

Pistol Panties
75 Westbourne Park Road, W2 5QH (7229 5286/www.pistolpanties.com). Westbourne Park tube. Open noon-6pm Tue-Sat; 1-5pm Sun.
Bikinis are a mix of flirty, frilly, '50s-styles and super-glam gold numbers, plus cut-out swimsuits.

Tallulah Lingerie
65 Cross Street, N1 2BB (7704 0066/www.tallulah- lingerie.co.uk). Angel tube. Open by appointment Mon; 11am-6pm Tue-Fri; 10.30am- 6.30pm Sat; 12.30-5pm Sun.
This elegant boudoir has a dreamy selection of lingerie from the likes of Fleur T, La Perla and Lejaby – from everyday bras to silky smalls.

GOING OUT
BEAUTY
FASHION
PARTIES
FOOD
HEALTH
ECO
OUTDOORS
HOME
CHILDREN
PETS
TRANSPORT
RESOURCES

Menswear

A Butcher of Distinction
*11 Dray Walk, 91 Brick Lane, E1 6QL
(7770 6111). Liverpool Street tube/rail.
Open 10am-7pm daily.*
Labels such as Haversack, Nom de Guerre
and Steven Alan are strewn over butcher-
block tables and meat hooks at this east end
boutique. Look out for simple, beautifully cut
pieces from Margaret Howell's diffusion line
MHL, and London stalwart YMC.

Albam ★
*23 Beak Street, W1F 9RS (3157 7000/www.
albamclothing.com). Oxford Circus tube.
Open noon-7pm Mon-Sat; noon-5pm Sun.*
Number one in *Time Out London*'s 100 Best
Shops List 2008, Albam focuses on high-
quality, mainly British-made designs with a
subtle retro edge. The airy store stocks
timeless staples: supersoft jersey Ts, waffle-
knit cardies and Italian leather accessories.

B-Store
For listings, see p65.
Leftfield B-Store attracts the capital's fashion-
forward types, who snap up Peter Jensen's
patchwork sneakers and pieces by Bernhard
Willhelm, Siv Støldal and Cosmic Wonder.
Don't miss owners Matthew Murphy and
Kirk Beattie's excellent B Clothing label.

Bread & Honey
*205 Whitecross Street, EC1Y 8QP (7253
4455/www.backin10minutes.com). Barbican
tube or Old Street tube/rail. Open 10am-
6.30pm Mon-Wed, Fri; 10am-7pm Thur;
11am-6pm Sat.*
The friendly, streetwear-focused store-cum-
gallery is great for fashion classics. Check out
Harrington's by Baracutta, Duffer of St George
knits, Penfield bags and a decent women's
section to distract bored girlfriends.

Diverse Men
*286 Upper Street, N1 2TU (7359 0081/
www.diverseclothing.com). Angel tube.
Open 10.30am-6.30pm Mon-Sat; noon-
5.30pm Sun.*

The brother store to Diverse (at no.294) has
been kitting out Islingtonites with an eclectic
mix of designer labels since 1986. APC, Nom
de Guerre, Marc by Marc Jacobs, the painfully
cool Superfine and a cherry-picked range of
accessories are among the temptations.

Goodhood
*41 Coronet Street, N1 6HD (7729 3600/
www.goodhood.co.uk). Old Street tube. Open
11am-7pm Tue-Sat.*
Wedged in between a sex shop and a sorry,
boarded-up old warehouse, Goodhood is
Hoxton's glittering luxe streetwear specialist,
stocking cult Australian brands PAM and
Rittenhouse along with Copenhagen label
Wood Wood and some excellent accessories.

Library
*268 Brompton Road, SW3 2AS (7589
6569). South Kensington tube. Open 10am-
6.30pm Mon, Tue, Thur-Sat; 10am-7pm
Wed; 12.30-5.30pm Sun.*
Pieces by Alexander McQueen and Dries Van
Noten hang from Library's rails, but the
recent addition of Brit menswear designer
Lou Dalton and knitwear specialist Claire
Tough underlines its ahead-of-trend ethos.

Matches Menswear
*60-64 Ledbury Road, W11 2AJ (7221
0255/www.matchesfashion.com). Notting
Hill Gate tube. Open 10am-6pm Mon-Sat;
noon-6pm Sun.*
Perfect for 'investment pieces', Matches
stocks pricey high-fashion brands – including
Marc Jacobs, Martin Margiela, Miu Miu, Paul
Smith, Lanvin and Prada.
Other locations *across the city.*

Sefton
*271 Upper Street, N1 2UQ (7226 9822/
www.seftonfashion.com). Highbury &
Islington tube/rail. Open 10am-6.30pm
Mon-Wed, Sat; 10am-7pm Thur, Fri;
noon-6pm Sun.*
Check out cult pieces by Comme des Garçons,
Alexander McQueen and Marni at this
Islington boutique. Brit newcomers Poltock
& Walsh and younger lines such as Edwin
and Acne Jeans are also present and correct.

Lesley Craze Gallery

Ring by Jo Hayes Ward

LESLEY CRAZE GALLERY is an internationally recognised showcase for contemporary jewellery, metalwork and textiles.

33 - 35a Clerkenwell Green London EC1R 0DU
Email: info@lesleycrazegallery.co.uk Web: www.lesleycrazegallery.co.uk

Tel: 020 7608 0393

The only place to see the entire Kirk Originals collection plus the best in hand made spectacles and sunglasses from around the world. Prescription lenses fitted onsite

www.kirkoriginals.com
info@kirkoriginals.com
29 Floral St WC2E 9DP
Tel 020 7240 5055

KIRK ORIGINALS

GOING OUT

BEAUTY

FASHION

PARTIES

FOOD

HEALTH

ECO

OUTDOORS

HOME

CHILDREN

PETS

TRANSPORT

RESOURCES

City Secret

Short of funds, but in need of a dazzling frock? Try **Marcos & Trump** (146 Columbia Road, E2 7RG, 7739 9008), a diminutive emporium of lovely vintage and designer wear. If you can't afford the exquisite gowns, the hire service lets you borrow an otherwise unaffordable frock for a special event – perfect for the affluent of taste, but not of purse.

Vintage

Beyond Retro
For listings see p65.
Packed with over 10,000 items, Beyond Retro is an east end legend, with a loyal following of fashion students, stylists, musicians and other skint but savvy shoppers. It's great for classics like prom dresses, leather jackets and embroidered cowboy boots.

East End Thrift Store ★
Unit 1A Watermans Building Assembly Passage, E1 4UT (7423 9700/www.theeast endthriftstore.com). Stepney Green tube. Open 11am-6pm Mon-Wed, Sun; 11am-7pm Thur-Sat.
Run by vintage specialists who edit a vast stock to reflect current runway trends, the clue's in the name: 'thrift' rather than 'vintage', which means you get yesteryear classics at prices around the £7-£10 mark – unheard of in most of the capital's better-known vintage emporiums.

Lost 'N' Found
25A Camden Stables Market, NW1 8AH (7482 2848). Camden Town tube. Open 11am-6pm Mon-Fri; 10am-7pm Sat, Sun.
One of the best vintage shops in Camden market, Lost 'N' Found has a bias towards 1950s Americana, with T-Bird leather jackets and cowboy boots aplenty, along with '30s floor-length gowns, elegant vintage heels and lacy wedding dresses.

Old Hat
66 Fulham High Street, SW6 3LQ (7610 6558). Putney Bridge tube. Open 10.30am-6.30pm Mon-Sat.
Fight off the stylists and designers from brands like Burberry and Dunhill who frequent this men's vintage boutique, and you might discover a Savile Row suit for £100, a pair of pristine moleskin trousers or the perfect pair of scuffed vintage brogues.

Palette London
21 Canonbury Lane, N1 2AS (7288 7428/www.palette-london.com) Highbury & Islington tube/rail. Open 11am-6.30pm Mon- Wed, Fri, Sat; 11am-7pm Thur; noon-5.30pm Sun.
Owner Mark Ellis specialises in collectable designer vintage and avant-garde labels. He has a vast range of desirable vintage pieces from Pucci, Courrèges and Ossie Clark.

Shikasuki
67 Gloucester Avenue, NW1 8LD (7722 4442/www.shikasuki.com). Camden Town or Chalk Farm tube. Open 11am-7pm Mon-Sat; noon-7pm Sun.
Shikasuki stocks a well-edited (but not overpriced) array of clothes and accessories, with every item graded A to E, depending on its condition, and priced accordingly.

Vintage Hart
96 Church Road, SE19 2EZ (07982 184657/www.vintagehart.co.uk). Crystal Palace rail. Open noon-8pm Fri; noon-6pm Sat, Sun.
This diminutive boutique offers carefully chosen vintage finds from the '50s onwards. If you're dragging an unwilling partner along, the shop has the advantage of being attached to the White Hart pub – so everyone's happy.

What The Butler Wore
131 Lower Marsh, SE1 7AE (7261 1353/www.whatthebutlerwore.co.uk). Lambeth North tube. Open 11am-6pm Mon-Sat.
A colourful array of heels and impeccably clean 1960s and '70s frocks awaits at this charming little shop, presided over by owner Bridget Duffy and her resident cat, Binky.

Address Book Secrets
Henry Holland
Fashion designer

If you want to get a feel for London fashion, then **Dover Street Market** (17-18 Dover Street, W1S 4LT, 7518 0680, www.doverstreetmarket.com) is such a great concept – it's almost like a department store, but with all the best bits packed together in a smaller, more exclusive environment. There's a really good cross-section of names, like Comme des Garçons, David David and Fred Perry, plus younger jeans labels like Number Nine and April 77. On the ground floor, there's the most amazing collection of vintage watches and jewellery.

B-Store (24A Savile Row, W1S 2XE, 7734 6846, www.bstorelondon.com) is a small independent boutique that handpicks really good designers from around Europe; people like Peter Jensen and Bless. Its staff are very embedded in London's fashion scene: Matthew Murphy, who runs it, works a lot with Topman. He's a really friendly guy too, so you're never in there for less than 45 minutes. Agyness [Deyn] always goes in there when she's in town.

I love **Beyond Retro** (110-112 Cheshire Street, E2 6EJ, 7613 3636, www.beyondretro.com) – it's like a one-stop vintage supermarket. You can literally go and get lost in there for a whole day – take some mates along and make everyone try on stupid stuff. There's the feeling you have to actually hunt for the best things, which is always really satisfying. So many classic items in my wardrobe have come from there.

In June, **Graduate Fashion Week** (7298 6530 www.gfw.org.uk) is always really interesting – especially the Saint Martins show, because it's where the future of London's design talent will be showing. It's open to the public. All the graduating students from fashion schools all over the country show their final collections which are put to a board, and then they make a selection of the best. I was a judge last year and so were Albert Elbaz and Victoria Beckham – she was wandering around all the stalls afterwards, buying things.

Bistroteque (23-27 Wadeson Street, E2 9DR, 8983 7900, www. bistrotheque.com) is a real hangout for the fashion pack, but it doesn't feel at all snotty – more like going to your friend's house for dinner. It serves good, hearty food like fish and chips, and there's a really nice bar as well. They put on cabaret in the room downstairs, and at Christmas they do the best pantos I've ever been to, with hilarious drag queens.

The **Andaz Hotel** (40 Liverpool Street, EC2M 7QN, 7961 1234, www.andaz. com), which used to be the Great Eastern, hosts some of the best fashion parties. It's in such a great, central location and has about five restaurants – including a fantastic sushi place. The best thing about it is that there's an amazing, windowless room in the middle: an old Masonic temple with a marble staircase, decked out with big thrones in the centre. What more could you want?

GOING OUT
BEAUTY
FASHION
PARTIES
FOOD
HEALTH
ECO
OUTDOORS
HOME
CHILDREN
PETS
TRANSPORT
RESOURCES

GOING OUT

BEAUTY

FASHION

PARTIES

FOOD

HEALTH

ECO

OUTDOORS

HOME

CHILDREN

PETS

TRANSPORT

RESOURCES

Services

Keep your wardrobe in good repair with our recommended alterations and mending services, dry-cleaners and cobblers.

Alterations & repairs

British Invisible Mending Service
32 Thayer Street, W1U 2QT (7935 2487/ www.invisible-mending.co.uk). Open 8.30am-5.30pm Mon-Fri; 10am-1pm Sat.
These miracle workers extract threads from a hidden section of a damaged garment, then reweave the fibres to blend in any holes or tears. It costs from £40 per hole, plus VAT.

Designer Alterations
220A Queenstown Road, SW8 4LP (7498 4360/www.designeralterations.com). Queenstown Road rail. Open 9am-6pm Mon-Wed, Fri; 9am-8pm Thur; 10am-4pm Sat.
Repairs and alterations are reasonably priced at this well-established company – you'll pay around £40 to shorten the hem on a dress, for example.

First Tailored Alterations
85 Lower Sloane Street, SW1W 8DA (7730 1400). Sloane Square tube. Open 9am-6pm Mon-Fri.
This traditional tailor is particularly good at working with delicate fabrics such as chiffon and silk, as well as sheepskin and tweed.

KS Tailoring Services
Lower Ground Floor, 13 Savile Row, W1S 3NE (7437 9345). Piccadilly Circus tube. Open 9.30am-5.30pm Mon-Fri; 10am-2pm Sat. No credit cards.
Quite appropriately, given the location, KS is known for its excellent alterations of suits and shirts. As a sample

indicative price, shortening a pair of jacket sleeves comes in at £21 plus VAT.

Manuela Alterations
Oriel Court, Heath Street, NW3 6TE (7431 9283). Hampstead tube. Open 10am-6pm Mon-Fri; 10am-5pm Sat. No credit cards.
Regulars are full of praise for Manuela Alterations' speedy, good value shortening, hemming and taking in; to have a pair of trousers taken up costs from £16.

Stitchcraft
3rd Floor, 7 South Molton Street, W1K 5QG (7629 7919/www.stitchcraftalterations. co.uk). Bond Street tube. Open 9am-5pm Mon-Fri; 10am-4pm Sat. No credit cards.
Both repairs and alterations are offered at reasonable rates. They'll tackle anything, insisting that 'no job is too big or too small'.

Dry-cleaning

The **Textile Services Association** (8863 7755, www.tsa-uk.org) lists a network of dry-cleaners and launderers that comply to its code of practice.

Blossom & Browne's Sycamore

73A Clarendon Road, W11 4JF (7727 2635/ www.blossomandbrowne.com). Holland Park tube. Open 8.30am-5.30pm Mon-Wed, Fri; 8.30am-4.30pm Thur; 8.30am-3pm Sat.
With Royal warrants aplenty, you know your dry-cleaning is in safe hands. Prices aren't too steep (a two-piece suit costs from £12.50) and if you set up an account, clothes can be picked up and delivered back with minimum hassle.
Other locations *across the city.*

Celebrity Cleaners

30 Brewer Street, W1F 0SS (7437 5324). Piccadilly Circus tube. Open 8.30am-6.30pm Mon-Fri.
Thanks to its regular work with West End theatres, this place knows how to shift make-up or sweat stains from pretty much anything, whether it be a common or garden men's shirt or your favourite LBB.

James of London

32 Upper Tachbrook Street, SW1V 1SW (7630 6596). Victoria tube/rail. Open 8.30am-7.30pm Mon-Fri; 9am-7pm Sat.
James offers a highly recommended invisible mending service as well as pristine dry-cleaning, at very reasonable prices; two men's suits can be done for £12.

Jeeves of Belgravia

8-10 Pont Street, SW1X 9EL (7235 1101/ www.jeevesofbelgravia.co.uk). Knightsbridge or Sloane Square tube. Open 8.30am-7pm Mon-Fri; 8.30am-6pm Sat.
It's not cheap, but you get what you pay for at Jeeves. Precious designer pieces and delicates are a speciality, while pick-up and delivery are free. Knitwear costs from £16.50; an overcoat from £42.50. Repairs, laundry washes and alterations are also available.
Other locations *across the city.*

Lewis & Wayne

13-15 Elystan Street, SW3 3NU (7589 5075/ www.lewiswayne.co.uk). South Kensington tube. Open 8am-5pm Mon-Fri; 8.30am-12.30pm Sat.
Fifty years of experience ensure a quality service at this South Kensington dry-cleaners. Staff are confident tackling anything from skiwear to haute couture gowns and wedding dresses.

Master Cleaners

189 Haverstock Hill, NW3 4QG (7431 3725). Belsize Park Tube. Open 8am-7pm Mon-Wed, Fri; 8am-6pm Thur, Sat; 10am-4pm Sun.
Eco-warriors with grubby suits take note: Master Cleaners offer a greener, more gentle wash. Dry-cleaning a day dress costs from £11.50 at standard prices; using the gentler F-clean process is £17.50.

Peter & Falla

281 New King's Road, SW6 4RD (7731 3255). Parsons Green tube. Open 8am-7.30pm Mon-Fri; 8.30am-5.30pm Sat.
This specialist cleaner will take good care of your best leather, sheepskin and suede gear. Transforming a limp and bashed-up leather jacket costs from £45.

Valentino

56B New Oxford Street, WC1A 1ES (7436 1660). Tottenham Court Road tube. Open 8.30am-6pm Mon-Fri; 9am-1pm Sat.
Specialising in cleaning and de-staining delicate designer pieces, suede and leather, Valentino offers great value for money, charging a mere £7.50 to spruce up a suede jacket. On orders over £40, collection and delivery is free.

Village Klean

1-20 St Johns Hill, SW11 1SA (7350 2562/ www.villageklean.com.). Clapham Junction rail. Open 7am-8pm Mon-Fri; 9am-6pm Sat.
Hand-finished shirts are £2.20 and a silk blouse £4 at this smart, eco-friendly dry-cleaning chain. It also offers alterations and re-heeling, along with dry-cleaning pick-ups.
Other locations *across the city.*

GOING OUT
BEAUTY
FASHION
PARTIES
FOOD
HEALTH
ECO
OUTDOORS
HOME
CHILDREN
PETS
TRANSPORT
RESOURCES

Shoe repair

Broadway Shoe Repairs
2 Bank Chambers, Tooting High Street, SW17 0SU (8682 0618/www.broadway-engraving.co.uk). Tooting Broadway tube. Open 8am-6pm Mon-Fri; 9am-6pm Sat.
Reasonable prices are matched by speedy efficiency at Broadway, with cobblers who'll take on well-worn shoes most other shoe-menders would write off. Ask for Henry, who comes highly recommended.

Chelsea Green Shoe Company
31 Elystan Street, SW3 3NT (7584 0776). South Kensington tube. Open 8am-5.30pm Mon-Fri; 9am-1pm Sat.
Regulars love this reliable cobblers, where staff are happy to attend to cracked heels and frayed straps. Re-heeling costs from £6.

Fifth Avenue Shoe Repairs
41 Goodge Street, W1T 2PY (7636 6705). Goodge Street tube. Open 8am-6.30pm Mon-Fri; 10am-6pm Sat. No credit cards.
This traditional cobblers handles shoe repairs, bag repairs and key cutting in an old-fashioned shop that also stocks a small range of traditional men's shoes and accessories such as shoe polish and luggage.

Jimmy's Shoes
129 Essex Road, N1 2SN (7226 4737). Essex Road rail or 73 bus. Open 9am-5.30pm Mon-Sat.
With 30 years in the business, this stalwart will re-sole those flapping shoes in a jiffy. Re-heeling costs from £7.95, re-soling from £12.

Well Heeled
443 Bethnal Green Road, E2 9QH (7739 3608). Bethnal Green tube. Open 7am-5pm Mon-Fri; 8am-4pm Sat.
Ken Holmes is the man in charge of your favourite strappies and brogues – and he's a safe pair of hands. You won't catch him solving problems with a slick of glue; this east end cobbling institution is strictly a needle and thread man.
Other locations *across the city.*

Specialist services

Bobbi Specialist Dyer
Winchmore Hill, London N21 1NG (8360 6148/www.bobbispecialistshoedyer.com). Open by appointment only.
With 20 years' experience, Bobbi dyes shoes, gloves and bags to match special occasion outfits. A self-confessed perfectionist, she's coloured heels from the likes of Christian Louboutin, Emma Hope and Jimmy Choo.

Chalfont Dyers & Cleaners
222 Baker Street, NW1 5RT (7935 7316). Baker Street tube. Open 8.30am-6.30pm Mon-Fri; 9.30am-1pm Sat.
Bored of that white shirt? As long as it's made from natural fibres, the expert dyers here will do the rest, with prices from £40. Disastrous colour runs can also be dealt with.

Hand & Lock
86 Margaret Street, W1W 8TE (7580 7488/ www.handembroidery.com). Oxford Circus tube. Open 9am-5.30pm Mon-Fri.
The crème de la crème of bespoke hand embroidery since 1767, Hand & Lock have honed their skills on film costumery and the Royal family. Shirt monogramming, beading and custom embroidery are all in a day's work.

Julia Taylor
7289 3966. Open by appointment only.
If you've stained your favourite silk or satin shoes or need to dye bridesmaids' shoes to match their frocks, Taylor's your woman. She can also sew beads or appliqué lace on to shoes.

City Secret
Beloved but battered cashmere can be posted (rather than taken) to the **Cashmere Clinic** (Flat 5, 53 Redcliffe Gardens, SW10 9JJ, 7584 9806) to be magically returned to its former glory. Repairing pesky moth holes costs from £15, while basic cleaning is from £20.

Parties

GOING OUT
BEAUTY
FASHION
PARTIES
FOOD
HEALTH
ECO
OUTDOORS
HOME
CHILDREN
PETS
TRANSPORT
RESOURCES

Caterers

A little forward-planning means minimum party stress.

Delis

Atari-ya
20 James Street, W1U 1EH (7491 1178/ www.atariya.co.uk). Bond Street tube. Open 11am-8pm daily.
Sushi and sashimi platters are made to order (collection only) at this takeaway branch of the Japanese grocery chain. An extensive list of fish and seafood includes eel, squid, surf clam and, at the pricier end of the spectrum, sea urchin and snow crab leg meat.

Flavours
For listings, see p82.
Former *Masterchef* winner Julie Friend creates a great range of dishes using produce from her two north London delis. Menus often have a Mediterranean slant, but British grub – such as shepherd's pie followed by trifle – is popular too. A finger-food buffet for ten starts at £7.50 per head.

Hand Made Food
40 Tranquil Vale, SE3 0BD (8297 9966/ www.handmadefood.com). Blackheath rail.

BIRTHDAY CAKES

Bea's of Bloomsbury
44 Theobald's Road, WC1X 8NW (7242 8330/www.beasofbloomsbury. com). Holborn or Chancery Lane tube. Open 8am-6pm Mon-Fri; 10.30am-4pm Sat.
Pastry chef Bea Vo's masterpieces range from pecan-topped cheesecake to rich chocolate concoctions. Better still, 'build-a-cake' allows you to design your dream cake. Gold leaf on top? Passionfruit or praline buttercream? It's entirely up to you.

Cake Boy
Unit 2, Kingfisher House, Juniper Drive, SW18 1TX (7978 5555/www. cake-boy.com). Wandsworth Town rail. Open 8am-7pm Mon-Fri; 9am-6pm Sat.
Master pâtissier Eric Lanlard creates the most glamorous gateaux in town: the A-list wouldn't buy their wedding cakes anywhere else. Options range from simple sachertorte or cheesecake

(from £24) to elaborate bespoke creations (from £5.50 per serving).

Euphorium Bakery
202 Upper Street, N1 1RQ (7704 6906/www.euphoriumbakery.com). Highbury & Islington tube/rail. Open 7.30am-11pm Mon-Fri; 8am-9pm Sat; 9am-11pm Sun.
With a few days' notice, Euphorium will create your ideal centrepiece – a luscious dark chocolate mousse cake, perhaps, or a fraises des bois-soaked vanilla sponge with chantilly cream. Prices start at £13 and a message is free, piped on to the cake or inscribed on a chocolate plaque.
Other locations *across the city.*

Hummingbird Bakery
133 Portobello Road, W11 2DY (7229 6446/www.hummingbirdbakery.com). Notting Hill Gate tube. Open 10am-5.30pm Tue-Sat; 11am-5pm Sun.

Open 9am-5pm Mon, Wed-Fri, Sun; 9am-2pm Tue; 9am-5.30pm Sat.

Fergus and Vicky Clague will cater for events of all sizes, rustling up party food for as few as 25 people. Canapés are a speciality, with an international menu that includes Jamaican beef patties, spanakopita and parmesan gnocchi (£1.50 each). Ingredients are sourced as locally as possible, and meat is organic.

Mimosa

16 Half Moon Lane, SE24 9HU (7733 8838/www.mimosafoods.com). Herne Hill rail. Open 9am-6pm Mon-Fri; 9am-5.30pm Sat; 9.30am-3.30pm Sun.

Covering Herne Hill and its surrounds, Mimosa offers Moroccan- and French-themed spreads alongside the more usual finger food; you can borrow Moroccan dishes for perfect presentation. A buffet for a party of ten costs from £13.75 a head.

The Hummingbird bakes a mean birthday cake; the Red Velvet (a red-hued vanilla sponge with a hint of chocolate, covered with cream cheese) always goes down a treat. Messages can be iced on to cakes or cupcakes, if you order ahead. **Other location** *47 Old Brompton Road, SW7 3JP (7584 0055).*

Konditor & Cook

10 Stoney Street, SE1 9AD (7407 5100/www.konditorandcook.com). Borough tube or London Bridge tube/rail. Open 7.30am-6pm Mon-Fri; 8.30am-5.30pm Sat.

As well as fabulous traditional birthday cakes (including the legendary Curly Whirly cake), this place is famed for its colourful little 'magic cakes': a letter can be iced on to each fondant-covered cake, spelling out a birthday message. **Other locations** *across the city.*

Mr Christian's

11 Elgin Crescent W11 2JA (7229 0501/www.mrchristians.co.uk). Notting Hill Gate tube. Open 6am-7pm Mon-Fri; 6am-6pm Sat; 7am-5pm Sun.

Pop into this Notting Hill deli and you might spot a local A-lister making arrangements for a small dinner party, or planning party catering for up to 200 guests. An enormous menu runs from tempting canapés to à la carte menus, along with sumptuous salads.

Pie Man

16 Cale Street, SW3 3QU (7737 7799/www.thepieman.co.uk). South Kensington or Sloane Square tube. Open 8am-5pm Mon-Fri; 8am-1pm Sat.

If you've ever tried anything from Murray Tollemache's Chelsea deli, you'll know you're in for a treat with his party catering service. A canapé selection (minimum 25 guests) starts at £12 per head and ranges from simple shots of gazpacho to the more elaborate likes of seared scallops with pea purée.

Rosslyn Deli

For listings, see p132.

The Rosslyn will cater for any event, with a finger-food buffet or an imaginative two-bite canapé list (from £1.35-£1.55 per portion), ranging from *FT*-wrapped mini fish and chips to lentil balls with spicy apricot sauce. It also offers various dinner party menus.

Independent caterers

Amaze in Taste

8981 8844/www.amazeintaste.com.

If you want your guests to fill up on proper food but still be able to mingle, serve 'bowl food': mushroom risotto with parmesan and parsley, perhaps, or lamb tagine and couscous. More traditional party food includes finger-food buffets, from £10 per head for 25 people.

Ang-McGuire Catering

8675 2577/www.angmcguirecatering.com.

Balham-based caterer Judy Ang-McGuire is Malaysian, though her cuisine ranges all over Asia. Presentation is polished, and there's no

GOING OUT
BEAUTY
FASHION
PARTIES
FOOD
HEALTH
ECO
OUTDOORS
HOME
CHILDREN
PETS
TRANSPORT
RESOURCES

GOING OUT

BEAUTY

FASHION

PARTIES

FOOD

HEALTH

ECO

OUTDOORS

HOME

CHILDREN

PETS

TRANSPORT

RESOURCES

A PERFECT MIX

Endlessly refilling your guests' glasses is no way to spend a party: instead, think about investing in a barman for the evening, or even hiring a mobile bar.

At Your Service (7610 8610, www.ays.co.uk) provides bar staff, while sister company Bamboo has experienced cocktail 'mixologists'. Prices start from £25 per hour. Alternatively, **High Society** (7228 0333, www.high-society.co.uk) charges a set rate of £49 per barman for the first four hours, then £10.75 per hour.

London's Mobile Bar (07757 025470, www.eventcocktails.com) offers mobile bars and mixologists, charging £135 for one person, then £95 each for extra staff. Or you can just hire the equipment, from mixers and blenders to strainers, tumblers, flutes and tongs.

Shaker Events (0870 720 2877, www.shaker-events.com) supplies all manner of bars, including a bamboo-clad tiki version, from which its professional bartenders will mix up a storm of cocktails. Prices start at £350 for a four-hour service, plus stock and VAT.

Wedding Trikes (07958 722251, www.weddingtrikes.com) offers the Cocktail Camper: a VW camper converted into a cocktail bar (hire from £1,200 for a 12-hour dry hire, with one helper), complete with its own sound system. More low key (and cheaper) is its Pimm's Trike.

If beery blurs are more your thing, **Rent a Keg** (0800 977 5113, www.rent-a-keg.com) has a good range of ice-cold lager kegs (88 pints of Becks, delivery, set-up and tap hire for £185), plus ales and cider. Proper pint glasses and a bar are also available.

minimum spend or number of guests; costs tend to average £20 per head plus overheads. It's best to give at least a week's notice.

El Vergel
7357 0057/www.elvergel.co.uk.
Stella de Garcia and Kiko Sanhueza blend Latin American and Mediterranean influences to create fabulous fusion food. Canapés (from £8 a head) might include Chilean village bread with refried bean spread or smoked salmon and guacamole. Vegetarian finger buffets served on fresh banana leaves cost around £15 per person, dinners from £25.

Gorgeous Gourmets ★
8944 7771/www.gorgeousgourmets.co.uk.
This Wimbledon-based stalwart deals in tried and trusted menus that span the globe – from traditional British cheddar scones to filo tartlets of devilled crab salad – and offers a range of catering options, including a finger-food buffet for ten from £16.25 per head (plus VAT and delivery).

Personal Chef Lucian
8699 7844/www.cheflucian.com.
Happy to cater for 20 or 200, chef Lucian Aldritch has worked with the likes of Marco Pierre White and Jamie Oliver. He can conjure up a wonderful array of party options, with a cold buffet for 35 starting at £350.

Simply Catering
07932 377069/www.simplycatering.co.uk.
Crowd-pleasing canapés, finger and bowl food, plus more unusual offerings such as the Cypriot BBQ, have helped to establish Theo Stylianou's reputation for approachable food at competitive prices. Finger buffet menus start from £5.50 per person, with a minimum order of 20. Service covers north London only.

Skye Cooks
07939 592724/www.skyecooks.co.uk.
Skye Cooks' imaginative party food is made from fairtrade and organic meat, fish and veg. Vegetarian and vegan menus are a speciality: think soba noodle and roast pumpkin salad, or aubergine and chickpea curry. A finger-food buffet for 40 costs from £15 per head.

theclerkenwellkitchen
catering for all events
celebrate
in our lovely venue with garden terrace
or at your chosen location

02071019959   www.theclerkenwellkitchen.co.uk

Profi - Dance Studios
...chin-up, smile & dance...

Rumba
Salsa   Ballroom
Cha-Cha-Cha   Freestyle   Argentine Tango
Foxtrot   - Every Friday from 20:30 till 23:30
- Dance Parties with Dance Classes   Rock'n'Roll   Jive
- Fully-Licensed Bar Open

www.profi-dance.com/events
POSK, 238-246 King Street, Hammersmith, W6 0RF

timeout.com
The hippest online guide to over 50
of the world's greatest cities

Time Out
Online

Party shops

From dressing-up to decorations.

Fancy dress

Angels
119 Shaftesbury Avenue, WC2H 8AE (7836 5678/www.fancydress.com). Leicester Square or Tottenham Court Road tube. Open 9.30am-5.30pm Mon, Tue, Thur, Fri; 10.30am-7pm Wed.
London's doyenne of fancy dress hires out an unparalleled array of outfits, with prices from £80 plus VAT. The website is devoted to cheaper costumes to buy, from naughty nurse and Batman outfits to Yoda costumes for dogs.

Contemporary Wardrobe
The Horse Hospital, Colonnade, WC1N 1HX (7713 7370/www.contemporarywardrobe. com). Russell Square tube. Open viewings noon-6pm Mon-Sat. Hire by appointment.
This specialist hire company has some gems among its 15,000-strong collection, including vintage Dior and Biba pieces, and outfits worn by pop icons such as David Bowie and the Beatles. Weekly hire prices for outfits are around £75, plus VAT.

Escapade
150 Camden High Street, NW1 0NE (7485 7384/www.escapade.co.uk). Camden Town tube. Open 10am-7pm Mon-Fri; 10am-6pm Sat; noon-5pm Sun.
The shop is always crammed with customers trying on wigs or peeking through sequin-encrusted masks. Outfits-wise, there are cheaper ensembles to buy outright, or higher-quality costumes to hire.

Mad World
69-85 Tabernacle Street, EC2A 4BA (0800 783 6582/www.madworldfancydress.com). Old Street tube. Open 9.30am-7pm Mon-Wed, Fri; 9.30am-8pm Thur; 10am-5pm Sat.
There's a mind-boggling array of costumes to hire, from pantomine horse two-parters to sequin-studded basques. If you'd prefer to throw caution – and your costume – to the winds, the company's make-up artists also offer body-painting.

Pantaloons
119 Lupus Street, SW1V 3EN (7630 8330/www. pantaloons.co.uk). Pimlico tube. Open 11am-5pm Mon, Tue; 11am-6pm Wed; 11am-7pm Thur; 11am-8pm Fri; 10am-6pm Sat.
Choose from more than 2,000 hire costumes, from Ali G's yellow tracksuit to Buzz Lightyear's spacesuit. A week's hire starts at £35. For a unique look, splash out on the 'haute couture' service, where your costume is custom-designed and fitted.

Prangsta Costumiers ★
304 New Cross Road, SE14 6AF (8694 9869/www.prangsta.com). New Cross Gate rail. Open 11am-7pm Mon-Sat.
More discerning dresser-uppers adore Prangsta's extravagant, beautifully made costumes. Burlesque-style basques and gowns are a forte, but you'll also find circus ringmaster suits, silky 1930s frocks and more. Hire ranges from £30 to £100 or so.

Party supplies

Circus Circus
176 Wandsworth Bridge Road, SW6 2UQ (7731 4128/www.circuscircus.co.uk). Fulham Broadway tube. Open 10am-6pm Mon-Sat; 10am-2pm Sun.
Head here for cheap and cheerful supplies, from multicoloured balloons to bosoms (of the fake plastic variety). There's a great selection of fancy dress costumes and accessories too, including luxuriant stick-on moustaches.

Oscar's Den
127-129 Abbey Road, NW6 4SL (7328 6683/ www.oscarsden.com). Swiss Cottage tube/ West Hampstead tube/rail. Open 9.30am-5.30pm Mon-Sat; 10am-2pm Sun.
Everything party-related, from invitations, helium balloons, paper plates and fireworks, to bubble machines and bouncy castles for hire.

Party Party
9-13 Ridley Road, E8 2NP (7254 5168/ www.ppshop.co.uk) Dalston Kingsland rail/67, 76, 149 bus. Open 9am-5.30pm Mon-Thur; 9am-6.30pm Fri, Sat.
This cheap and cheerful three-floor shop is filled to the brim with party paraphernalia.

Party Plus
4 Acton Lane, W4 5NB (8987 8404/www. partyplus.co.uk). Chiswick Park tube. Open 9.30am-5pm Mon-Fri; 9am-5pm Sat.
Party Plus is packed with every kind of party goods imaginable, from brightly coloured piñatas to bar mitzvah balloons.

GOING OUT

BEAUTY

FASHION

PARTIES

FOOD

HEALTH

ECO

OUTDOORS

HOME

CHILDREN

PETS

TRANSPORT

RESOURCES

PRESENTS BY POST

A monthly delivery of little luxuries has to be the ultimate gift.

Neal's Yard Dairy
7500 7653/www.nealsyarddairy shop.co.uk.
What cheese lover wouldn't covet a subscription to Neal's Yard Dairy's Cheese of the Month service? Each delivery comprises four superb cheeses – often unusual, small-scale, artisan affairs – which are sent out with tasting notes and information on the cheesemakers. Options range from one-off deliveries (£47) to quarterly (£180) and monthly boxes (£520), while a more modestly sized bi-monthly three-cheese box is £222.

Panty Postman
7229 4904/www.pantypostman.com.
Pamper your beloved with Coco Ribbon's ingenious Panty Postman service. Every three months, two pairs of gorgeous smalls (choose between thongs or briefs) will land on the lucky recipient's doorstep. At £58 a year, it seems a small price to pay for a resplendent knicker drawer.

Real Flower Company
01730 818300/www.realflowers.co.uk.
What could be more romantic than receiving a hand-tied bouquet of seasonal, headily scented roses every month for a year? True love doesn't come cheap, though, with prices starting at £420 per year for the posy-sized option, not including postage.

Stone, Vine & Sun
01962 712351/www.stonevine.co.uk.
Wine merchants can seem offputtingly stuffy – but not the friendly Stone, Vine & Sun. One-off gift boxes are available, or you can opt for a gift that keeps on giving with the Doorstep Dozen (from £72.50/month). This brings a monthly (or bi-monthly) case of reds and whites, mixing classic buys with notable new discoveries and with tasting notes included.

GOING OUT

BEAUTY

FASHION

PARTIES

FOOD

HEALTH

ECO

OUTDOORS

HOME

CHILDREN

PETS

TRANSPORT

RESOURCES

Venues

Perfect party venues – whatever your budget.
For children's parties, *see p176*.

CENTRAL

Bourne & Hollingsworth
*28 Rathbone Place, W1T 1JF (7636 8228/
www.bourneandhollingsworth.com). Goodge
Street or Tottenham Court Road tube.
Available for hire 5pm-midnight Mon-Thur,
Sun; 5pm-12.30am Sat. Capacity 90
standing. Minimum spend £1,500.*
Hire out this soigné little one-room basement
bar (available any night but Friday) for small
but select gatherings. The 1920s-style decor
and floral wallpaper is sweet without being
twee, while good cocktails are another draw.
There's a decent sound system and decks,
plus a screen and projector.

Carpenter's Arms
*68-70 Whitfield Street, W1T 4EY (7580
3186). Goodge Street tube. Available for hire
venue noon-midnight Sat, Sun; 1st floor
noon-midnight Mon-Wed, Sat, Sun. Capacity
venue 200 standing; 1st floor 50 standing.
Minimum spend venue from £2,500; 1st
floor from £400.*

This boho boozer has three areas for hire.
Downstairs, the backroom has a kitsch,
working men's club feel thanks to its '70s-
style floral wallpaper and bench seating; for
more intimate gatherings, there's a smaller
front-of-bar space. The real gem is upstairs,
where a second bar leads on to one of
Fitzrovia's prettier outdoor drinking spots: a
small, wooden-decked terrace with four
tables, fairy light-draped bird cages and a
back wall decorated with bird prints.

Cellar Door
*Zero Aldwych, WC2R 0HT (7240 8848).
Covent Garden or Temple tube. Available
for hire 4pm-1am daily. Capacity venue
60 standing; private room 60 standing.
Minimum spend venue from £2,000;
private room from £500.*
Once a gentlemen's public convenience, this
place has been transformed into a suitably
louche bar, often host to jazz and cabaret
nights. Lipstick-red walls and racy toilets (the
clear glass turns opaque when the door's
locked) add risqué appeal, while clever design
makes the space feel intimate rather than
claustrophobic. An SMS jukebox allows you
to choose tunes without leaving your seat,
and the cocktails are inspired.

Positively 4th Street
*119 Hampstead Road, NW1 3EE (7388
5380/www.positively4thstreet.co.uk). Warren
Street tube/Euston tube/rail. Available for
hire 5-11pm Mon-Thur; 5pm-1am Fri; 7pm-
1am Sat. Capacity 120. Hire charge £135.
Minimum spend £1,500.*
A few minutes' walk from Warren Street
tube, Positively 4th Street is a little-known
gem. Part Prohibition-style speakeasy, part
Japanese diner, it serves inventive cocktails
and Japanese food in seductive surrounds:

> ## City Secret
>
> Celebrate with crafts rather than
> cocktails at the **Make Lounge** (49-
> 51 Barnsbury Street, N1 1TP, 7609
> 0275, www.themakelounge.com).
> Host to some of London's niftiest
> workshops, the lounge also hosts
> private parties (from around £45 a
> head for three hours), where you can
> learn to make anything from sparkly
> jewellery to flirty fascinator hats.
> Bring your own wine or champagne
> to help the inspiration flow.

think deep red decor, art deco mirrors and sultry lighting. Bring your own decks or simply plug in the iPod; there's also a mic and projector for more arty entertainment.

NORTH

Harrison
28 Harrison Street, WC1H 8JF (7278 3966/www.harrisonbar.co.uk). King's Cross tube/rail. Available for hire noon-11.30pm Sat. Capacity 100 standing. Minimum spend £300.
A stone's throw from King's Cross and in fine fettle after a 2008 refurbishment, the Harrison is a warm, inviting place to throw a party. You can rent out the entire pub on Saturday nights and make full use of the DJ decks, PA and stage at no extra charge – or just connect up your iPod. The pub can get an extended licence a few times a year, so ask nicely and you may get lucky.

Monkey Chews ⭐
3 Queens Crescent, NW5 4EP (7267 6406/ www.monkeychews.com). Chalk Farm tube. Available for hire 5-11pm Mon-Thur; 5pm-1am Fri, Sat; noon-11pm Sun. Capacity private room 60 standing/30 seated. Hire charge £75. Minimum spend £500.
The upstairs room at this hip lounge bar is the perfect setting for wild and wonderful parties – even if this place is slightly off the beaten track. Stripped wooden flooring, velvet banquette seating and dim red lighting create a suitably louche backdrop; at one end of the room is the bar, backlit with pink fairy lights, while opposite there's a stage and DJ booth. Canapés are available on request from the downstairs restaurant.

Old Queen's Head
44 Essex Road, N1 8LN (7354 9993/www. theoldqueenshead.com). Angel tube. Available for hire noon-midnight Mon-Wed, Sun; noon-1am Thur. Capacity private room 200 standing/100 seated. Minimum spend from £1,000.
The elegantly proportioned upstairs room offers a vast parquet dancefloor, professional sound system and proper DJ booth, along

SPECIAL SERVICES

Boothnation
7613 5576/www.boothnation.com.
Always forget to take party pictures in the heat of the moment? Hire a mobile photo booth for the evening and watch as your guests squeeze in to strike a pose. The Classic Booth is a 1950s US import, but for sheer glamour it's hard to beat the sparkly, silver-clad Glitterbox, complete with silver lamé curtains. Prices include on-the-day prints, and start at £1,545 for four hours.

Lola's on Ice
07871 797260/www.lolason ice.co.uk.
Lola's purple-painted van dispenses gloriously grown-up ice-creams and sorbets – think burnt orange caramel ice-cream or crisp gin and tonic sorbet – made from fresh, organic ingredients. Hire within London costs £200 for two hours, then £3 per double scoop of ice-cream; you get to choose six flavours, so pick wisely and well.

London Jukeboxes
8318 2852/www.london-jukeboxes.com.
Personalise your party soundtrack by hiring out a cool retro jukebox. Options range from the 50-CD Wurlitzer-shaped Rockola Bubbler (£245) to the boxy, all-vinyl Jakovich (£165); you can choose the tunes you want loaded. Delivery is charged outside SE postcodes.

with a well-stocked bar and artfully battered chesterfields. If that's beyond your means, smaller private areas (with a capacity of up to 20 people each) can be booked either upstairs or in the downstairs bar for £50 – just beware your guests getting snarled up in long queues to get in.

GOING OUT

BEAUTY

FASHION

PARTIES

FOOD

HEALTH

ECO

OUTDOORS

HOME

CHILDREN

PETS

TRANSPORT

RESOURCES

GOING OUT BEAUTY FASHION PARTIES FOOD HEALTH ECO OUTDOORS HOME CHILDREN PETS TRANSPORT RESOURCES

Paradise by Way of Kensal Green

19 Kilburn Lane, W10 4AE (8969 0098/ www.theparadise.co.uk). Kensal Green tube/ Kensal Rise rail. Available for hire noon-midnight Mon-Wed, Sun; noon-1am Thur; noon-2am Fri, Sat. Capacity reading room 14 seated/40 standing; dining room 20 seated/70 standing; music room 50 seated/ 150 standing. Minimum spend music room £3,000 Fri, call for details other days; dining room £1,000; reading room £300.

This deliciously theatrical gastropub offers three different rooms. Downstairs, the book-lined reading room hosts private dinners or 'host a roast' three-course feasts (£29 a head). Upstairs there's a more secluded and opulently decorated dining room, with a door leading on to the roof terrace. Finally, there's the spacious music room, complete with deer antlers, a stuffed peacock and a professional-quality sound system and decks.

Rosemary Branch

2 Shepperton Road, N1 3DT (7704 2730/ www.rosemarybranch.co.uk). Old Street tube/ rail, then 21, 76, 141 bus. Available for hire noon-11pm Mon-Thur; noon-midnight Fri, Sat; noon-10.30pm Sun. Capacity venue 200 standing; private room 80 standing; theatre 90 seated. Hire charge venue from £5,000; private room £200-£500; theatre £200.

This mellow pub and theatre offers a beautifully decorated function room, with startling pink-flowered wallpaper, stripped floors and an ornate bar. With a proper sound system, film-screening facilities and decks on request, it's well set up for celebrations. If you're feeling ambitious, you can hire out the theatre and put on your own production; the hire price includes technical support, lighting and use of the battered grand piano.

EAST

dreambagsjaguarshoes

34-36 Kingsland Road, E2 8DA (7729 5830/ www.dreambagsjaguarshoes.com). Old Street tube/rail. Available for hire noon-midnight Mon; noon-1am Tue-Fri; 5pm-1am Sat; noon-12.30am Sun. Capacity private room 100 standing. Minimum spend £500.

This former shoe shop-turned bar remains a cornerstone of the East End's drinking scene. Changing art exhibitions hang against the white and turquoise wallpaper, while trendy regulars lounge on slouchy couches. The brick-walled basement can be hired out for parties (mainly Monday to Wednesday). You can't choose the music, though, so only those who like electro and alt-rock need apply.

Drunken Monkey

222 Shoreditch High Street, E1 6PJ (7392 9606/www.thedrunkenmonkey.co.uk). Liverpool Street tube/rail. Available for hire noon-midnight daily. Capacity venue 250 standing; private rooms (2) 28-35 standing/ 12-15 seated. Minimum spend venue £2,000-£7,000; private rooms free.

Lit by glowing paper lanterns and serving dim sum as well as drinks, the Drunken Monkey is a raucous, rollicking party venue. Your options include a quieter private dining area, plus 'concubine rooms' along the sides that seat 12. For serious partying, the entire venue can be hired out. Music is loud and housey, while stellar staff do their utmost to accommodate special party requests.

Gramaphone

60-62 Commercial Street, E1 6LT (7377 5332/www.thegramaphone.co.uk). Aldgate East tube. Available for hire noon-2.30am Mon-Fri; 9am-2.30am Sat; noon-midnight Sun. Capacity private room 200 standing. Hire charge £150-£300.

Popular with band and club promoters, the Gramaphone's basement is also perfect for big birthday bashes. Decks are set up so you can bring your own DJs; if you'd prefer a band to play, the hire fee includes full PA and engineer. The battered wooden floor and furniture and low-level lighting are worn-in but welcoming; best of all, you have your own bar, with staff serving until 2.30am.

SOUTH

Balham Bowls Club ★

7-9 Ramsden Road, SW12 8QX (8673 4700/www.antic-ltd.com). Balham tube/rail. Available for hire 4-11pm Mon-Thur; 4pm-

midnight Fri; noon-midnight Sat; noon-
11pm Sun. Capacity private rooms (2)
50-100 standing. Hire charge £100-£250.
Once home to Balham's Bowls Club, this
charming venue still brims with original
fixtures, from the old wooden scoreboard and
framed rosettes on the wall to the wonky
seating. The entire right-hand side is
available for hire, and perfect for anything
from a quirky wedding reception to a proper
birthday knees-up. The smaller front room
can hold 50 people, but for larger dos the
doors open up and the room extends into the
snooker hall. Dancing to tunes from your
iPod is encouraged, while food can be
arranged on request. *See also p33.*

Bar du Musée
17 Nelson Road, SE10
9JB (8305 3091/www.
bardumusee.com). Cutty
Sark DLR. Available for
hire 7pm-1am Mon-Fri,
Sun; 7pm-2am Sat.
Capacity venue 80 seated/
250 standing; private room
20 seated/50 standing. Hire
charge venue call for prices;
private room £150.
This Greenwich bistro and late-night bar
has a sophisticated party space in the shape
of the adjoining George Room. Despite not
having its own bar (an obliging waiter takes
the drinks orders), it's a charming room, with
a lofty ceiling, granite-topped tables (which
can be arranged or removed as you please),
walls adorned with etchings and paintings,
and welcoming leather sofas. Music can be
provided courtesy of your own iPod (just
plug it in and you're good to go), while
canapés can be arranged. Perfect for more
elegant gatherings.

Dusk
339 Battersea Park Road, SW11 4LS (7622
2112/www.duskbar.co.uk). Battersea Park
rail. Available for hire 6pm-midnight Tue-
Wed; 6pm-1am Thur; 6pm-2am Fri, Sat;
call for details Mon, Sun. Capacity venue
300 standing; private areas (4) 50-150
standing. Hire charge venue £400-£800.
Minimum spend £2,000-£4,200. Private
areas free.
This sleek, candlelit cocktail bar makes for a
pleasingly grown-up party venue – and one
that's worth seeking out, despite its slightly
out-of-the-way location. There are four
different party areas to choose from: the
Montgomery lounge, the VIP area, the
cocktail tables or the larger private playroom.
On quieter nights, exclusive hire of the whole
bar is sometimes available; call the venue for
details. *See also p28.*

Harrison's
15-19 Bedford Hill,
SW12 9EX (8675 6900/
www.harrisonsbalham.com).
Balham tube/rail. Available
for hire noon-midnight Mon-Wed,
Sun; noon-1am Thur-Sat. Capacity
private room 15 seated/40 standing.
Minimum spend £400 Mon-Wed, Sun;
£800 Thur-Sat.
Hidden away at the bottom of a spiral
staircase leading off the plush main
restaurant lies Harrisons' private bar. Lined
with leather banquettes, and with its own
Barbarella-ish bar, it's totally separate from
the rest of the venue and provides a
sophisticated setting for a really special
occasion. Music comes in the form of an
MP3 connection, the cocktails are mixed to
perfection, and food can be arranged to suit
your needs.

GOING OUT

BEAUTY

FASHION

PARTIES

FOOD

HEALTH

ECO

OUTDOORS

HOME

CHILDREN

PETS

TRANSPORT

RESOURCES

Hide Bar

39-45 Bermondsey Street, SE1 3XF (7403 6655/www.thehidebar.com). London Bridge tube/rail. Available for hire 10am-11pm Mon; 10am-midnight Tue; 10am-1am Wed, Thur; 10am-2am Fri; 5pm-2am Sat. Capacity venue 100 standing; private room 50 standing. Minimum spend venue £5,000; private room free.

Known for its stellar cocktails (*see p28*), Hide is also nicely set up for parties. Behind the main bar there's a low-lit lounge with leather seating, beautiful wallpaper and a chandelier made from crystal decanter tops, available for private hire. Alternatively, enquire about hiring the whole place out. The cocktail-making classes are especially popular with discerning hen parties.

WEST

Defectors Weld

170 Uxbridge Road, W12 8AA (8749 0008/ www.defectors-weld.com). Shepherd's Bush tube. Available for hire noon-midnight Mon-Thur; noon-1am Fri, Sat; noon-11pm Sun. Capacity 50 seated/70 standing. Minimum spend £300-£800 Mon-Thur, Sun; £1,100-£1,200 Fri, Sat.

Hidden away from the after-work throng crowding the bar below, the private room has become a hip photo-shoot location of late, thanks to its muted colour palette and country house-style decor. By night it becomes a cosy party venue, probably better suited to dining and conversation than raving (the bar menu is top-notch, and party food can be arranged on request). That said, you can bring your own DJs (decks provided), or music can be piped up from downstairs. Attentive staff and stylish surrounds give this place the feel of a private members' club, at a fraction of the cost.

Grand Union

45 Woodfield Road, W9 2BA (7286 1886). Westbourne Park tube. Available for hire noon-11pm Mon-Thur; noon-midnight Fri, Sat; noon-10.30pm Sun. Capacity private room 60 standing (minimum 20). Minimum spend call for details.

The Grand Union is ideal for a low-key summer celebration – although if you hire the downstairs room, you may have to share the outside canalside space with the pub's regulars. For a price, however, it can all be yours. In summer there's no better spot to tuck into a jug of Pimms and make the most of the outdoor barbecue grill (even if the views are more urban than idyllic, thanks to the bus depot opposite). As night draws in, retire into the snug indoor space, which has its own bar and a selection of board games.

Idlewild

55 Shirland Road, W9 2JD (7266 9198/ www.ruby.uk.com/idlewild). Warwick Avenue tube. Open 4-11.30pm Mon-Thur; 4pm-midnight Fri, 11am-midnight Sat; 11am-11pm Sun. Capacity private room 80 standing. Minimum spend £1,500-£3,000.

This modish Maida Vale pub has bookable booths on the ground floor, but the real gem is on the first floor. Head straight up the magnificent staircase (lined with cases of framed insects and butterflies) to the grand, petrol-blue cocktail lounge. Here, stately Murano glass chandeliers and floor-to-ceiling draped windows will wow even the most jaded gastropub-goer. There's a fierce sound system, along with decks, and canapés are available on request. As you'd expect, there's a sizeable minimum spend.

Westbourne House

65 Westbourne Grove, W2 4UJ (7229 2233/ www.westbournehouse.net). Bayswater or Royal Oak tube. Available for hire 11am-11.30pm Mon-Thur; 11am-midnight Fri, Sat; 11am-11pm Sun. Capacity private areas (3) 25-40 standing. Hire charge £100 Mon-Thur, Sun; £200 Fri, Sat.

This handsome venue is part cosy gastropub, part sleek cocktail bar – and it works. Expert Italian bar staff mix cracking cocktails from a list designed by drinks supremo Mat Perovetz, with treats like the dangerous 'martini with a spot': Plymouth gin with vermouth and a spot of Pernod absinthe. Rather than private rooms, there are three mid-sized areas that can be reserved, including a mezzanine space.

Food

GOING OUT

BEAUTY

FASHION

PARTIES

FOOD

HEALTH

ECO

OUTDOORS

HOME

CHILDREN

PETS

TRANSPORT

RESOURCES

Cafés & restaurants

From bring-your-own bargains to the capital's most romantic spots for a candlelit tryst – plus where to find a decent dinner after midnight.

Breakfast & brunch

CENTRAL

Crescent
Montcalm Hotel Nikko, 34-40 Great Cumberland Place, W1H 7TW (7402 4288/ www.montcalm.co.uk). Marble Arch tube. Meals served 7-10am Mon-Fri; 7-11am, 6-10.30pm Sat, Sun. ££.
The Crescent offers an exquisitely presented Japanese breakfast of grilled fish, miso soup, rice and *onsen tamago* (lightly poached egg).

Dehesa
25 Ganton Street, W1F 9BP (7494 4170/ www.dehesa.co.uk). Oxford Circus tube. Meals served noon-11pm Mon-Fri; 10am-11pm Sat; noon-11pm Sun. ££.
Head here for a Spanish-Italian brunch of Tuscan sausages, scrambled duck eggs with morcilla, or *churros* with thick hot chocolate, served weekends only.

Fernandez & Wells
For listings see p90. £.
Indulge in a breakfast bun brimming with pancetta and egg mayonnaise, washed down with a perfect cappuccino.

NORTH

Brilliant Kids Café & Arts Centre
For listings see p166. £.
Organic sausages and bacon from Devon Rose and buttery scrambled eggs start the day off in style at this child-friendly café.

Flavours
10 Campdale Road, N7 0EA (7281 6565/ www.delibelly.com). Tufnell Park tube. Meals served 10am-6pm Tue; 9.30am-6pm Wed-Fri; 10am-6pm Sat; 10am-2pm Sun. £.
This modest little café-deli tempts with its overflowing baskets of artisan breads and delicious (and immense) almond croissants.

Ottolenghi
287 Upper Street, N1 2TZ (7288 1454/ www.ottolenghi.co.uk). Angel tube/Highbury & Islington tube/rail. Meals served 8am-11pm Mon-Sat; 9am-7pm Sun. £.
Heaped plates of scrambled eggs and salmon or moreish cinnamon French toast with fruit compôte are served at communal tables at this cool, white-painted deli and bakery.
Other locations *across the city.*

EAST

Clerkenwell Kitchen ★
27-31 Clerkenwell Close, EC1R 0AT (7101 9959/www.theclerkenwellkitchen.co.uk). Angel tube/Farringdon tube/rail. Meals served 8am-5pm Mon-Fri. £.
Full English breakfasts, made with free-range and organic produce, or porridge with fruit compôte are prepared in the open kitchen; if you're lucky, pancakes may be on the menu.

Climpson & Sons
67 Broadway Market, E8 4PH (7812 9829/ www.climpsonandsons.com). Bethnal Green tube/London Fields rail. Meals served 8am-4pm Mon-Fri; 8.30am-4pm Sat; 9am-3pm Sun. £. No credit cards.

GOING OUT

BEAUTY

FASHION

PARTIES

FOOD

HEALTH

ECO

OUTDOORS

HOME

CHILDREN

PETS

TRANSPORT

RESOURCES

City Secret

If the very idea of getting out of bed is all too much, call in **Brunch Bed** (07527 049327, www.brunchbed. com), who'll deliver breakfast to your doorstep. Offerings are more of the croissant and freshly squeezed orange juice variety than the full English, with prices starting at £20 for two. The service is currently only available in west London, and you need to give a day's notice.

Coffees are faultless and breakfasts inspired: smoked salmon on toast with wasabi mayo, perhaps, or spiced baharat beans on toast.

E Pellicci
332 Bethnal Green Road, E2 0AG (7739 4873). Bethnal Green tube/rail/8, 253 bus. Meals served 7am-4.30pm Mon-Sat. £.
A legend, famed for its fry-ups, Grade II-listed '50s interior and Cockney-Italian charm.

Flâneur Food Hall
41 Farringdon Road, EC1M 3JB (7404 4422/ www.flaneur.com). Farringdon tube/rail. Meals served 8.30-10.30am, noon-3pm, 6-10pm Mon-Fri; 10am-3pm, 6-10pm Sat. ££.
Plump for French toast with banana and pecans, or the more inventive likes of pan-fried sheep's cheese with pistachios and honey.

Little Georgia
87 Goldsmiths Row, E2 8QR (7739 8154). Liverpool Street tube/rail, then 26, 48 bus. Meals served 9am-5pm Mon; 9am-11pm Tue-Sat; 9am-10pm Sun. £.
The hearty 'Full Georgian' breakfast (served weekends only) is a treat, with its handmade sausages and herby baked beans.

SOUTH

Dosa n Chutny
68 Tooting High Street, SW17 0RN (8767 9200). Tooting Broadway tube. Meals served 10am-10.30pm daily. £.

Scoff superb dosas (lentil and rice flour cakes) with accompanying sambhar (a spicy vegetable and lentil 'soup') at this early-opening South Indian caff.

Maggie's Café
322 Lewisham Road, SE13 7PA (8244 0339/ www.maggiesrestaurant.co.uk). Lewisham rail/DLR. Meals served 7am-8pm Mon-Fri; 7am-2pm Sat. £.
This Lewisham institution is known for its Irish charm, bargain all-you-can-eat brekkies and bottomless cups of tea and coffee.

Organic Café Company
12-14 Greenwich Church Sreet, SE10 9BJ (8465 5577). Cutty Sark DLR/Greenwich rail/DLR. Meals served 8.30am-6pm Mon-Fri; 8.30am-7pm Sat, Sun. £.
Healthy, Med-style breakfasts with pan-fried halloumi cheese and sun-dried tomatoes or sunshine-yellow scrambled eggs are the main draw at this organic eatery.

WEST

Harp
304 Uxbridge Road, W12 2LJ (8723 2820). Shepherd's Bush tube. Meals served 7am-3.30pm Mon-Sat. £. No credit cards.
This cheery greasy spoon on the Uxbridge Road is known to serve the best bacon and egg butties in the neighbourhood.

Regency Café ★
17-19 Regency Street, SW1P 4BY (7821 6596). Pimlico tube. Meals served 7am-2.30pm, 4-7pm Mon-Fri; 7-11.45am Sat. £.
Declared the 'prince of caffs' by locals, the iconic Regency serves perfectly fluffy chips alongside its superb fry-ups.

202 Café
202-204 Westbourne Grove, W11 2RH (7792 6888). Notting Hill Gate tube. Meals served 10am-6pm Mon; 8.30am-6pm Tue-Sat; 10am-5pm Sun. ££.
The superlative breakfasts and brunches at this boutique's café fuel Notting Hill's finest; maple syrup-drizzled French toast with chargrilled bacon is heavenly.

BYO eateries

CENTRAL

Ali Baba

32 Ivor Place, NW1 6DA (7723 7474). Baker Street tube/Marylebone tube/rail. Meals served noon-midnight daily. Corkage no charge. £.
From street-food staples (*fuul*, falafels) to fusion favourites such as *macarona* (macaroni in béchamel sauce), Ali Baba covers the full spectrum of Egyptian cuisine.

Patogh

8 Crawford Place, W1H 5NE (7262 4015). Edgware Road tube. Meals served 12.30-11pm daily. Corkage no charge. £. No credit cards.
Competition is fierce for Patogh's half-dozen or so tables, where the lucky few devour sesame-studded flatbread and superb kebabs, prepared over the smoky charcoal grill.

The Place Below ✈

St Mary-le-Bow, EC2V 6AU (7329 0789/ www.theplacebelow.co.uk). St Paul's tube/ Bank tube/DLR. Meals served 7.30am-3pm Mon-Fri. Corkage no charge. £.
Dine in the cool crypt of St Mary-le-Bow, where friendly staff dish up fresh, satisfying vegetarian quiches, sandwiches, soup and salads, along with a hot daily special.

NORTH

Bintang

93 Kentish Town Road, NW1 8NY (7813 3393). Kentish Town tube/rail. Meals served 5.30-11pm Mon-Sat. Corkage no charge. £.
The kitsch dining room at this Thai-Malaysian eaterie is always packed. Oven-baked sea bass in fragrant bintang sauce and red curry, packed with plump king prawns, are among the menu highlights.

Jai Krishna

161 Stroud Green Road, N4 3PZ (7272 1680). Finsbury Park tube/rail. Meals served noon-2pm, 5.30-11pm Mon-Sat. Corkage £1.75. £.

This modest little South Indian fends off the competition from nearby Turkish cafés and pizzerias: most dishes from the delicious, all-vegetarian menu only cost around £3.

19 Numara Bos Cirrik I

34 Stoke Newington Road, N16 7XJ (7249 0400). Dalston Kingsland rail/76, 149, 243 bus. Meals served noon-midnight daily. Corkage £5. £.
Dalston's original Turkish grill continues to impress with its succulent kebabs and spare ribs, cooked to perfection on the *ocakbasi* grill.

SOUTH

Amaranth

346-348 Garratt Lane, SW18 4ES (8874 9036). Wandsworth tube. Meals served 5.30-10.30pm Mon-Sat. Corkage £2.50. £.
Booking is essential at this buzzing, no-frills little Thai restaurant in Earlsfield, thanks to its freshly-made food and budget prices.

Cah Chi ✈

34 Durham Road, SW20 0TW (8947 1081). Raynes Park rail/57, 131 bus. Meals served noon-3pm, 5-11pm Mon-Fri; noon-11pm Sat, Sun. Corkage 10% of bill. £.
This friendly Korean establishment serves honest, authentic fare at reasonable prices – its *yukkaejang* (spicy beef soup) is outstanding.

Nouvelle Spice

315 New Cross Road, SE14 6AS (8691 6644/www.nouvellespice.co.uk). New Cross or New Cross Gate rail. Meals served noon-11.30pm daily. Corkage no charge. £.
Nouvelle Spice serves top-notch Indian food at fair prices in comfortable surrounds (and also delivers); there are some interesting vegetarian options, such as pumpkin massala or panir cheese pasandra.

EAST

Lahore Kebab House

2 Umberston Street, E1 1PY (7488 2551). Aldgate East or Whitechapel tube. Meals served noon-midnight daily. Corkage no charge. £.

Delicious Pakistani fare makes an early arrival essential at this basic, brightly lit BYO. The mixed grill starters are superlative, and the kulfis a must-try.

Rochelle Canteen

The Canteen, Old School Building, Arnold Circus, E2 7ES (7729 5677/www.arnoldand henderson.com). Old Street tube/rail. Meals served noon-2.30pm Mon-Fri. Corkage £3.50-£5. £.

Set in an old school bike shed, this charming little eaterie attracts fashionistas and foodies alike. A pleasingly concise, daily-changing menu includes Mediterranean-inspired delights alongside modern British dishes; sorrel and pea soup, perhaps, or jellied ham.

Tay Do Café

65 Kingsland Road, E2 8AG (7729 7223). Old Street tube/rail/26, 48, 55, 67, 149, 242, 243 bus. Meals served 11.30am-3pm, 5-11.30pm daily. Corkage £1 per person. £.

This tiny Vietnamese canteen is packed to the rafters every night with hungry Hoxtonites; order the refreshing *chao tom* (prawn paste on sugar cane) or crunchy, shrimp-filled *bo bia* summer rolls.

Wild Cherry

241-245 Globe Road, E2 0JD (8980 6678). Bethnal Green tube/8 bus. Meals served 10.30am-4pm Tue, Thur-Sun; 10.30am-7pm Wed. Corkage £1. £.

A calming, Buddhist-run vegetarian restaurant, Wild Cherry offers imaginative – and delicious – food in mellow surrounds. In summer, head for the flower-filled courtyard.

WEST

Adam's Café

77 Askew Road, W12 9AH (8743 0572). Hammersmith tube, then 266 bus. Meals served 7-11pm Mon-Sat. Corkage £3. £.

Adam's delivers superb African food in laid-back surroundings; the Tunisian-style starter of *brik au thon* (crisp, light *ouarka* pastry stuffed with egg, tuna and herbs) and grilled *merguez* are stellar staples. Service is amiable and efficient.

Alounak

10 Russell Gardens, W14 8EZ (7603 7645). Kensington (Olympia) tube/rail. Open noon-midnight daily. Corkage no charge. ££.

Iranian stalwart Alounak offers meltingly tender lamb and chicken kebabs, accompanied by own-made *doogh* (a salty yoghurt drink), fluffy Persian rice and piping-hot *taftoon* bread, fresh from the oven.

Miraggio

510 Fulham Road, SW6 5NJ (7384 9774/ www.miraggio.co.uk). Fulham Broadway tube. Meals served noon-3pm, 6-11pm daily. Corkage £3. £.

Charming Italian staff serve impressive pizzas to share and classic home-made pasta (risotto ai funghi, spaghetti carbonara, linguine alle vongole) at this small, family-run restaurant near Parson's Green.

Polanka

258 King Street, W6 0SP (8741 8268/www. polanka-rest.com). Ravenscourt Park tube. Meals served noon-10pm Mon-Sat; noon-8pm Sun. Corkage £2 wine, £5 spirits. £.

Located in the heart of west London's Polish community, Polanka serves up honest-to-goodness traditional Polish cooking: *pierogi* (dumplings), herring, *golabki* (cabbage rolls) and other traditional fare. For those with room, there's a fine array of cakes, including Polish cheesecake.

City Secret

One of London's best lunchtime deals is dished up daily at the **Indian YMCA** (41 Fitzroy Square, W1T 6AQ, 7387 0411, www. indianymca.org) in Fitzrovia. The decor may be slightly spartan, but for £4.25, two bowls of freshly-made curry, a generous heap of pilau rice and a chapatti is not to be sniffed at. It's open for lunch between noon and 2pm on weekdays, or 12.30pm and 1.30pm at weekends.

GOING OUT

BEAUTY

FASHION

PARTIES

FOOD

HEALTH

ECO

OUTDOORS

HOME

CHILDREN

PETS

TRANSPORT

RESOURCES

Cafés

CENTRAL

In addition to the cafés listed below, **Bea's of Bloomsbury** (*see p70*) offers expertly made coffees and Valrhona hot chocolate alongside an inspired selection of cakes, salads and sarnies. **Fernandez & Wells** (*see p90*) is another sterling operation.

Bullet
Snow & Rock, 4 Mercer Street, WC2H 9QA (7836 4922/www.bullet-coffee.com). Covent Garden tube. Meals served 10am-6pm Mon-Wed, Fri, Sat; 10am-7pm Thur; 10am-4.30pm Sun. £.
Perched above a sports shop, this Kiwi-run café is a gem. The Fairtrade coffee is exemplary, while the food runs from dense, dreamy brownies to savoury snacks and pies.

Cake Therapy
59 Shaftesbury Avenue, W1D 6LF (07939 574315). Piccadilly Circus tube. Meals served 7am-10.30pm Mon-Fri; 10am-11pm Sat; 11am-8pm Sun. £.
A calming retreat from the chaos of central London, this cream-coloured café serves soothing teas in funky Betty Jackson cups and saucers; the honey cake is sublime.

Flat White ✸
17 Berwick Street, W1F 0PT (7734 0370/ www.flat-white.co.uk). Leicester Square tube. Meals served 8am-7pm Mon-Fri; 8am-6pm Sat, Sun. £.
This Antipodean-run café specialises in its namesake brew, a coffee made with a large shot of espresso and generous slosh of milk (frothed slightly less than in a cappuccino).

Kastner & Ovens
52 Floral Street, WC2E 9DA (7836 2700). Covent Garden tube. Meals served 8am-5pm Mon-Fri. £.

This little café attracts hordes of hungry office workers during weekday lunchtimes, eager to chow down on the fresh and tasty home-made salads, hot mains, quiches and cakes made by owners Sue and Ann-Marie.

London Review Cakeshop
14-16 Bury Place, WC1A 2JL (7269 9030). Tottenham Court Road tube. Meals served 10am-6pm Mon-Sat; 12.30-5pm Sun. £.
This charming bookshop café is run by Terry Glover, formerly of Maison Blanc. Literary types can sip Jing teas and enjoy superb cakes and baguettes while perusing their purchases.

Nordic Bakery ✸
14 Golden Square, W1F 9JG (3230 1077). Piccadilly Circus tube. Meals served 8am-8pm Mon-Fri; 11am-7pm Sat; 11am-6pm Sun. £.
Clean lines and modern Scandinavian design make this café a standout. The cinnamon buns are spectacular, while open-faced rye sandwiches feature typical Finnish toppings such as gravadlax with sweet mustard.

Ray's Jazz Café
1st floor, Foyles, WC2H 0EB (7440 3205). Tottenham Court Road tube. Meals served 9.30am-9pm Mon-Sat; 11.30am-6pm Sun. £.
On the first floor of Foyle's bookshop, Ray's Jazz Café offers a laid-back jazz

soundtrack, generous hunks of cake and fresh mint tea and fruit smoothies – if you can score a seat, that is.

Sacred
13 Ganton Street, W1F 9BL (7734 1415/ www.sacredcafe.co.uk). Oxford Circus tube. Meals served 7.30am-8pm Mon-Fri; 9am-8pm Sat; 10am-7.30pm Sun. £.
Excellent fairtrade coffees are matched by an extensive loose-leaf tea menu (with green, fruit, ayurvedic and black blends) at this cosy, two-floor Soho café.

NORTH

Café Mozart
17 Swains Lane, N6 6QX (8348 1384). Gospel Oak rail/214, C2, C11, C12 bus. Meals served 9am-9pm Mon-Fri; 9am-10pm Sat, Sun. £.
Savouries at this Austrian café include *borscht*, sausages and schnitzel, but most customers are here to eye up the legendary sweets: rich chocolate tortes, plum tarts and cheesecakes.

Lemon Monkey
188 Stoke Newington High Street, N16 7JD (7241 4454). Stoke Newington rail. Meals served 8.30am-8pm Mon-Sat; 10am-8pm Sun. £.
This French café and deli delivers top-notch cheese, charcuterie and coffee; sweet tooths will adore the own-made macaroons.

Louis Pâtisserie
32 Heath Street, NW3 6TE (7435 9908). Hampstead tube. Meals served 9am-6pm daily. £. No credit cards.
After admiring the alluring window display, take a seat in the wood-panelled tearoom for an unhurried pot of tea and a chestnut slice.

The Tea Rooms
155 Stoke Newington Church Street, N16 0UH (7923 1870). Stoke Newington rail/bus 73, 476. Meals served 11am-7pm Mon, Wed-Sun. £. No credit cards.
This lovely '50s-style tearoom makes all of its cakes and pastries on the premises. Afternoon tea, with delectable scones, is £10.

FREE WI-FI

Free Wi-Fi is spreading fast in London's café culture; these are some dependable central hotspots.

Apostrophe
9 Tottenham Court Road, W1T 7PT (7436 6688/www.apostropheuk. com). Goodge Street tube. Open 7.30am-6.30pm Mon-Fri; 9.30am-5.30pm Sat.
Tucked away behind Tottenham Court Road, this branch tends to be nice and peaceful, so you should get a seat at the long communal tables.

Benugo Bar & Kitchen
BFI Southbank, Belvedere Road, SE1 8XT (7401 9000/www.benugo. com). Waterloo tube/rail. Open 9.45am-11pm Mon-Fri; 11am-11pm Sat; 11am-10.30pm Sun.
During the daytime, Benugo's plush couches are a supremely comfy spot to check your emails.

Hummus Brothers
88 Wardour Street, W1F 0TJ (7734 1311/www.hbros.co.uk). Oxford Circus tube. Meals served 11am-10pm Mon-Wed; 11am-11pm Thur, Fri; noon-11pm Sat; noon-10pm Sun.
Perfect for laptop-toting houmous lovers. After the lunchtime rush, you can linger over a fresh mint tea.

Peyton & Byrne
Wellcome Collection, 183 Euston Road, NW1 2BE (7611 2138/www. peytonandbyrne.com). Euston tube/ rail. Meals served 10am-6pm Mon-Wed; 10am-10pm Sun; 8am-8pm Fri-Sun.
This chic café serves large pots of tea and scrummy cakes; if you're in need of something more solid, the salads and pies are excellent.

GOING OUT

BEAUTY

FASHION

PARTIES

FOOD

HEALTH

ECO

OUTDOORS

HOME

CHILDREN

PETS

TRANSPORT

RESOURCES

EAST

Jones' Dairy Café

23 Ezra Street, E2 7RH (7739 5372/www. jonesdairy.co.uk). Bus 26, 48, 55. Meals served 9am-3pm Fri, Sat; 8am-3pm Sun. No credit cards. £.

Located just off Columbia Road Flower Market, this boho café welcomes an influx of shoppers on Sundays, so you'll have to queue to sample the own-baked cakes and bagels.

Tea Smith

6 Lamb Street, E1 6EA (7247 1333/www teasmith.co.uk). Liverpool Street tube/rail. Meals served 11am-6pm daily. £.

Unusual teas can be sipped at the counter at this airy, architect-designed shop and tearoom. Cakes come courtesy of the renowned William Curley pâtisserie (*see p95*).

Venetia

55 Chatsworth Road, E5 0LH (8986 1642). Homerton rail/242, 308 bus. Meals served 8am-5pm Mon-Fri; 8am-5.30pm Sat; 9am-5pm Sun. £.

Cake stands at this elegant little eaterie groan with chunky brownies, almond croissants and own-made victoria sponge. Look out, too, for the delicious daily sandwich specials.

SOUTH

Café Crema

306 New Cross Road, SE14 6AF (8320 2317). New Cross or New Cross Gate rail. Meals served 10.30am-10pm Mon-Sat. £. No credit cards.

Goldsmiths College students flock here for the scrumptious vegetarian food and creamy hot chocolates. There's a little back garden, and a selection of books to browse.

Café St Germain

16-17 Crystal Palace Parade, SE19 1UA (8670 3670). Crystal Palace rail. Meals served 8am-6pm Mon-Fri, Sun; 8am-11pm Sat. £.

Go continental with a croque monsieur and potent black coffee at south-east London's answer to a Parisian café.

Jack's Tea & Coffee House

85 Pellatt Road, SE22 9JD (8693 0011/ www.jacks-coffeehouse.co.uk). North Dulwich rail. Meals served 10am-5pm Mon-Fri; 10am-3pm Sat. £. No credit cards.

One of Dulwich's best-kept secrets, a place to tuck into a glorious caramelised french onion tart, or a meatball and beetroot mayo baguette.

Petitou

63 Choumert Road, SE15 4AR (7639 2613). Peckham Rye rail. Meals served 9am-5.15pm Tue-Sat; 10am-5.15pm Sun. £.

There's a 1940s charm to Petitou, with its brown earthenware teapots, mismatched china and moist slabs of own-made cake.

WEST

Books For Cooks

4 Bleinheim Crescent, W11 1NN (7221 1992/ www.booksforcooks.com). Ladbroke Grove tube. Meals served 10am-3pm Tue-Sat. £.

Arrive before 12.30pm if you want to lunch at this bijou culinary bookshop. The kitchen cooks up a three-dish set menu (a steal at £7) every day, but there's only a handful of tables.

Lisboa Pâtisserie

57 Golborne Road, W10 5NR (8968 5242). Ladbroke Grove or Westbourne Park tube/ 23, 52 bus. Open 8am-7.30pm daily. £.

Queues often form at the weekend, thanks to the café's famed freshly-made *pasties de nata* (custard tarts) and *bicas* (espressos).

City Secret

In the heart of Mayfair, **Postcard Teas** (9 Dering Street, W1S 1AG, 7629 3654, www.postcardteas.com) is a labour of love, run by tea enthusiast Timothy d'Offay. Primarily a tea boutique selling top-quality Indian, Japanese and Sri Lankan blends, it also has a tasting table where you can sample the wares – including the unique coffee blossom tea – for a mere £1.50 per pot.

The Providores and **Tapa Room**
Seven days a week in the heart of Marylebone Village

The Tapa Room – ground floor café/wine bar. All day dining from legendary breakfasts through to creative suppers.
The Providores – first floor restaurant. Intimate dining offering Peter Gordon's inventive and creative Fusion Cuisine.
PLUS one of the largest selections of premium New Zealand wines, and some of the finest coffee in town.

109 Marylebone High Street, London, W1U 4RX
tel (+44) 020 7935 6175
anyone@theprovidores.co.uk
www.theprovidores.co.uk
www.peter-gordon.net

EL FARO
THE FINEST SPANISH CUISINE IN A SPECTACULAR WATERFRONT LOCATION

3 TURNBERRY QUAY
PEPPER STREET
LONDON
E14 9RD
TELEPHONE: 020 7987 5511
EMAIL: INFO@EL-FARO.CO.UK

OPENING HOURS:
12PM - 3.30 PM & 5PM - 11 PM MONDAY TO SATURDAY
12PM - 3.30PM SUNDAY

SPECIAL
SUCKLING PIG FROM **SEGOVIA**
MONDAY TO THURSDAY

London winner Remy Martin Restaurant Awards 2008
London Restaurant Awards 2008-Iberian Restaurant of the Year- Nominee

Address Book Secrets
Angela Hartnett,
Chef

My favourite market is **Broadway Market** in Hackney (*see p101*) on a Saturday (9am-5pm). It's a farmers' market and not ridiculously expensive. There's a great tomato stall with a woman selling every variety you can imagine, only in season, all grown on the Isle of Wight.

There's a real feel of the Italian community at the **Gazzano Deli** (167 Farringdon Road, EC1R 3AL, 7837 1586), near the Italian church in Clerkenwell. It doesn't look pretty-pretty, but the quality is great. It's always packed to capacity, and you see unusual things you can't get in any supermarket, like *fregola* and *ditalini* – which are variations on pasta that Italians put in their minestrone.

Lina Stores (18 Brewer Street, W1F 0SH, 7437 6482) and **I Camisa & Son** (61 Old Compton Street, W1 6HS, 7437 7610, www.camisa.co.uk) are similar – you can close your eyes and almost believe you're in Bologna. Camisa is stacked floor to ceiling with produce, and I've been going there since my grandmother used to send us to pick groceries up as kids; if we had a family get-together, that's where we'd go for salami and cheeses.

Another really lovely little place in Soho is **Fernandez & Wells** (73 Beak Street, W1F 9SR , 7287 8124, www.fernandezandwells.com). The café does great coffee, which you can also buy at the deli, just around the corner in Lexington Street. It also sells Spanish ham and sausages, with lots of different chorizos and salamis, plus cheeses and wines. The staff in there are very sweet too.

La Fromagerie (2-6 Moxon Street, W1U 4EW, 7935 0341, www.lafromagerie.co.uk), sells everything you need to put together a lovely meal. At the front there are vegetables like treviso from Italy, which is hard to find elsewhere, and wonderful vine tomatoes. Everything's labelled with where it comes from too. You go in attempting to buy a small piece of parmesan and come out having spent £80 because it all looks so tempting.

In Peckham, on the way to my uncle's allotment, there's an old, traditional wet fish shop, **Soper's** (141 Evelina Road, SE15 3HB, 7639 9729). It's always packed, so the stock turnover is fast and the prices are kept low. The stall extends on to the road, and is piled high with great-looking shrimps and English fish, like mackerel.

Near where I live at Old Spitalfields Market there's a great food market on Sundays (www.oldspitalfieldsmarket.com). I go to the **Estro** stall for wonderful organic vegetables from East Anglia. The stallholders really seem to care about the environment – it's somewhere you make an effort to take your own plastic bag. **Tony Booth** at Borough Market (Stoney Street, SE1 www.boroughmarket.org.uk) is also very good for veg. He always keeps up with the seasons and sells salad leaves loose, so you can help yourself and feel how fresh they are.

Late-opening cafés & restaurants

CENTRAL

Aaya
66-70 Brewer Street, W1F 9UP (7319 3888). Piccadilly Circus tube. Meals served noon-12.30am Mon-Sat; 6-10pm Sun. ££.
Modern interpretations of Japanese classics and top-quality sushi are expertly executed, while the wine list, though pricey, is well crafted and wide-ranging.

Balans
60 Old Compton Street, W1D 4UG (7437 5212/www.balans.co.uk). Leicester Square or Piccadilly Circus tube. Meals served 8am-5am Mon-Sat; 8am-2am Sun. ££.
This slightly retro Soho brasserie attracts the post-clubbing crowd with amazing spiced scrambled egg burritos for vegetarians, as well as substantial mains such as bengal prawn curry or steak and chips.

Café TPT
21 Wardour Street, W1D 6PN (7734 7980). Leicester Square or Piccadilly Circus tube. Meals served noon-1am daily. £.
Often filled with weary students in need of late-night sustenance, this clean, modern Chinatown caff offers great value for money; try the barbecue pork or soy sauce chicken.

HK Diner ★
22 Wardour Street, W1D 6QQ (7434 9544). Leicester Square or Piccadilly Circus tube. Meals served 11am-4am daily. £.
Take note: go for the specials menu, not the unexceptional stir-fries. Cheery surrounds, semi-private booths and hangover-curing bubble teas and juices make this a popular pitstop for young Chinese Londoners.

Joe Allen
13 Exeter Street, WC2E 7DT (7836 0651/ www.joeallen.co.uk). Covent Garden tube. Meals served 8am-12.30am Mon-Fri; 11.30am-12.30am Sat; 11.30am-11.30pm Sun. ££.
A classic post-show stopover, Joe Allen's is a theatreland institution. It's all about the buzzing atmosphere, with a thespian crowd gathering to toast that night's performance and devour grilled tuna, ribs and steaks.

Woo Jung
59 St Giles High Street, WC2H 8LH (7836 3103). Tottenham Court Road tube. Meals served noon-1am Mon-Sat; 5pm-midnight Sun. £.
We can't think of better late-night food than a stodgy bowl of *bibimbap* (rice topped with meat and vegetables), or warming beef stew. Filling, homestyle Korean cooking and low prices mean it's always busy, despite the tatty decor and lackadaisical service.

NORTH

Gilgamesh
Stables Market, Chalk Farm Road, NW1 8AH (7482 4922/www.gilgameshbar.com). Chalk Farm tube. Meals served Bar 6pm-2.30am Mon-Thur; noon-2.30am Fri-Sun. Restaurant noon-3pm, 6pm-midnight daily. ££.
The unashamedly over-the-top decor and DJs make this a distracting place to dine; luckily the pan-Asian food is consistently excellent, from elegant sushi to smart little dim sum. The restaurant closes at midnight, but the bar menu should satisfy late-night cravings.

Mangal II
4 Stoke Newington Road, N16 8BH (7254 7888/www.mangal2.com). Dalston Kingsland rail/76, 149, 243 bus. Meals served 3pm-1am Mon-Fri; 2pm-1am Sat, Sun.
Grilled fish and good-quality kebabs satisfy late-night hunger pangs at this cheery blue-and yellow-painted Turkish eaterie. If you're merely peckish, order pide and delicious yoghurt-based dips.

EAST

Somine
131 Kingsland High Street, E8 2PB (7254 7384). Dalston Kingsland rail/76, 149, 236, 343 bus. Meals served 24hrs daily. £. No credit cards.

GOING OUT

BEAUTY

FASHION

PARTIES

FOOD

HEALTH

ECO

OUTDOORS

HOME

CHILDREN

PETS

TRANSPORT

RESOURCES

Many come to this brightly lit 24-hour café purely for the tasty lentil soup (£3), served with soft, squidgy bread. Otherwise, choose from the ever-changing selection of hearty, no-nonsense stews at the counter; the staff will explain what's what.

Stone Cave
111 Kingsland High Street, E8 2PB (7241 4911). Dalston Kingsland rail/76, 149, 236, 343 bus. Meals served 11.30am-2am Mon-Wed; 11.30am-3am Thur-Sat; 4pm-midnight Sun. £.
A local favourite in Dalston, Stone Cave serves good-value kebabs and traditional Turkish food in fantasy-like surroundings, complete with live bands.

Tinseltown
44-46 St John Street, EC1M 4DT (7689 2424/www.tinseltown.co.uk). Farringdon tube/rail. Meals served 24hrs daily. £.
This chilled-out Hollywood-themed diner sees clubbers slurping phenomenal peanut butter milkshakes and chomping burgers alongside insomniacs and cabbies on a break.
Other locations 104 Heath Street, NW3 1DR (7435 2396).

SOUTH

Meze Mangal
245 Lewisham Way, SE4 1XF (8694 8099/www.meze-mangal.co.uk). Lewisham DLR/rail/St John's rail. Meals served noon-1am Mon-Thur; noon-2am Fri, Sat; noon-midnight Sun. £.
Lewisham locals head here for flavoursome, traditional Turkish fare; start with nutty, rough-textured *kisir*, then order a dish of tender *çop sis* (marinated chunks of lamb) and salad.

Vingt-Quatre
325 Fulham Road, SW10 9QL (7376 7224/ www.vingtquatre.co.uk). South Kensington tube. Meals served 24hrs daily. £.
The short but classic menu at Vingt-Quatre ranges from grilled club sandwiches to spaghetti: if you're feeling decadent, wash it all down with a bottle of Krug.

WEST

Cecconi's
5A Burlington Gardens, W1S 3EP (7434 1500/www.cecconis.co.uk). Green Park or Piccadilly Circus tube. Meals served 7am-1am Mon-Fri; 8am-1am Sat; 8am-midnight Sun. ££-£££.
One of the only restaurants in London to serve Italian tapas (*cichetti*), Cecconi's is perfect for sophisticated late-night nibbles in stylish art deco surrounds. Delicacies might range from foie gras and asparagus crostini to oysters.

High Road Brasserie ★
162-166 Chiswick High Road, W4 1PR (8742 7474/www.highroadhouse.co.uk). Turnham Green tube. Meals served noon-11pm Mon-Thur; noon-midnight Fri; 5pm-midnight Sat; 5-10pm Sun. ££.
This chic offshoot of Nick Jones' Soho House impresses with its classic brasserie menu, catering for all appetites at all hours of the day (well, up until midnight on Fridays and Saturdays at least).

O Fado
49-50 Beauchamp Place, SW3 1NY (7589 3002/www.ofado. co.uk). Knightsbridge or South Kensington tube. Meals served noon-3pm, 6.30-11pm Mon-Sat. ££.
Incongruously set in showy Knightsbridge, this homely little restaurant is one of London's oldest Portuguese eateries. Expect classics such as *pastéis de bacalhau* (salt

LATE-NIGHT TAKEAWAYS

Brick Lane Beigel Bake
159 Brick Lane, E1 6SB (7729 0616).
Liverpool Street tube/rail. Meals
served 24hrs daily. £. No credit cards.
This 24-hour East End institution has
the best freshly-baked bagels in the
capital. Service is brisk but charming,
and the bagels top-notch, whether you
visit at lunchtime or 3am.

Fishcotheque
79A Waterloo Road, SE1 8UD (7928
1484). Waterloo tube/rail. Meals
served 11am-midnight Mon-Sat;
noon-10pm Sun. £. No credit cards.
Don't let the unenticing exterior and
boozy regulars deter you: the fish
here is fresh, the portions generous.
Chicken kebabs, doused with own-
made chilli sauce, are also delicious.

Kebab Kid
90 New Kings Road, SW6 4LU (7731
0427). Parson's Green tube. Meals
served noon-midnight daily. £. No
credit cards.
A foodie crowd (including off-duty
chefs) are among the regulars queuing
for fresh houmous- or taramosalata-
topped chicken *shawarma*.

Kurz & Lang
1 St John Street, EC1M 4AA (7253
6623/www.kurzandlang.com).
Farringdon tube/rail. Meals served
11am-midnight Mon-Wed; 11am-
1.15am Thur; 11am Fri-7am Sun;
noon-midnight Sun. £.

This cheerful caff does a roaring trade
in bratwurst sausages, topped with
lashings of mustard, ketchup and
sauerkraut. On weekends it's open
nonstop from Friday night until Sunday
morning, to feed the post-party crowds.

Manzara
24 Pembridge Road, W11 3HL (7727
3062). Notting Hill Gate tube. Meals
served 8am-1am Mon-Wed; 8am-3am
Thur-Sat; 8am-11.30pm Sun. £.
Piping-hot pide and top-notch kebabs
are the mainstay at this predominantly
Turkish eatery; the yoghurt-slathered
lamb shish in pitta is a reliable choice.

Maoz
43 Old Compton Street, W1D 6HG
(7851 1586). Leicester Square or
Tottenham Court Road tube. Meals
served 11am-1am Mon-Thur; 11am-
2am Fri, Sat; 11am-midnight Sun. £.
Maoz offers much-needed sustenance
to the late-night prowlers of Soho's
bars and clubs. It's surprisingly
healthy fare: falafels, houmous and
flavoursome couscous salad – though
there are chunky chips as well.

Ranoush Juice
43 Edgware Road, W2 2JR (7723 5929).
Marble Arch tube. Meals served 8am-
3am daily. No credit cards. £.
Watch as staff assemble lamb or
chicken *shawarma* at lightning speed:
the final result, oozing garlic sauce at
every bite, is sublime.

cod fritters) and *clam ameijoa a bulhao pato*
(clams poached in garlic and white wine).

Rossopomodoro ★
214 Fulham Road, SW10 9NB (7352
7677). South Kensington tube, then 14 bus.
Meals served noon-midnight daily. £-££.

The busy open kitchen at Rossopomodoro
churns out consistently delicious antipasti,
pizza and pasta dishes from a menu so long
it unfolds off the table and into your lap. For
a calorific treat, try the deep-fried pizza.
Other location *50-52 Monmouth Street,*
WC2H 9EP (7240 9095).

GOING OUT
BEAUTY
FASHION
PARTIES
FOOD
HEALTH
ECO
OUTDOORS
HOME
CHILDREN
PETS
TRANSPORT
RESOURCES

brilliant  **kids**

...cafe & arts centre

"Crisply turned out, the bright polished cafe with an airy art room at the back, beyond which blossoms a lovely garden, is a ray of sunshine among the dowdy shopfronts of Kensal Rise" Time Out Eating & Drinking 2007

7/8 Station Terrace, London NW10 5RT

020 8964 4120   www.brilliantkids.co.uk

GABY'S
DELI

30 Charing Cross Road, London WC2H 0DB
(Next to Leicester Square Tube Station)

Tel: 020 7836 4233
www.gabys.net

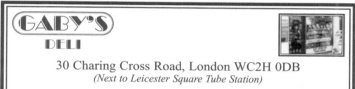

SACRED CAFÉ

A hidden gem for those who appreciate gourmet coffee, tea and food in sublime surroundings.

"The Place for Coffee Worship"
Time Out London

Discover us in the heart of Carnaby Street
13 Ganton Street, W1F 9BL   0207 734 1415   www.sacredcafe.co.uk

Romantic restaurants

CENTRAL

Andrew Edmunds

46 Lexington Street, W1F 0LW (7437 5708).
Oxford Circus or Piccadilly Circus tube.
Meals served 12.30-3.30pm, 6-10.45pm
Mon-Sat; 1-3.30pm, 6-10.30pm Sun. ££.
The snug tables here are perfect for romantic
tête-à-têtes – though to avoid becoming too
intimate with your neighbours, reserve on the
marginally more spacious ground floor.
Classic Modern European dishes are quietly
satisfying: in-season asparagus or chicken
liver parfait, perhaps, followed by rib-eye
steak or wild halibut. The wine list is good
value, with champagne at £6.50 a glass.

Aurora

49 Lexington Street, W1F 9AP (7494 0514).
Oxford Circus or Piccadilly Circus tube.
Meals served noon-10.30pm Mon-Sat. £-££.
With seating for 20 and a few tables in the
garden, Aurora is delightfully intimate.
There are sometimes two sittings an evening:
make sure you're on the later one, so you can
linger over dessert. Food is unfussy, with
generous portions of modern British fare,
while the wine list is short and sweet.

Le Comptoir Gascon ★

61-63 Charterhouse Street, EC1M 6HJ (7608
0851/www.comptoirgascon.com). Farringdon
tube/rail. Meals served noon-2pm, 7-11pm
Tue-Fri; 10.30am-10pm Sat. ££.
This French bistro focuses on cooking from
the south-western provinces – much of it
unashamedly carnivorous. The blackboard-
scrawled specials might include roast suckling
pig or quail salad, while menu fixtures include
a 'piggy treats' charcuterie board. Prices are
reasonable, and the atmosphere's relaxed.

Crazy Bear

26-28 Whitfield Street, W1T 2RG (7631
0088/www.crazybeargroup.co.uk). Goodge
Street or Tottenham Court Road tube.
Meals served noon-10.45pm Mon-Fri; 6-
10.45pm Sat. ££.
Despite the zany name, Crazy Bear surprises
with its belle époque-style decor and Eastern
influenced menu. The moodily-lit dining room
is lined with leather banquettes and art deco
lamps, while the menu ranges from dim sum
to wok-fried lobster. Downstairs, the bar's
padded alcoves are equally seductive.

Hakkasan ★

8 Hanway Place, W1T 1HD (7907 1888).
Tottenham Court Road tube. Meals served
noon-3pm, 6-11pm Mon-3pm;
6pm-midnight Thur, Fri; noon-4pm,
6pm-midnight Sat; noon-4pm Sun. £££.
With its sultry good looks, dim lighting and
underground location, it doesn't matter what
time of day you eat here – Hakkasan's always
romantic. Arrive early to quaff saké-infused
cocktails at the long, back-lit bar before
sampling the impressive menu.

NORTH

Green Room

182 Broadhurst Gardens, NW6 3AY (7372
8188). West Hampstead tube/rail. Meals
served 6.30-11.30pm Tue-Fri; 6.30pm-
midnight Sat; 12.30am-3.30pm; 6.30-
10.30pm Sun. ££.
This Hampstead bistro's deliciously pretty
chandelier-lit dining room is perfect for more
intimate soirées. An inviting Modern
European menu sticks to the classics, cooked
with real flair, while the interesting but
inexpensive wine list adds to the appeal.

City Secret

One of the city's sweetest venues
for a date is the dessert bar at
William Curley (32-34 Shepherd
Market, W1J 7QN, 7495 0302,
www.williamcurley.co.uk). Perch at
the bar and watch as the *pâtissier*
skilfully assembles delectable
concoctions such as chocolate
tart with green tea ice-cream and
raspberry compôte. Note that the
dessert bar is closed on Sundays.

GOING OUT
BEAUTY
FASHION
PARTIES
FOOD
HEALTH
ECO
OUTDOORS
HOME
CHILDREN
PETS
TRANSPORT
RESOURCES

GOING OUT
BEAUTY
FASHION
PARTIES
FOOD
HEALTH
ECO
OUTDOORS
HOME
CHILDREN
PETS
TRANSPORT
RESOURCES

NO BOOKING? NO PROBLEM

Forgotten to make that all-important reservation? Here's the solution.

Anchor & Hope
36 The Cut, SE1 8LP (7928 9898). Southwark or Waterloo tube/rail. Meals served 6-10.30pm Mon; noon-2.30pm, 6-10.30pm Tue-Sat; 2pm sitting Sun. ££
The pared-down, daily-changing menu at this foodie favourite offers inviting gastropub fare: rich chicken pithivier, perhaps, or a classic cassoulet.

Barrafina
54 Frith Street, W1D 4SL (7813 8016/ www.barrafina.co.uk). Tottenham Court Road tube. Meals served noon-3pm, 5-11pm Mon-Sat. £.
Once you've scored a coveted seat at the broad, L-shaped bar, relax and enjoy the sensational tapas.

Busaba Eathai
8-13 Bird Street, W1U 1BU (7518 8080). Bond Street tube. Meals served noon-11pm Mon-Thur; noon-11.30pm Fri, Sat; noon-10pm Sun. £.
Low lighting, stylish decor and a well-priced menu of soups, salads, stir-fries and curries keep Busaba buzzing.

Dehesa
For listings see p82. ££.
Sumptuous charcuterie boards and Italian-influenced tapas are the draw at Dehesa; don't miss the Monte Enebro-stuffed courgette flowers.

The Providores & Tapa Room
109 Marylebone High Street, W1U 4RX (7935 6175/www.the providores.co.uk). Baker Street tube. Meals served noon-10.30pm Mon-Fri; 4-10.30pm Sat; 4-10pm Sun. £-££.

Le Mercury
140A Upper Street, N1 1QY (7354 4088/ www.lemercury.co.uk). Angel tube or Highbury & Islington tube/rail. Meals served noon-1am Mon-Sat; noon-11.30pm Sun. £.
For Gallic charm at a fraction of the cost, head to Le Mercury, where starters cost a mere £3.95, mains – ranging from sea bass to rib-eye steak – £6.45. There are plenty of tables for two (upstairs is more romantic), plus flickering candles set in vintage wine bottles.

EAST

Bistrotheque
23-27 Wadeson Street, E2 9DR (8983 7900/ www.bistrotheque.com). Bethnal Green tube/ rail. Meals served 6.30-10.30pm Mon-Thur; 6.30-11pm Fri; 11am-4pm, 6.30-11pm Sat; 11am-4pm, 6.30-10.30pm Sun. ££.
Housed in a lofty warehouse space, Bistrotheque walks the line between street and sophistication. Cooking is unpretentious and punchy: chorizo and seafood stew, say, or garlicky roast chicken (perhaps best avoided on a first date). After dinner retire to the Cabaret Room, with its candlelit tables and intimate decor; pre-book tickets.

Les Trois Garçons
1 Club Row, E1 6JX (7613 1924/www. loungelover.co.uk). Liverpool Street tube/ rail/8, 388 bus. Meals served 7-10pm Mon-Thur; 7-10.30pm Fri, Sat. £££.
Generously gilded and crammed with bizarre *objets trouvés*, the dining room at Les Trois Garçons defiantly flouts the modern less-is-more aesthete. The food is equally artistically presented, with elaborate menu descriptions: more importantly, cooking is spot on.

Ubon
34 Westferry Circus, E14 8RR (7719 7800). Canary Wharf tube/DLR/Westferry DLR. Meals served noon-2.15pm, 6-10.15pm Mon-Fri; 6-10.15pm Sat. £££.

Upstairs is the more grown-up Providores restaurant; below, the Tapa Room offers a delightfully fresh, eclectic menu. Traditional tapas dishes rub shoulders with unexpected delights: deep fried baby *kumara*, say, or asparagus with ginger miso sauce.

Vinoteca
7 St John Street, EC1M 4AA (7253 8786/www.vinoteca.co.uk). Farringdon tube/rail. Meals served noon-2.45pm, 6.30-10pm Mon-Fri; 6.30-10pm Sat. ££.
A simple menu complements the stellar wine list, which boasts over 275 bottles. Options range from Spanish meat or cheese platters to robust, seasonal mains, such as pan-fried halibut with Jersey royals or steak with sorrel butter.

Nobu may look out across Hyde Park, but Ubon trumps its sister operation with a stunning view across the Thames at dusk. Reserve a window table then sit back to enjoy Nobu classics such as black cod with miso and sublime *o-toro sashimi* (the highest grade of tuna belly). While City suits dominate at lunchtimes, evenings are perfect for those who find candlelit soirées a touch too cloying.

SOUTH

Tentazioni
2 Mill Street, SE1 2BD (7237 1100/www. tentazioni.co.uk). Bermondsey tube/London Bridge tube/rail. Meals served noon-2.45pm, 6.30-10.45pm Tue-Fri; 6.30-10.45pm Sat. £££.
With its opulent plum-and-red decor and hidden-away location, Tentazioni is ideal for illicit rendezvous. Dishes are ambitious but accomplished, with bold flavours and polished presentation.

Upstairs
89B Acre Lane, entrance on Branksome Road, SW2 5TN (7733 8855). Brixton tube. Meals served 6.30-9.30pm Tue-Thur; 6.30-10.30pm Fri, Sat. ££.
An unmarked door adds an air of exclusivity to this discreet little gem, where diners must ring a bell to gain admittance. Up the winding stairs lies a chilled out bar area, with another set of stairs leading to the Lilliputian dining room. The prix fixe menu offers three starters and three mains, with a strong seasonal focus.

WEST

Angelus ✱
4 Bathurst Street, W2 2SD (7402 0083/ www.angelusrestaurant.co.uk). Lancaster Gate tube. Meals served noon-2.15pm, 6-11pm Tue-Sun. ££.
Chef Olivier Duret offers a modern take on classic brasserie fare – notably with his famed foie gras crème brûlée. The art nouveau surrounds are as elegant as the food, with polished dark wood fittings and burgundy leather banquettes, and service is charming.

La Poule au Pot
231 Ebury Street, SW1W 8UT (7730 7763). Sloane Square tube. Meals served 12.30-2.30pm, 6.45-11pm Mon-Fri; 12.30-4pm, 6.45-11pm Sat; 12.30-4pm, 6.45-10pm Sun. ££.
This rustic, dimly lit French bistro is one of London's classic romantic hotspots. Things don't change much here, including the menu: expect robust dishes such as coq au vin or rabbit in creamy mustard sauce. Fairly priced house wines help conversation flow.

Saigon Saigon
313-317 King Street, W6 9NH (0870 220 1398). Ravenscourt Park or Stamford Brook tube. Meals served 6-10pm Mon; noon-3pm, 6-11pm Tue-Thur; noon-3pm, 6-11.30pm Fri, Sat; noon-3pm, 6-10pm Sun. £-££.
Bamboo screens, dark wood flooring and photos of '40s Saigon evoke the glamour of a bygone age at this chic Vietnamese restaurant. Sophisticated dishes such as chargrilled quail and buttered frogs' legs won't fail to impress.

GOING OUT
BEAUTY
FASHION
PARTIES
FOOD
HEALTH
ECO
OUTDOORS
HOME
CHILDREN
PETS
TRANSPORT
RESOURCES

Sunday lunch

There's no shortage of gastropubs offering Sunday lunch, but only a select few truly shine: the following serve a roast that's second only to your mum's.

Charles Lamb

16 Elia Street, N1 8DE (7837 5040/www. thecharleslambpub.com). Angel tube. Meals served 4-11.30pm Mon, Tue; noon-11.30pm Wed-Sat; noon-10.30pm Sun. ££.
It's well worth getting lost in the backstreets of Angel to stumble across the diminutive, wooden-floored Charles Lamb. There's a glorious array of world beers, ales and wines, while food is hearty and accomplished: a Sunday roast with all the trimmings is £12.

Duke of Cambridge

30 St Peter's Street, N1 8JT (7359 3066/ www.dukeorganic.co.uk). Angel tube. Meals served noon-3pm, 6.30-11pm Mon-Fri; 12.30-4pm, 6.30-11pm Sat, Sun. ££.
The original organic gastropub, the Duke dishes up a hearty Sunday lunch, made with seasonal, local and, of course, organic ingredients. The roast changes weekly, and arrives generously anointed with gravy and accompanied by crisp, fluffy-centred spuds.

Gipsy Moth

60 Greenwich Church Street, SE10 9BL (8858 0786/www.thegipsymothgreenwich. co.uk). Cutty Sark DLR/Greenwich rail. Meals served noon-10pm Mon-Thur; noon-11pm Fri, Sat; noon-9.30pm Sun. ££.
The Gipsy Moth's huge beer garden is perfect for sunny Sunday lunches. Choose from roast pork belly with generous slabs of crackling and textbook-perfect mash and leeks, or half a roast chicken. A fine selection of draught beers, ales and ciders is another plus.

Gun ★

27 Coldharbour, E14 9NS (7515 5222/ www.thegundocklands.com). Blackwall or Canary Wharf DLR. Meals served noon-3pm, 6-10.30pm Mon-Fri; 11.30-4pm, 6-10.30pm Sat, Sun. £££.

The terrace overlooking the Thames is a lovely spot for a leisurely Sunday lunch, if you can score a table; enormous Yorkshire puddings are the star of the show.

Herne Tavern

2 Forest Hill Road, SE22 0RR (8299 9521/ www.theherne.net). Peckham Rye rail. Meals served noon-2.30pm, 6.30-9.45pm Mon-Fri; noon-3pm, 6.30-9.45pm Sat; noon-2.30pm, 6.30-9.30pm Sun. ££.
Gorge yourself on a groan-inducing roast for £11.50 at this welcoming, oak-panelled pub. Chef David Fegan uses organic and free-range produce, and there's a beer garden out back for the children to let off steam in.

Marquess Tavern ★

32 Canonbury Street, N1 2TB (7354 2975/ www.marquesstavern.co.uk). Angel tube/ Essex Road rail. Meals served 5-11pm Mon-Thur; 5pm-midnight Fri; noon-midnight Sat; noon-11pm Sun. ££.
Free-range and traditionally reared meat is the order of the day at this superior gastropub, where a roast beef Sunday dinner or pork belly with black pudding and apple sauce round off the weekend in style.

Norfolk Arms

28 Leigh Street, WC1H 9EP (7388 3937/ www.norfolkarms.co.uk). Euston tube/rail. Meals served noon-3pm, 6.30-10.15pm Mon-Sat; noon-10.15pm Sun. ££.
Best known for its sterling tapas, the Norfolk Arms is no slouch when it comes to inventive mains. You might find basque fish stew or marinated octopus on the menu, but Sunday brings trad roasts: Gloucester Old Spot pork belly, perhaps, or a leg of Welsh lamb.

Royal Oak

73 Columbia Road, E2 7RG (7729 2220/ www.royaloaklondon.com). Old Street tube/ rail/26, 48, 55 bus. Meals served 6-10pm Mon; noon-4pm, 6-10pm Tue-Sat; noon-4pm, 5-10pm Sun. ££.
Sunday lunch here means a whopping plate, filled to the brim with succulent roast. Veggie options are well thought out, and no-nonsense puddings round things off nicely.

Shopping

A culinary tour of the capital's markets and specialist food shops.

Markets

The capital's markets scene is thriving, with farmers' markets cropping up across town. Another trend is street food markets, where stalls and vans take over the road to serve lip-smackingly good, hot and cold food to hungry passers-by. Last but not least, there are the traditional markets, where stallholders vie with each to shout their bowl-for-a-pound bargains.

Fifteen of the city's farmers' markets are officially verified by **London Farmers' Markets** (www.lfm.org.uk), which means they must adhere to strict guidelines, including only selling produce from farms located within 100 miles of the M25.

CENTRAL

Borough Market

Southwark Street, SE1 1TL (7407 1002/ www.boroughmarket.org.uk). London Bridge tube/rail. Open 11am-5pm Thur; noon-6pm Fri; 9am-4pm Sat.
London's oldest food market is guaranteed to bring out your piggish side. Free samples abound, as do all manner of enticing lunch options: Brindisa's barbecued chorizo rolls and Raclette's grilled cheese sarnies or bubbling namesake raclette are standouts. Take-home goodies range from fruit and veg to rare-breed meats, bread and cakes: Flour Power City Bakery's brownies are heavenly.

Cabbages & Frocks

St Marylebone Parish Church Grounds, Marylebone High Street, W1 (7794 1636/ www.cabbagesandfrocks.co.uk). Baker Street tube. Open 11am-5pm Sat.
Fashionistas and foodies happily mingle at this Saturday-only market. Pick up bread, olives, cupcakes and homemade preserves along with the eponymous frocks, then recover with a cream tea, served from 4pm. On the last Saturday of the month, don't miss the Moroccan tent, manned by former Momo's chef Abdul.

Marylebone Farmers' Market

Cramer Street car park, off Marylebone High Street, W1 (7833 0338/www.lfm. org.uk). Bond Street or Baker Street tube. Open 10am-2pm Sun.
Just off chi chi Marylebone High Street, this farmers' market is brimming with fresh produce – from bounteous displays of fruit and veg to quality meats and excellent breads. A sneaky slice from Downland Produce's whole hog roast is a must-buy.

Whitecross Food Market

Whitecross Street, EC1Y 8JH (7378 0422/ www.whitecrossstreetmarket.co.uk). Old Street tube. Open 11am-5pm Thur, Fri.
This buzzing market attracts droves of hungry office workers, thanks to its enticing spread of takeaway vans and stalls. Options

---

City Secret

Appease mid week cravings for a roast with a visit to **Fuzzy's Grub** (6 Crown Passage, SW1Y 6PP, 7925 2791, www.fuzzysgrub.com). Here, takeaway lunchtime roasts are served Monday to Friday – in traditional and sarnie form. Choose your meat, add some potatoes and trimmings (sage and onion stuffing or crackling), then select a relish: own-made red onion marmalade, perhaps, or a dollop of sweet chilli jam.

GOING OUT
BEAUTY
FASHION
PARTIES
FOOD
HEALTH
ECO
OUTDOORS
HOME
CHILDREN
PETS
TRANSPORT
RESOURCES

THE LODGE
TAVERN

2 FOR 1 LUNCH*

LIVE JAZZ/SOUL SESSIONS EVERY SUNDAY

TRADITIONAL SUNDAY ROASTS

HAND CRAFTED COCKTAILS

BBQ PARTIES AVAILABLE ON OUR VERANDA
[During the warmer months]

*SEE OUR WEBSITE FOR HIRE INFO, DEALS,
SPECIAL EVENTS AND DJ LISTINGS

53 The Mall, Ealing Broadway, London, W5 3TA T:: 0208 567 0173 www.thelodgetavern.co.uk

SAGAR
BEST VEGETARIAN RESTAURANT
www.gosagar.com

New to Percy Street
* Private room for parties.
* We cater for Weddings,
Christmas Parties & loads more.
Please call Percy Street below
for details.

'One of the Best South Indian
Vegetarian Restaurants in London'
-Time Out

Sagar Hammersmith
157 King Street, Hammersmith, London W6 9JT
Reservations:
020 8741 8563

Sagar Twickenham
27 York Street, Twickenham, London TW1 3JZ
Reservations:
020 8744 3868

Sagar West End
17A Percy Street, off Tottenham Court Road, London W1T 1DU
Reservations:
020 7631 3319

include Thai food, salads and bratwurst, with Luardo's burritos always attracting a queue. While you're there, pick up some of Manor Farm Game's superb sausages, which range from pigeon and peach to venison and herb.

NORTH

Chapel Market

Chapel Street, N1 ORW (7289 4371).
Angel tube. Open 9am-6pm Tue-Sat;
8.30am-4pm Sun.
This lively street market in the heart of Angel sells fresh fruit and veg for a song, alongside cheap toiletries, knickers and other bits and bobs. The French cheese stall and fish stalls (complete with jellied eels) are worth a visit; if you're in need of refuelling, pop into Manze's traditional pie and mash shop at no.74.

Islington Farmers' Market

William Tyndale School, Richmond Grove,
N1 2AQ (7833 0338/www.lfm.org.uk). Angel
tube/bus 38, 56, 73. Open 10am-2pm Sun.
This popular farmers' market was the first to begin operating in London, back in 1999, and continues to thrive. There's a wealth of seasonal produce, from asparagus and broad beans in spring to pheasant, apples and native oysters in the autumn. Other goodies include specialist cheeses, organic meat and seafood.

EAST

Brick Lane Sunday UpMarket

91 Brick Lane, E1 6QL (7770 6028/www.
sundayupmarket.co.uk). Aldgate East tube.
Open 10am-5pm Sun.
The takeaway food court keeps expanding, with more and more interesting vendors pitching up alongside the fashion and art stalls. At the market's Brick Lane end you can try homestyle Moroccan dishes and piping-hot Japanese *takoyaki* (battered octopus) or quaff Ethiopian coffee, brewed in clay pots.

Broadway Market

London Fields, E8 (07709 311869/www.
broadwaymarket.co.uk). Bethnal Green tube/
London Fields rail/26, 48, 55, 106, 253, 263,
277, 388, 394, D6 bus. Open 9am-5pm Sat.

Delectably whiffy cheeses, charcuterie and artisanal desserts are among the wares at this charming East End market. Highlights include Vietnamese coffee and curious artichoke tea from Cà Phê VN, and dainty cupcakes from Violet's antique cakestands.

Spitalfields Food Market

Commercial Street, between Lamb Street
& Brushfield Street, E1 (7247 8556/www.
spitalfields.org.uk). Liverpool Street tube/rail.
Open 10am-5pm Wed, Fri, Sun.
The thrice-weekly artisan food market sees Spitalfields come alive, with traders touting everything from freshly-shucked oysters to prosciutto sandwiches and unusual beers. Sample a few choice olives and pickled garlic, then take home some fine salami for tea.

Stoke Newington Farmers' Market

William Patten Primary School, Stoke
Newington Church Street, N16 0NX
(7502 7588/www.growingcommunities.org).
Stoke Newington rail/73, 393, 476 bus.
Open 10am-2.30pm Sat.
This modestly proportioned local farmers' market features some top-notch producers, selling organic greens and fruits, seafood, cakes, cheeses and meat. Once a month, look out for the Stour Valley Organic Lavender Company's wonderfully fragrant honey.

SOUTH

Blackheath Farmers' Market

Station car park, 2 Blackheath Village,
SE3 0ZH (7833 0338/www.lfm.org.uk).
Blackheath rail/54, 89, 108, 202, 380 bus.
Open 10am-2pm Sun.
In operation since late 2000, Blackheath is a veteran among the city's farmers' markets. Fresh, in-season fruit and vegetables all come from within 100 miles of the M25, and stallholders change from Sunday to Sunday. Keep an eye out for the Garlic Farm's roasted garlic butter, and excellent goat's cheeses from Nut Knowle Farm in Sussex.

Brixton Market

Electric Avenue/Pope Road/Atlantic Road/
Brixton Station Road, SW9 8HE. Brixton

GOING OUT

BEAUTY

FASHION

PARTIES

FOOD

HEALTH

ECO

OUTDOORS

HOME

CHILDREN

PETS

TRANSPORT

RESOURCES

GOING OUT

BEAUTY

FASHION

PARTIES

FOOD

HEALTH

ECO

tube/rail. Open 10am-6pm Mon, Tue; 10am-4pm Wed; 10am-6pm Thur-Sat.

This sprawling market is the best place in London to find African and Caribbean produce, from custard apples to yams and exotic fish. It can be overwhelming for the novice shopper, but take your time to peruse the stalls and ask the traders for cooking tips.

Clapham Farmers' Market

Bonneville Primary School, off Abbeville Road, SW4 9LB (7833 0338/www.lfm.org.uk). Clapham South tube. Open 10am-2pm Sun.

Stalls offer organic breads, pies, vegetables and cheeses, along with juices, cakes, jams and relishes. Take a leisurely look round as you devour a freshly-grilled sausage bun.

Greenwich Food Court

Cutty Sark or Island Gardens DLR/ Greenwich DLR/rail. Open 9.30am-5.30pm Sat, Sun.

Treats at this well-designed food court range from freshly rolled sushi to flaky, sweet baklava. Quality charcuterie and cheeses are available, as are olives, spices and all sorts of bread and cakes. A fresh fruit and vegetable market also opened here in 2008.

Wimbledon Farmers' Market

Wimbledon Park First School, Havana Road, SW19 8EJ (7833 0338/www.lfm.org.uk). Wimbledon Park tube/rail/156 bus. Open 9am-1pm Sat.

Organised by London Farmers' Markets, Wimbledon's market is an unhurried, enjoyable affair. Some stalls rotate monthly, others fortnightly, though regular fixtures include Horti Halcyon, with its abundance of organic vegetables.

WEST

Notting Hill Farmers' Market

Car park behind Waterstone's, access via Kensington Place, W8 (7833 0338/www.lfm. org.uk). Notting Hill Gate tube. Open Sat 9am-1pm.

In the opposite direction to the infinitely more touristy Portobello Road lies this gem of a market. There's a great range of organic produce stalls, mostly manned by farmers from Kent, Surrey and Sussex.

Partridges Food Market

Outside Duke of York Square, SW3 4LY (www.partridges.co.uk/foodmarket). Sloane Square or South Kensington tube. Open 10am-4pm Sat.

Myriad stalls set up camp here each week, with high-quality foods to tempt well-heeled locals: look out for the artisanal pâtés and darling cupcakes from Crumbs and Doilies.

Shepherd's Bush Market

East side of railway viaduct, between Uxbridge Road & Goldhawk Road, W12. Goldhawk Road or Shepherd's Bush tube. Open 8.30am-6pm Tue, Wed, Fri, Sat; 8.30am-1pm Thur.

There's an impressive array of ethnic foods at this lively local market, including Indian and Polish grub. Follow your nose to the stalls selling fragrant spices and juicy mangoes.

PASTIES + PIES

Specialist shops

CENTRAL

For a taste of *la dolce vita*, Soho's much-loved **I Camisa & Son** (*see p90*) is another must-visit.

Japan Centre
212 Piccadilly, W1J 9HG (7255 8255/www. japancentre.com). Piccadilly Circus tube. Open 10am-7pm Mon-Fri; 10.30am-8pm Sat; 11am-7pm Sun.
With over 1,000 Japanese food items in stock, this bustling store has everything from *nori* seaweed and spices to wasabi peas and fabulously packaged sweets to snack on.

Lina Store
For listings, see p90.
Beyond the 1950's green ceramic frontage at this Italian family-run deli lies a wealth of quality products – wooden crates full of dried pastas, plus a deli counter filled with excellent antipasti and (in season) truffles.

NORTH

Andreas Michli & Son
405-411 St Ann's Road, N15 3JL (8802 0188). Harringay Green Lanes rail. Open 10am-7pm Mon-Sat; 11am-3.30pm Sun.
Charming proprietor Mr Michli oversees operations at this Cypriot store, where staff will happily answer questions about the stock – from fresh yellow dates to hollyhock leaves, and seasonal fruit and veg from Cyprus or Mr Michli's Hertfordshire farm.

The Food Hall
22-24 Turnpike Lane, N8 0PS (8889 2264). Turnpike Lane tube. Open 8.30am-7pm Mon-Sat; 10am-3pm Sun.
The speciality at this Ethiopian food shop is the freshly-milled flour (including rice, millet and maize flour) used for making traditional breads such as soft, slightly sour *injera*. Other finds include aged spice butter (used to flavour stews) and the pungent, peppery West African 'grains of paradise' spice.

Le Péché Mignon
6 Ronalds Road, N5 1XH (7607 1826/www. lepechemignon.co.uk). Holloway Road tube/ Highbury & Islington tube/rail. Open 8am-7pm Mon-Fri; 9am-6pm Sat; 9am-5pm Sun.
Set on a quiet residential side street, this impressive deli and café stocks plentiful supplies of cheese, charcuterie and products from all over Europe, from panettone to paella rice.

Polsmak ★
39 Balls Pond Road, N1 4BW (7275 7045/ www.polsmak.co.uk). Dalston Kingsland rail/bus 30, 36, 56, 277. Open 9am-8pm Mon-Fri; 9am-6pm Sat, Sun.
This little shop is so authentic, everything is labelled in Polish; happily, staff are at hand to explain. There's also a small café area where you can enjoy delicious Polish *packzi* (cream buns) and *drozdzowka* (yeast cake).

EAST

London Star Night Supermarket & Video
203-213 Mare Street, E8 3QE (8985 2949). Hackney Central or London Fields rail/bus 26, 48, 55, 253. Open 10am-10pm daily.
Even the Vietnamese restaurants down the road rely on this place for the occasional ingredients run. Stock includes aromatic herbs such as Asian basil and saw-tooth herb, as well as staples such as rice noodles, fish sauce and bundles of morning glory.

Taj Stores
112-114A Brick Lane, E1 6RL (7377 0061/ www.tajstores.co.uk). Aldgate East tube or Liverpool Street tube/rail. Open 9am-9pm daily.
This Bangladeshi grocer does a brisk trade in halal meat, exotic herbs and fish. Freshly prepared naan and samosas are stocked, as are more unusual vegetables such as *lata* and *danga*, pulses, grains, spices and tiffin tins.

Turkish Food Centre
89 Ridley Road, E8 2NT (7254 6754). Dalston Kingsland rail/30, 56 or 236 bus. Open 8am-9pm Mon-Sat; 8.30am-9pm Sun.

GOING OUT
BEAUTY
FASHION
PARTIES
FOOD
HEALTH
ECO
OUTDOORS
HOME
CHILDREN
PETS
TRANSPORT
RESOURCES

GOING OUT

BEAUTY

FASHION

PARTIES

FOOD

HEALTH

ECO

OUTDOORS

HOME

CHILDREN

PETS

TRANSPORT

RESOURCES

A formidable purveyor of Turkish foodstuffs, this Dalston stalwart has been in operation for more than 20 years. Fresh fruit and veg are flown in from Turkey, Greece and Cyprus, while pomegranate syrup is a bargain buy.

SOUTH

The Cheese Block
69 Lordship Lane, SE22 8EP (8299 3636). East Dulwich rail. Open 9am-6.30pm Mon-Fri; 9am-6pm Sat.
With hundreds of cheeses, this is a haven for fromage lovers. Choosing can be tough, but staff are always happy to help; the mature Old Amsterdam gouda is one of our top picks.

Deepak Cash & Carry
953-959 Garrat Lane, SW17 0LW (8767 7819). Tooting Broadway tube. Open 8.45am-8pm Mon-Sat; 10am-4pm Sun.
If you're looking for a South Indian product and can't find it here, you're unlikely to find it anywhere. For dried goods and spices, this place has no peer. Best buys are pulses such as *malawi toor dahl* and *channa dahl*.

Gennaro Delicatessen
23 Lewis Grove, SE13 6BG (8852 1370). Lewisham rail/DLR. Open 9am-6pm Mon-Sat.
This family-run deli, passed down through generations, sells anything an Italian food aficionado could desire: quality prosciutto, fresh buffalo mozzarella, coffee and more. The own-brand Sicilian olive oil is top-notch.

Persepolis ✦
28-30 Peckham High Street, SE15 5DT (7639 8007). Peckham Rye rail. Open 10.35am-10pm daily.
Owner Sally Peck, author of the acclaimed *Persia in Peckham* cookbook, is often on hand to answer queries about the Iranian produce available in her corner shop, from fresh herbs and pomegranates to saffron and *sumak*.

Talad Thai
326 Upper Richmond Road, SW15 6TL (8789 8084/www.taladthai.co.uk). Putney rail. Open 9am-8pm Mon-Sat; 10am-8pm Sun.

Talad Thai crams plenty in to its modest premises. Fresh fruit and vegetables are imported from Thailand, with hard-to-find delights such as mangosteens, the 'queen of fruits', as well as essentials such as kaffir lime leaves and Asian holy basil. There's a formidable range of curry pastes too.

WEST

R Garcia & Sons
248-250 Portobello Road, W11 1LL (7221 6119). Ladbroke Grove or Westbourne Park tube. Open 9am-6pm Mon-Fri; 9am-7pm Sat; 10am-6pm Sun.
A one-stop shop for all things Spanish, R Garcia stocks a comprehensive range of sherries, and a feast of cheeses and *jamon*. Even the tinned olives, imported from Spain, are excellent. The shop also sells clay cookware and dishes for entertaining at home.

Natural Natural
20 Station Parade, Uxbridge Road, W5 3LD (8992 0770/www.natural-natural.co.uk). Ealing Common tube. Open 9am-8pm daily.
This quaint Japanese store offers an excellent range of groceries, from saké and fresh fruit to ready-packaged and marinated cod and mackerel. Prime picks include *mentaiko* (spicy cod roe), jars of *yamamomo* (Japanese mountain peaches) and *yuzu* salad dressing.

Teaspoon Leluu & Dewdhory
195 Praed Street, W2 1RH (7402 0499/www.leluu.com). Paddington tube/rail. Open 9am-7pm Mon-Sat.
Teaspoon offers an unrivalled selection of specialist teas, and an appealing array of tea accessories. From Earl Grey Supreme to Moroccan Mint and first-pick Shizuoka Sencha, this is an inspirational little place.

VB & Sons
147 Ealing Road, Wembley, Middlesex HA0 4BU (8795 0387). Alperton tube. Open 9.30am-6.30pm daily.
Head here for a wealth of Gujarati products: cobra saffron, soapnuts, mango-ginger, malucca nuts, freshly-made pickles, own-made paneer cheese and Indian noodles.

Health

GOING OUT

BEAUTY

FASHION

PARTIES

FOOD

HEALTH

ECO

OUTDOORS

HOME

CHILDREN

PETS

TRANSPORT

RESOURCES

Health

The essential contacts – plus our pick of the city's best alternative practitioners and yoga classes.

Alternative health

Individual practitioners' working hours vary, so we've only listed opening hours for centres with set times.

GENERAL CLINICS

Hale Clinic
7 Park Crescent, W1B 1PF (7631 0156/ www.haleclinic.com). Regent's Park tube. Open 8.30am-8.30pm Mon-Fri; 9am-5pm Sat.
If you're unsure about alternative health treatments, the Hale, with its focus on integrating conventional medicine with complementary techniques, is a good place to start. In total, there are around 100 treatments on offer, from homeopathy to hypnotherapy.

Inside Out Retreats
9 Brewers Lane, Richmond, Surrey TW9 1HH (8332 6566/www.insideoutretreats. com). Richmond tube/rail. Open 10am-6pm Tue-Sat; 11am-5pm Sun.
Familiar treatments such as homeopathy and reflexology sit alongside colour therapy, primordial sound meditation and ayurvedic facial rejuvenation at this chic centre, owned by life coach and energy healer Alison Pothier. Sound therapy sessions with Margaret Teggin PhD are highly recommended.

Neal's Yard Remedies Therapy Rooms
12 Foubert's Place, W1F 7PG (7494 9862/ www.nealsyardremedies.com). Oxford Circus tube. Open 10am-7pm Mon-Wed, Fri, Sat; 10am-8pm Thur; 11am-5pm Sun.
Along with the ever-popular facials and aromatherapy, this bright new treatment centre offers lesser-known therapies such as

Bowen Technique. Among the excellent practitioners is Yeen Au, who has found that shiatsu and craniosacral therapy are particularly effective when used together.

SPECIALISTS

Eastern Clinic (Ayurvedic Medical Centre)
1079 Garratt Lane, SW17 0LN (8682 3876/www.easternclinic.co.uk). Tooting Broadway tube. Open 10.30am-7.30pm Mon-Fri; 10.30am-4pm Sat.
Ayurveda ('science of life' in Sanskrit) is an intriguing field; its medical practitioners train for a minimum of five years at university, followed by a year's hospital internship in India and Sri Lanka. As well as founding the Ayurvedic Medical Association of the UK, Dr Moorthy Sathiya consults for the NHS. Ayurveda is famed for its massage treatments, but clinical diagnosis of your ayurvedic body type and dietary advice are fundamental.

Garden Health Practice
63 Long Acre, WC2E 9JN (07886 308715/ 07886 242872/www.gardenhealthpractice. co.uk). Covent Garden tube. Open 10am-7pm Mon-Sat; 11.30am-5.30pm Sun.
A basement below the London Marathon Store may seem an unusual place to find traditional Chinese medicine, but Suzanne Turner and Graham Waterworth have a special expertise in sports injuries. A typical session with Turner will incorporate acupuncture, massage and herbal remedies, addressing issues as diverse as RSI, migraines and depression.

The Keet Clinic
14-16 Betterton Street, WC2H 9BU (7240 1438/www.reflexologycollege.com). Covent Garden tube. Open 10am-7pm daily.

Podiatrist Michael Keet is principal of the London College of Reflexology, which is based at this clinic. Hour-long sessions with a newly qualified reflexologist start at £35 and rise according to the therapist's experience and expertise.

Micheline Arcier Aromathérapie

7 William Street, SW1X 9HL (7235 3545/ www.michelinearcier.com). Knightsbridge tube. Open 10am-6pm Mon, Fri; 9.30am-6.30pm Tue-Thur; 9am-6pm Sat.

This smart aromatherapy company has been awarded a Royal Warrant. Micheline Arcier distinguishes true aromatherapy – the use of essential oils to promote holistic well-being – from the sort of 'aromatherapy' massage using nice smelly oil you often get in salons.

Milton Natural Health Centre

33 Milton Avenue, N6 5QF (8340 7062). Highgate tube. Open by appointment only.

A treatment at highly-qualified Mark Mordin's home clinic may comprise everything from magnetic therapy to shiatsu. Wife Linda specialises in aromatherapy, with particular emphasis on mothers-to-be.

Paul Lennard Energy Healer

Ella Clinic, 106 Harley Street, W1G 7JE (7935 5281/www.paullennard.co.uk). Baker Street tube. Open by appointment only.

One-hour sessions with energy healer Paul Lennard vary widely according to the needs of the client, but may incorporate craniosacral

City Secret

If you're on a tight budget, check out the **Polyclinic** (115 New Cavendish Street, W1W 7UW, 7911 5041, www.westminster.ac.uk/sih). Here, students from the University of Westminster's School of Integrated Health offer the public supervised, low-cost alternative treatments, with everything from acupuncture and herbal medicine to osteopathy, for a flat-rate £20 charge.

therapy, *chi nei tsang* (a Thai deep massage technique) and discussion of past traumas.

Vena Ramphal Crystal Resonance

Venues vary; call for details (07852 329826).

Crystal resonance with Vena Ramphal is a gentle, usually hands-off therapy that can help you deal with major transitions, such as a divorce or career change. Crystals are selected according to the client's needs and placed around the body: some people feel hot or cold sensations; others simply fall asleep.

West London Osteopaths

65 Vespan Road, W12 9QG (8749 0581/ www.westlondonosteopaths.com). Shepherds Bush or Stamford Brook tube. Open 8am-5.30pm Mon, Tue, Thur, Fri; 8am-7pm Wed; 9am-1pm Sat.

In addition to running this innovative clinic, owner David Tatton is Chairman of the London Osteopathic Society. Holistic massage and Pilates matwork sessions are offered to assist osteopathy sessions, which can benefit back pain, respiratory function, arthritis and accident trauma, among other conditions.

Yoga Biomedical Trust

90-92 Pentonville Road, N1 9HS (7689 3040/www.yogatherapy.org). Angel tube. Open by appointment only.

Asthma, diabetes, cancer, mild MS and Parkinsons are just some of the medical conditions that can be helped with yoga therapy. After a consultation with a therapist (a yoga teacher who has undertaken two years of specialised training), you then undertake prescribed classes and home practice.

Zita West Clinic

37 Manchester Street, W1U 7LJ (7224 0017/ www.zitawest.com). Baker Street tube. Open 9am-6pm Mon-Thur; 9am-5pm Fri, Sat.

Fronted by renowned midwife Zita West, this is the place to come if you're having trouble getting pregnant or want to boost your chances for successful IVF. Nutritional therapy, hypnotherapy and acupuncture are among the complementary techniques used – and the clinic is integrated, so you also have access to a wide variety of medical tests.

Key contacts

The **NHS Direct** (0845 4647/www.nhs direct.nhs.uk) is a one-stop-shop for free health advice, and should be your first port of call if you're feeling unwell, or need to find your nearest doctor, A&E, minor injuries unit, pharmacist, dentist or support group. Alternatively, the main NHS website at www.nhs.uk has a good range of search criteria which will enable you to find the best service for your condition, whether it be a sports and fitness injury or a dental emergency.

A&E DEPARTMENTS

Accident and Emergency departments cover the whole of the capital; to find your nearest call the **NHS Direct** (*see above*).

EMERGENCY EYE CLINICS

London has two 24-hour emergency departments dealing specifically with eye injuries, although if your injuries are more extensive you should go to a regular A&E department.

Moorfields Eye Hospital
162 City Road, EC1V 2PD (7253 3411/ www.moorfields.nhs.uk). Old Street tube/rail. Moorfields also has a nurse-led telephone helpline on 7566 2345, open 8.30am-4.30pm Monday to Friday.

Western Eye Hospital
171 Marylebone Road, NW1 5PN (7886 6666/www.imperial.nhs.uk). Marylebone tube/rail. Western Eye Hospital is open 24 hours a day for ambulance and walk-in cases.

DENTISTS

Find your nearest dentist via the **British Dental Association** website at www.bda.org. The search facility allows you to specify a range of different criteria, including NHS dentists and those with disabled access. NHS dentists who are taking on new patients are also listed at www.nhs.uk.

If you need an emergency dentist, your first call should be to your own dentist. Even out of hours, they should have emergency information on their answerphone. If you don't have a dentist, call the **NHS Direct** or ring Guy's Hospital's **Dental Emergency Care Service** on 7188 0512. Guy's also provides free walk-in emergency treatment (Guy's Hospital, St Thomas Street, SE1 9RT, 7188 0511); it's open 9am-5pm Monday to Friday, but queues start forming at 8am. Arrive by 10am if you're to be seen at all.

WALK-IN CENTRES

NHS Walk-in Centres offer confidential advice and treatment for minor injuries and illnesses. Staffed by experienced nurses, they're often open seven days a week (hours vary) and you don't need an appointment. Find your nearest through the **NHS Direct** (*see left*).

Canary Wharf NHS Walk-In Centre
30 Marsh Wall, E14 9TP (7517 3300). Canary Wharf tube or South Quays DLR. Open 7am-7pm Mon-Fri and bank holidays.

City and Hackney Teaching PCT Walk In Centre *Tollgate Primary Care Centre, 57 Stamford Hill, N16 5SR (7689 3140). Seven Sisters tube. Open 8am-8pm Mon-Fri; 8am-6pm Sat, Sun.*

Charing Cross NHS Walk-In Centre
Charing Cross Hospital, Fulham Palace Road, W6 8RF (8846 1234). Hammersmith Broadway tube. Open 8am-10pm Mon-Fri; 9am-10pm Sun.

Hackney NHS Walk-In Centre
Homerton University Hospital, Homerton Row, E9 6SR (8510 5342). Homerton rail. Open 8am-10pm Mon-Fri; 9am-10pm Sat, Sun.

GOING OUT

BEAUTY

FASHION

PARTIES

FOOD

HEALTH

ECO

OUTDOORS

HOME

CHILDREN

PETS

TRANSPORT

RESOURCES

Liverpool Street Walk-In Centre
Exchange Arcade, EC2M 3WA (0845 880 1242). Liverpool Street tube/rail. Open 7am-7pm Mon-Fri.

Parsons Green NHS Walk-In Centre
5-7 Parsons Green, SW6 4UL (8846 6758). Parsons Green tube. Open 8am-8pm Mon-Fri; 9am-1.30pm Sat, Sun.

Soho NHS Walk-In Centre *1 Frith Street, W1D 3HZ (7534 6500). Tottenham Court Road tube. Open 8am-8pm Mon-Fri; 10am-8pm Sat, Sun.*

Victoria NHS Walk-In Centre *63 Buckingham Gate, SW1E 6AS (7340 1190). Victoria or St James Park tube. Open 7am-7pm Mon-Fri.*

Whitechapel NHS Walk-In Centre
Whitechapel Hospital, 174 Whitechapel Road, E1 1BZ (7943 1333). Whitechapel tube. Open 7am-10pm Mon-Fri; 9am-10pm Sat, Sun.

LATE-NIGHT CHEMISTS

Below are details for late-night, central London branches of Boots, along with a couple of independent chemists that stay open late.

Boots Queensway *114 Queensway, W2 4QS (7229 9266). Bayswater or Queensway tube. Open 9am-midnight Mon-Sat; noon-6pm Sun.*

Boots Piccadilly *44-46 Regent Street, W1B 5RA (7734 6126). Piccadilly Circus tube. Open 8am-midnight Mon-Fri; 9am-midnight Sat; noon-6pm Sun.*

Boots Victoria Station
Victoria Station, SW1V 1JT (7834 0676). Victoria tube/rail. Open 7am-10pm Mon-Fri; 8am-10pm Sat; 9am-9pm Sun.

Zafash *233-235 Old Brompton Road, SW5 0EA (7373 2798). Earl's Court tube. Open 24hrs daily.*

Bliss Chemists *5-6 Marble Arch, W1H 7EL (7723 6116). Marble Arch tube. Open daily 9am-midnight.*

SEXUAL HEALTH

In addition to the services of **NHS Direct** (*see p108*), the 24-hour service **Sexual Healthline** (0800 567123, www.playingsafely.co.uk) is free and confidential. Either service will locate your nearest NHS Genito-Urinary Clinic. These provide free, confidential treatment of STDs and other problems such as thrush and cystitis; they also offer counselling and advice on HIV and other STDs and can carry out blood tests. **Sexwise** (0800 282930), is an advice centre aimed at young people aged 18 and under that can provide free, confidential advice about sex and contraception, as well as on relationships in general. The **British Pregnancy Advice Service** (0845 730 4030, www.bpas.org) offers callers advice, contraceptives, the morning-after pill, pregnancy tests and referrals to BPAS nursing homes for private abortions, and has outposts across the city. For under-25s, **Brook** (0800 0185 023, www.brook.org.uk) runs ten London clinics.

The **Terence Higgins Trust** (0845 122 1200, www.tht.org.uk) is an excellent source of information and advice on sexual health and particularly HIV, with an advice and support line, plus friendly drop-in centres in Waterloo, Peckham and Notting Hill.

GOING OUT
BEAUTY
FASHION
PARTIES
FOOD
HEALTH
ECO
OUTDOORS
HOME
CHILDREN
PETS
TRANSPORT
RESOURCES

Yoga

For children's yoga classes, try **Yoga Bugs** (www.yogabugs.com), which caters for three- to seven-year-olds. The **Sitaram Partnership** (*see p168*), meanwhile, runs excellent family yoga sessions and toddler and parent classes.

Iyengar Yoga Institute
223A Randolph Avenue, W9 1NL (7624 3080/www.iyi.org.uk). Maida Vale tube. Open call for details. Classes £6-£11.
Housed in two airy, light studios in a leafy Maida Vale street, the Iyengar Institute runs some 50 classes, with a maximum of 35 people per class. Novices can try a free class; the six-week beginners' course costs £60.

Jeff Phenix Yoga
07870 569466/www.yogajeff.co.uk. Classes £8-£12.
British Wheel of Yoga-accredited Jeff Phenix runs classes at several top centres, including Triyoga at Covent Garden and Primrose Hill and the Life Centre in Notting Hill, with an emphasis on meditation; see the website for details.

Jivamukti Yoga
300 Kensal Road, W10 5BE (8960 3999/ www.jivamuktiyoga.co.uk). Ladbroke Grove or Westbourne Park tube. Open 7.30am-2pm, 5-9pm Mon-Fri; 9am-2pm, 3-7pm Sat, Sun. Classes £8-£14.
Jivamukti offers ashtanga-based yoga in a range of vigorous classes, with an emphasis on spiritual elements such as chanting and meditation. This is the London offshoot of the successful New York studio.

The Life Centre ✦
15 Edge Street, W8 7PN (7221 4602/www. thelifecentre.com). Notting Hill Gate tube. Open 8am-9.30pm Mon-Fri; 8am-7.30pm Sat, Sun. Classes £12-£14.
One of London's first yoga studios, and still one of its prettiest. The space is small enough to feel intimate, but there's still a great selection of classes – more than 60 a week – and the teaching quality is superb.

PILATES

You can do Pilates pretty much anywhere these days. To ensure the best tuition, look for classes and studios led by dance and choreography experts, and for instructors whose work is based on the classical Pilates repertoire. Do a little homework before you sign up and investigate your instructor's professional background and training, such as who they trained with and for how long.

The where is not so important as the who; the Pilates class at **Sobell Leisure Centre** (7609 2166, www.aquaterra.org) on Wednesdays is beloved by regulars, thanks to its energetic Australian teacher, Michael, and value-for-money prices. And while **Studio 74** (Pilates 07775 687585, Gyrotonic 07801 565310, www.studioseventyfour.co.uk) won't win any prizes for high-tech wizardry, the friendly, warm centre offers a well-priced range of classes in a characterful 18th-century building.

You won't go far wrong if you stick with the likes of the **Body Maintenance Studio** at the Pineapple Dance Studio (7 Langley Street, WC2H 9JA, 7379 6043, www.pineapple.uk.com), where Lesley Ackland, a former remedial exercise consultant to the Birmingham Royal Ballet, leads a team teaching individually designed programmes as well as group classes.

At **Chiswick Pilates Practice** (venue varies, 8994 5822, www.chiswick pilates.co.uk), ex-ballerina Gaby Lewis concentrates on Pilates for

The Studio

Basement East, 36/42 New Inn Yard, EC2A 3EY (7729 0111/www.studiopt.org). Old Street tube/rail. Open times vary; call for details. Classes £8.

This newly opened studio hosts a whole range of yoga and Pilates classes. Of particular note are the weekday morning (6am-8.30am) Mysore-style ashtanga vinyasa classes with Charlie Taylor Rugman, a highly experienced teacher directly authorised by yoga master Sri K Pattabhi Jois.

Triyoga

6 Erskine Road, NW3 3AJ (7483 3344/ www.triyoga.co.uk). Chalk Farm tube. Open 6am-10pm Mon-Fri; 8am-8.30pm Sat; 9am-9.30pm Sun. Classes £12-£15.

The original Triyoga studio, and still the best. Most of London's top teachers lead classes here. It's a mecca for serious enthusiasts as well as a great starting ground for beginners. **Other locations** *Triyoga Covent Garden, 2 Dryden Street, WC2E 9NA (7483 3344); Triyoga Soho, 2nd Floor, Kingly Court, W1B 5PW (7483 3344).*

rehabilitation, using matwork, equipment sessions and Gyrotonic.
   Christine Hocking (7240 5922, www.pilatesbodyawareness.co.uk) also has a dance background, and uses it to offer five levels of group matwork classes at different venues around central London.
   If you must have the big names, then have the best: at **NY Pilates Studio** (20 Lonsdale Road NW6 6RD, 7372 3490, www.nypilates. co.uk), all the instructors have been fully trained by Joseph Pilates' protégé Romana Kryzanowska, and you'll find the complete repertoire of Gratz equipment, built to the exact specifications stipulated by the great man himself.

Yoga Biomedical Trust

For listings see p107. Classes £7-£12.

The Yoga Biomedical Trust's centre is dedicated to the development of yoga therapy as an integral part of complementary and alternative medicine. The pregnancy yoga classes with Françoise Barbira-Freedman are highly recommended, while various other specialisms include yoga for menopause, yoga for depression and anxiety, and sessions for children with asthma.

Yogahome

11 Allen Road, N16 8SB (7249 2425/ www.yogahome.com). Highbury & Islington tube/rail or Angel tube, then 73 bus or Dalston Kingsland rail. Open 10am-9pm Mon-Thur; 10am-2pm Fri; 9am-2pm Sat; 10am-2pm Sun. Classes from £7.50.

Set up by Maria Gandy and Billie Chan in 1998, Yogahome has won a loyal fan base. An extensive range of classes (including pregnancy yoga led by Billie and hatha fusion yoga by Maria) are taught in the warm, friendly studio.

Yoga Junction

Unit 24 City North, Fonthill Road, N4 3HF (7263 3113/www.yogajunction.co.uk). Finsbury Park tube/rail. Open 10am-9.15pm Mon; 7am-9.30pm Tue-Thur; 10am-7.30pm Fri; 9am-6pm Sat; 10am-8.30pm Sun. Classes £8.50-£10.

A nicely chilled space (albeit located in a business centre) with a good mix of classes and styles, including ashtanga self-practice, vinyasa flow and hatha. Therapeutic sessions for sufferers of Parkinson's Disease and ME, as well as children's classes, are held in the bright and peaceful studio.

Yoga Place

1st Floor, 449-453 Bethnal Green Road, E2 9QH (7739 5195/www.yogaplace.co.uk). Bethnal Green tube. Open times vary; check online for details. Classes £10-£12.

Some 30 classes are held each week, from shadow yoga and deep relaxation sessions to post-natal classes. The calm, warm space feels a long way from the grit and grime of Bethnal Green Road outside.

GOING OUT

BEAUTY

FASHION

PARTIES

FOOD

HEALTH

ECO

OUTDOORS

HOME

CHILDREN

PETS

TRANSPORT

RESOURCES

Start The Fun...
Learn to Dance! Ballroom & Latin
Singles and Couples are Welcome

77 Baker Street, London W1U 6RF
+44 (0)20 7486 4511 • www.ambakerstreet.com

PARAÍSO SCHOOL OF SAMBA

Weekly Samba Dance & Percussion
Workshops in North & South London

- Carnival
- Parties
- Corporate Events
- Shows

For more info visit:
www.paraisosamba.co.uk
For workshop info:
020 3291 2390
info@paraisosamba.co.uk

Hang out with Westway

LONDON'S TOP CLIMBING CENTRE
Try a taster now – no experience needed

**Plus 12 tennis courts, 6 football pitches,
4 handball courts, netball, basketball...**

CALL US FOR TAILORED EVENTS & PARTIES

020 8969 0992

BOOK ONLINE NOW!
www.westway.org/sports

ADULT & JUNIOR PROGRAMMES IN ALL SPORTS

Sport & fitness

Some of the city's finest fitness venues, from climbing centres to ice rinks. For yoga centres, *see p110.*

Climbing centres

Along with dedicated climbing centres, six of London's sports centres with climbing walls have clubbed together to form **Climb London** (0845 363 1144, www.climblondon.co.uk). Taster sessions, workshops and weekends away are all offered.

Castle
Green Lanes, N4 2HA (8211 7000/www. castle-climbing.co.uk). Open 2pm-10pm Mon-Fri; 10am-7pm Sat, Sun. Admission £6-£11.50.
Spectacularly set in a converted Victorian water-pumping station, the Castle offers over 400 routes (changed every four months). It can get very crowded, though.

Mile End Climbing Wall
Haverfield Road, E3 5BE (8980 0289/www. mileendwall.org.uk). Mile End tube. Open noon-9.30pm Mon-Thur; noon-9pm Fri; 10am-6pm Sat, Sun. Admission £7-£12.
Housed in an old pipe-engineering works, the huge climbing wall caters to all levels and provides a range of surfaces. A first climb deal, including shoe hire, is just £12.

Vertical Chill at Ellis Brigham
Tower House, 3-11 Southampton Street, WC2E 7HA (7395 1010/www.vertical-chill. com). Covent Garden tube. Open 12.30pm-5.30pm Tue; 10.30am-3.30pm Wed-Fri; 10.30am-6.30pm Thur; 10am-5pm Sat; noon-4pm Sun. Admission £20-£40.
This eight-metre indoor ice wall offers a unique climbing adventure: a lesson with a qualified guide costs £40, with cheaper rates if you bring your own equipment.

Westway Climbing Complex ★
Westway Sports Centre, 1 Crowthorne Road, Ladbroke Grove, W10 6RP (8969 0992/ www.westway.org). Ladbroke Grove or Latimer Road tube. Open 10am-10pm Mon-Wed, Fri; 8am-10pm Thur; 10am-8pm Sat, Sun. Admission £7-£8.50.
The largest indoor climbing facility in the country, Westway caters to all climbing levels.

Dance

The **London Dance Network** (www. londondance.com) has a full directory of classes and workshops in everything from tango to wedding dance tuition.

Cecil Sharp House
2 Regent's Park Road, NW1 7AY (7485 2206/www.efdss.org). Camden Town tube. Open times vary; call for details. Classes £3-£10. No credit cards.
If salsa's too saucy and rumba too raunchy, this might be the place for you: the home of the English Folk Dance and Song Society. There are lessons in everything from cajun to clog dancing, and a whole range of ceilidhs.

Chisenhale Dance Space
64-84 Chisenhale Road, E3 5QZ (8981 6617/www.chisenhaledancespace.co.uk). Mile End tube. Open 10am-9pm daily. Classes £8-£15; £3.50 reductions.
Chisenhale runs children's and adults' African and creative dance classes, and also offers cheap studio space.

Danceworks
16 Balderton Street, W1K 6TN (7629 6183/www.danceworks.net). Bond Street tube. Open 8.30am-10pm Mon-Fri; 9am-

6.30pm Sat, Sun. Membership call for details. Classes £4-£8, plus £5 charge for non-members.

An enormously diverse spread of classes, held in six well-appointed studios, ranges from bhangra and ballet to flamenco and jazz.

The Factory Gym and Dance
407 Hornsey Road, N19 4DX (7272 1122/ www.factorylondon.com). Archway tube/ Finsbury Park tube/rail. Open 9.30am-10pm Mon-Fri; 9.30am-7pm Sat; 9.30am-6pm Sun. Membership from £25. Classes £6-£10.
The Factory's individual and group lessons include pole-dancing and Argentinian tango, as well as wedding first dance lessons.

Greenwich Dance Agency
Borough Hall, Royal Hill, SE10 8RE (8293 9741/www.greenwichdance.org.uk). Greenwich rail. Open 9am-9pm Mon-Fri; 9am-3pm Sat. Classes £3.50-£6.
Greenwich Dance Agency runs an appealing range of drop-in classes and courses.

Laban
Creekside, SE8 3DZ (8691 8600/www.laban. org). Deptford rail. Open 8am-8pm Mon-Fri; 8am-4pm Sat, Sun. Classes £76-£114/term.
Laban offers year-long evening courses for keen amateurs, including classical ballet, Africanist Movement and jazz.

Pineapple
7 Langley Street, WC2H 9JA (7836 4004/ www.pineapple.uk.com). Covent Garden tube. Open 9am-10pm Mon-Fri; 9am-7pm Sat; 10am-6pm Sun. Classes £5-£8.
Founded in 1979, Pineapple hosts more than 30 dance classes every day. Prices are affordable, and beginners warmly welcomed.

The Place
17 Duke Road, WC1H 9PT (7121 1101/ www.theplace.org.uk). Euston Square tube/ Euston tube/rail. Open noon-7pm Mon-Sat. Classes £4-£10.
Known for its excellent professional training, the Place also offers ballet and contemporary classes and courses for amateurs, whether adults or children.

Ice skating

The first stop for anyone looking to glide their way to fitness should be the **London Skaters** website (www. londonskaters.com), which lists all of the capital's indoor rinks.

INDOOR RINKS

Alexandra Palace Ice Rink
Alexandra Palace Way, N22 7AY (8365 4386/www.alexandrapalace.com). Wood Green tube/Alexandra Palace rail/W3 bus. Open see website for details. Admisson £5-£7 (inc skate hire).
This huge rink in North London has an attached café and bar, and offers regular classes and private tuition.

Lee Valley Ice Centre
Lea Bridge Road, E10 7QL (8533 3154/ www.leevalleypark.org.uk). Clapton rail. Open see website for details. Admission £6.50; £2.50-£5.50 reductions (plus £1.50 skate hire).
Lee Valley's modern, well-maintained rink attracts both nervous novices and confident figure skaters, but rarely feels crowded.

Queens Ice Bowl
17 Queensway, W2 4QP (7229 0172/ www.queensiceandbowl.co.uk). Bayswater or Queensway tube. Open 10am-11pm Mon-Sat; 10am-10.30pm Sun. Admission £10 (plus £1 skate hire).
Our favourite indoor rink organises disco nights on Friday and Saturday nights, and also runs very friendly drop-in classes for beginners (*see p172*).

Streatham Ice Arena ★
386 Streatham High Road, SW16 6HT (8769 7771/www.streathamicearena.co.uk). Streatham rail. Open see website for details. Admission £8; £6 reductions (plus £2 skate hire).
Beloved by locals, Streatham's rink offers six-week courses for all ages – including special sessions for toddlers.

OUTDOOR RINKS

Call for season dates and opening times.

Broadgate Ice Arena
Broadgate Circle, EC2M 2QS (7505 4068). Liverpool Street tube/rail.
A small, resolutely urban spot that's often less crowded than other outdoor rinks.

Natural History Museum
Cromwell Road, SW7 5BD (7942 5725/www. nhmskating.com). South Kensington tube.
A fairytale winter ice rink and Christmas fair.

Somerset House
Strand, WC2R 1LA (7845 4600/www. somersethouse.org.uk). Covent Garden, Charing Cross or Temple tube.
Somerset House's magnificent courtyard is the most attractive rink in London.

Tower of London
Tower Hill, EC3N 4AB (0870 950 4466/ www.toweroflondonicerink.com). Tower Hill tube/Tower Gateway DLR/Fenchurch Street rail.
This rink is set right in the Tower's moat.

Lidos

For **Hampstead Heath Ponds**, *see p137.*

Brockwell Lido *Brockwell Park, Dulwich Road, SE24 0PA (7274 3088/www.brockwell lido.com). Herne Hill rail. Open late June-Sept 6.45am-8pm Mon-Fri; 10am-6pm Sat, Sun. Admission £5.20; £3.10-£3.60 reductions.*

Hampton Pool *High Street, Hampton, Middlesex TW12 2ST (8255 1116/www. hamptonpool.co.uk). Hampton rail. Open 6am-8pm Mon-Fri, 8am-8pm Sat, Sun. Admission £4.50-£6.20; £2.75-£3.30 reductions.*

London Fields Lido *London Fields Westside, E8 3EU (7254 9038). Liverpool Street tube/rail then 48, 55 bus. Open Apr-May 7am-7pm Mon-Fri; 8am-5pm Sat, Sun. June-Sept 6.30am-8pm Mon-Fri; 8am-7pm Sat, Sun. Admission £4; £2-£2.40 reductions.*

Parliament Hill Lido *Parliament Hill Fields, Gordon House Road, NW5 2LT (7485 3873). Gospel Oak rail. Open May-Sept 7-9am, 10am-6pm Tue, Wed, Fri-Sun; 7-9am, 10am-6pm, 6.45-8pm Mon, Thur. Oct-Apr 7am-noon daily. Admission £2-£4.30; £1-£2.70 reductions.*

Richmond Lido *Twickenham Road, Richmond, Surrey TW9 2SF (8940 0561/ www.springhealth.net). Richmond rail. Open Apr-Sept 6.30am-8pm Mon-Fri; 8am-5.45pm Sat; 7am-5.45pm Sun. Admission £3.90; £1.60-£3.10 reductions.*

Serpentine Lido *Hyde Park, W2 2UH (7706 3422/www.serpentinelido.com). Knightsbridge or South Kensington tube. Open mid June-mid Sept 10am-6pm daily. Admission £4; £1-£3 reductions.*

Tooting Bec Lido *Tooting Bec Road, SW16 1RU (8871 7198/www.bdleisure centres.co.uk). Streatham rail. Open late May-Aug 6am-7.30pm daily. Oct-May members only. Admission £4.50; £3 reductions.*

GOING OUT

BEAUTY

FASHION

PARTIES

FOOD

HEALTH

ECO

OUTDOORS

HOME

CHILDREN

PETS

TRANSPORT

RESOURCES

GOING OUT
BEAUTY
FASHION
PARTIES
FOOD
HEALTH
ECO
OUTDOORS
HOME
CHILDREN
PETS
TRANSPORT
RESOURCES

Riding stables

For a full list of **British Horse Society**-approved riding stables in the capital, visit www.bhs.org.uk. Lessons must be booked in advance, and you should discuss equipment needs with the venue. If you're just after a simple pony ride, a number of city farms offer children's riding sessions, among them **Kentish Town**, **Vauxhall**, and **Mudchute** (*see pp169-170*).

Ealing Riding School

Gunnersbury Avenue, W5 3XD (8992 3808/ www.ealingridingschool.biz). Ealing Common tube. Lessons Group £24/hr. Individual £34/hr. Lessons for beginners through to advanced; pony days (£55) include stable management.

Hyde Park & Kensington Stables

63 Bathurst Mews, W2 2SB (7723 2813/ www.hydeparkstables.com). Lancaster Gate tube. Lessons Group £55-£59/hr. Individual £74-£95/hr.

Ride down Rotten Row and explore Hyde Park's five miles of charming bridle paths; unsurprisingly, steep prices reflect the centre's glamorous setting.

Lee Valley Riding Centre

Lea Bridge Road, E10 7QL (8556 2629/ www.leevalleypark.org.uk). Clapton rail/48, 55, 56 bus. Lessons Group £23.90/hr; £18.20/hr reductions. Individual £31-£33/30mins; £12.60/30mins reductions. The centre's 35 horses and ponies enjoy the open spaces of Walthamstow Marshes and delight a devoted band of regulars. More experienced riders can try the jumping facilities and cross-country course.

London Equestrian Centre

Lullington Garth, N12 7BP (8349 1345/ www.londonridingschool.com). Mill Hill East tube. Lessons Group £27/30mins; £23/30mins reductions. Individual £24-£30/30mins. Set in 34 rolling acres, riding here feels like being in the heart of the country, rather than a mere eight miles away from Oxford Street.

FREE EVENTS

Instead of shelling out to join a gym, sign up for some of London's free sporting events. One of the most high-profile is the **Critical Mass Monthly Cycle** (www.criticalmasslondon.org.uk) on the last Friday of every month. These monthly mass outings welcome all manner of wheels, including cyclists, skateboarders and wheelchair users. Meet by the BFI Southbank under Waterloo Bridge at 6pm.

Friday Night Skates (www.thefns. com) are equally adrenaline-charged, as hundreds of skaters take to the city streets on weekly changing routes, accompanied by a pounding sound system. Be warned: the ten- to 12-mile route is fast and furious, so you'll need to be able to keep up. Skaters

assemble at 7.30pm at the Duke of Wellington Arch, at Hyde Park Corner.

For a more calming ride, join a Sunday outing with the **Pollards Hill Cyclists** (www.pollardshillcyclists. org.uk). The group takes its cycling seriously, but with plenty of stops for lunch, tea and a quick half. Routes often venture beyond south London into the Surrey countryside.

If jogging, yoga or Pilates are more your thing, clothing brand **Sweaty Betty** organises free group fitness events across London; see www. sweatybetty.com/sweatyclub for details of upcoming gatherings.

The **Richmond Park Time Trial** (Richmond Gate, TW10, www.parkrun. com), held every Saturday at 9am, is

Newham Riding School

Docklands Equestrian Centre, 2 Claps Gate Lane, E6 6JF (7511 3917). Beckton DLR. Lessons Group £20/hr; £15/hr reductions. Individual £32/hr; £25/hr reductions.
Twenty horses and ponies are housed at this much-loved neighbourhood stables.

Trent Park Equestrian Centre

Bramley Road, N14 4UW (8363 9005/ www.trentpark.com). Oakwood tube. Lessons Group £30-£37/hr; £23-£30/hr reductions. Individual £40-£48/hr; £38-£42/hr reductions.
The leafy acres of Trent Park make this a popular place to ride, and there are twice-weekly women-only riding sessions (£20) – the Blazing Saddles Ladies' Riding Club.

Willowtree Riding Establishment

The Stables, Ronver Road, SE12 0NL (8857 6438/www.willowtreeridinglondon.co.uk). Grove Park or Lee rail. Lessons Group from £9/30mins. Individual from £18/30mins.
This friendly local offers some of the cheapest prices around and is home to over 40 ponies and horses, including some pure-bred Arab.

another sociable event. The free 5km runs are open to all; simply register online by Friday noon.

Another energetic option is the one-of-a-kind **Brick Lane Bike Polo**, held on Sunday afternoons at the corner of Shacklewell Street and Brick Lane (www.bricklanebikepolo. wordpress.com). Mallets and balls are provided and anyone's welcome.

Finally, you can get to grips with Tai Chi for free every Wednesday, thanks to the **London Spirituality Network** (Rosslyn Hill Unitarian Chapel, Pilgrims Place, NW3 1NG, 7433 3267, www.rosslynhill chapel.com). The class begins at 5.45pm and is suitable for all ages and levels.

Wimbledon Village Stables ★

24 High Street, SW19 5DX (8946 8579/ www.wvstables.com). Wimbledon tube/rail. Open 9am-5pm Tue-Sun. Lessons Individual £50-£55/hr, £28/30mins.
A wide range of lessons, courses and pony riding sessions on quiet, safe ponies is available at this bucolic London stables.

Skateparks

Skaters often prefer unofficial street spots such as the South Bank under the Royal Festival Hall or the northside approach to the Millennium Bridge, but the capital has some decent dedicated skate parks too. **Stockwell Skatepark** (www.stockwell skatepark.com), also known as Brixton Beach, was scheduled to re-open in summer 2008 after a major refurbishment and resurfacing project that began in 2007.

Baysixty6 Skate Park

Bay 65-66, Acklam Road, W10 5YU (8969 4669/www.baysixty6.com). Ladbroke Grove tube. Open 11am-4pm and 5-9pm Mon, Thur, Fri; 11am-4pm and 5-10pm Tue, Wed; 10am-4pm and 5-9pm Sat, Sun. Admission £6.
This famed skatepark's features include four halfpipes, a mini-ramp and loads of funboxes, grind boxes, ledges and rails.

Cantelowes Skatepark

Cantelowes Gardens, Camden Road, NW1 (www.cantelowesskatepark.co.uk). Camden Town tube. Open daily summer 11am-9pm.
Opened in April 2007 as part of the park's £1.5m redevelopment, this free skatepark is phenomenally popular. The local BMX and skateboarders' group, the Cantelocals, helped with the park's design.

Meanwhile

Meanwhile Gardens, off Great Western Road, W10 5BN (8960 4600/www.mgca.f2s.com). Westbourne Park tube.
This community garden's skatepark offers three concrete bowls of varying steepness but no flatland, so it's not for beginners.

Tennis

Plenty of parks around the city have affordable council-run courts, while **London Tennis** (www.londontennis. co.uk) will match you up with an opponent if you need one. The site also has a very good tennis courts database.

For grass courts, consult the **Lawn Tennis Association** (8487 7000, www. lta.org.uk), and for a useful list of London's free courts by borough, see **Tennis for Free** (www.tennisforfree.com).

If your racket needs restringing, take it in to **Wigmore Sports** (79-83 Wigmore Street, W1U 1QQ, 7486 7761, www. wigmoresports.co.uk). The service takes 24 to 48 hours and costs between £15-£60. The shop also lend outs certain racquets for a week's trial for £20 (plus £100 deposit), redeemable against purchase.

COURTS FOR HIRE

Battersea Park

Battersea Park Millennium Arena, Battersea Park Road, SW11 4NJ (8871 7542/www. wandsworth.gov.uk/sports). Battersea Park rail. Open 7am-10pm Mon-Fri; 7.30am-7.30pm Sat, Sun. Court hire £6-£8/hr. Membership £26-£36/yr.
Battersea Park's 19 floodlit courts are bookable seven days in advance.

Highbury Fields

Baalbec Road, N5 1QN (7226 2334). Highbury & Islington tube/rail. Open 8am-9pm daily. Court hire £6.60-£7.60/hr; £2.80-£3.80/hr reductions.
The 11 very popular pay and play courts (seven are floodlit) are set in a pretty location on the edge of the park.

Islington Tennis Centre

Market Road, Islington, N7 9PL (7700 1370/www.aquaterra.org). Caledonian Road tube/Caledonian Road & Barnsbury rail. Open 7am-10pm Mon-Fri; 7am-9pm Sat, Sun. Court hire Indoor £19/hr; £12/hr reductions. Outdoor £9/hr; £7/hr reductions.

The centre offers subsidised coaching and tennis courses; non-members are welcome.

Parliament Hill Fields Tennis Courts

Highgate Road NW5 1QR (7284 3648/www. cityoflondon.gov.uk). Kentish Town tube/rail. Open 8am-sunset daily. Court hire £4.90; £2.60 reductions. Membership £11/yr.
Ten hard courts are bookable in advance, or you can try your luck on the day. Group coaching sessions with qualified LTA coaches are held throughout the summer.

Paddington Recreation Grounds

Randolph Avenue, W9 1PD (7641 3642/ www.westminster.gov.uk). Maida Vale or Kilburn Park tube. Open Summer 8am-9pm daily. Winter 8am-dusk. Court hire £6.45-£10.80/hr.
There are 15 pay and play courts – seven open tarmac, two enclosed tarmac and six synthetic. Members can book in advance.

Redbridge Sports & Leisure Centre

Forest Road, Barkingside, Essex IG6 3HD (8498 1000/www.rslonline.co.uk). Fairlop tube. Open 9am-11pm Mon-Fri; 9am-9pm Sat; 9am-10pm Sun. Court hire varies; call for details.
This outstanding multi-sports centre has eight indoor and six outdoor courts.

Regents Park Tennis Centre

York Bridge Road, Inner Circle, Regents Park, NW1 4NU (7486 4216/www.tennis intheparks.co.uk). Regent's Park tube. Open call for details. Court hire varies; call for details.
Along with four pay and play floodlit courts, this popular centre offers drop-in coaching, tournaments and a dedicated children's zone.

Westway Tennis Centre

1 Crowthorne Road, W10 6RP (8969 0992/ www.westway.org). Latimer Road tube. Open 8am-10pm Mon-Fri; 8am-8pm Sat; 10am-10pm Sun. Court hire Indoor £16-£20/hr; £8-£10/hr reductions. Outdoor £8-£9/hr; £5-£7/hr reductions.
Eight indoor and four outdoor clay courts – the only ones in London open to the public.

GOING OUT

BEAUTY

FASHION

PARTIES

FOOD

HEALTH

ECO

OUTDOORS

HOME

CHILDREN

PETS

TRANSPORT

RESOURCES

Food

It's a growth industry, and no mistake.

Allotments

See yourself pottering around a green and pleasant plot, picking home-grown tomatoes and watching the pumpkins swell? Sadly, lots of other Londoners have exactly the same idea. Getting your hands on an allotment requires luck, perseverance and a lengthy stint on a waiting list. If you succeed, expect to pay around £30-£40 per year for the plot.

In some boroughs waiting lists are closed: at the time of writing, this was the case in **Lambeth** (7926 9000, www. lambeth.gov.uk), **Richmond** (8831 6110, www.richmond.gov.uk) and for the **Hackney Allotments Society** (www.hackneyallotments.org.uk).

We've listed London boroughs with available plots or waiting lists of five years or under; details were correct at the time of going to press. In other areas, the lists are much longer: it can take over 15 years in **Camden** (7974 8819, www. camden.gov.uk) and eight to ten years in **Islington** (7527 4953, www.islington. gov.uk). Note there are no allotments in **Westminster**, **Kensington & Chelsea** or the **City of London**.

PLOTS AVAILABLE

Barnet
8359 7829/www.barnet.gov.uk.
See also www.bfahs.org.
Certain plots were available at the time of writing, costing £65 per year for residents, more if you live outside the borough.

Bexley
8294 6494/www.bexley.gov.uk.
See also www.bfalg.co.uk.

Eight of Bexley's 36 sites currently have available plots; you don't have to live in the borough to get your hands on one.

Bromley
8461 7520/www.bromley.gov.uk.
One or two of Bromley's 52 sites currently have free plots; elsewhere, waiting lists apply. Applicants don't have to live in the borough.

Ealing
8825 5938/www.ealing.gov.uk.
With 46 council-managed sites, Ealing has limited plots available (for local residents only) in Greenford, Northolt and Southall.

Enfield
8379 3722/www.enfield.gov.uk.
There are free plots at several of Enfield's 39 sites. The yearly rate is £30 for locals, slightly more for non-borough residents.

Harrow
8424 1756/www.harrow.gov.uk/allotments.
See also www.harrowinleaf.org.uk.
Limited plots are available at some of Harrow's 32 sites; others have lengthy waits.

Hillingdon
01895 250635/www.hillingdon.gov.uk.
Half of Hillingdon's 35 sites currently have vacant plots, while the longest waiting list is a mere six months. You don't have to live in the borough to sign up.

Hounslow
0845 456 2796/www.hounslow.gov.uk.
Borough residents may currently be able to nab a site in central Hounslow, but waiting lists of up to five years apply in Chiswick.

Merton
8545 3665/www.merton.gov.uk.

Of Merton's 18 sites, three currently have available plots; certain sites only accept applications from borough residents.

Redbridge
8708 3091/www.redbridge.gov.uk.
Sixteen of 23 sites have vacancies, with higher rates for applicants living outside the borough.

Sutton
8770 5070/www.sutton.gov.uk.
Around a third of the 36 sites have available plots, at a mere £28.35 a year.

WAITING LISTS

Barking & Dagenham
8227 3381/www.barking-dagenham.gov.uk.
All 14 sites currently have waiting lists.

Brent
8937 5633/www.brent.gov.uk.
Waiting lists vary from six months to nine years at Brent's 23 sites.

Croydon
8726 6900/www.croydon.gov.uk. See also www.spahill.org.uk.
The shortest wait is currently four years, and lists may close in the near future.

Greenwich
8856 2232/www.greenwich.gov.uk.
Waiting lists range from three to ten years at Greenwich's 18 sites.

Hammersmith & Fulham
8748 3020/www.lbhf.gov.uk.
Just two sites, and waiting lists of two years.

Haringey
8489 0000/www.haringey.gov.uk.
The average wait for a plot is four years, though 11 waiting lists remain open.

Havering
01708 434343/www.havering.gov.uk. See also www.romfordsmallholderssociety.org.uk.
Call for vacancies at the 25 allotment sites.

Kingston upon Thames
8399 1274/www.kingston.gov.uk.
Waiting lists remain open at these 23 sites.

Lewisham
8314 2277/www.lewisham.gov.uk.
The average wait in Lewisham is 11 months, with a healthy 36 sites; residents get priority.

Newham
8430 2000/www.newham.gov.uk.
Waiting times at the seven allotments vary; four years is currently the longest wait.

Southwark
7525 1050/www.southwark.gov.uk.
Nine allotment sites, all with waiting lists.

Tower Hamlets
7364 5020/www.towerhamlets.gov.uk.
The seven sites all have waiting lists.

Waltham Forest
8496 2612/www.walthamforest.gov.uk.
You'll wait around a year for a plot at one of Waltham's 32 sites.

Wandsworth
8871 6441/www.wandsworth.gov.uk. See also www.roehamptonallotments.co.uk.
Wandsworth's nine sites have an average wait of three to four years.

GOING OUT
BEAUTY
FASHION
PARTIES
FOOD
HEALTH
ECO
OUTDOORS
HOME
CHILDREN
PETS
TRANSPORT
RESOURCES

GOING OUT
BEAUTY
FASHION
PARTIES
FOOD
HEALTH
ECO
OUTDOORS
HOME
CHILDREN
PETS
TRANSPORT
RESOURCES

Groceries

See also **Daylesford Organic** (*p132*).

Bumblebee

*30, 32 & 33 Brecknock Road, N7 0DD
(7607 1936). Kentish Town tube/rail. Open
9am-6.30pm Mon-Sat.*
This friendly, old-school health food store
sells quality organic groceries and delicious
home-made goodies: bread, cakes and a small
but excellent selection of takeaway dishes.

Farm W5

*19 The Green, W5 5DA (8566 1965/www.
farmw5.com). Ealing Broadway tube. Open
8am-7.30pm Mon-Fri; 9am-7.30pm Sat;
10am-6pm Sun.*
This organic and Slow Food market supports
small British producers – so fish comes fresh
from Cornwall, chutney from the New Forest
and honey from down the road in Ealing.

Natural Kitchen

*77-78 Marylebone High Street, W1U 5JX
(7486 8065/www.thenaturalkitchen.com).
Open 8am-8pm Mon-Fri; 9am-7pm Sat;
11am-6pm Sun.*
The ethical ethos here centres on seasonality,
sustainability, traceability and good animal
welfare, while suppliers include Royal Farms,
the Well Hung Meat Company and organic
vintner Vintage Roots.

City Secret

Serving seasonal menus and run on
environmentally sound principles,
Acorn House (69 Swinton Street,
WC1X 9NT, 7812 1842, www.acorn
houserestaurant.com) also provides
training for ten young adults a year.
Happily, it's not remotely dull or
worthy, with breezy, fresh decor and
a terrific menu. Mains are superb,
but save room for dessert: rice
pudding with hazelnut biscotti,
or a plate of English cheeses.

Unpackaged

*42 Amwell Street, EC1R 1XT (7713 8368/
www.beunpackaged.com). Angel tube. Open
10am-7pm Mon-Fri; 10am-6pm Sat.*
Bring your own pots and bags to this lovely
little grocery store, and get a discount on
washing powder, grains, spices, coffee and
pulses, ladled from handsome glass jars.

Whole Foods Market

*The Barkers Building, 63-97 Kensington
High Street, W8 5SE (7368 4500/www.
wholefoodsmarket.com). Open 8am-10pm
Mon-Sat; noon-6pm Sun.*
This vast supermarket-style space groans
with a huge range of organic and natural
produce, cosmetics and homeware.

Organic box schemes

For details of London's **farmers'
markets**, *see p99.*

Abel & Cole

*0845 262 6262/www.abel-cole.co.uk.
Boxes £10.95-£24.*
The king of delivery boxes in London, Abel
& Cole offers organic meats, sustainably
caught fish, dairy and freshly baked bread as
well as seasonal fruit and veg from over 50
British producers. A small mixed box of fruit
and veg, at £10.95, contains four vegetables
and three fruits, plus potatoes.

Capricorn Organics

*8306 2786/www.capricornorganics.co.uk.
Boxes prices vary; call for details.*
This south-east London company specialises
in individual orders (though mixed boxes are
available too), which you make up from a list
on the website – so if you want just two
tomatoes in your veg selection (minimum of
£10), that's what you'll get. Deliveries to
south-east London cost around 50p to £1.

Everybody Organic

*0845 345 5054/www.everybodyorganic.com.
Boxes £9-£26.*
Produce is rigorously organic, though not
necessarily local; bananas from Peruvian

growers and a host of other fairly traded produce is sold too. Stock ranges from the usual fruit and veg to deli products, booze, eggs and cereals. Prices are fair for the quality – a small mixed fruit and veg box is £10.99 – and delivery is free in London.

Farmaround ★

7627 8066/www.farmaround.co.uk.
Boxes £8-£14.
Farmaround delivers organic fruit and veg boxes all over London. Produce is seasonal and as local as possible, and the site is updated regularly with recipes to use up your supplies – plus customers receive occasional gifts of chutney and honey. A vegetable bag for one person is £8, though the minimum spend is £11.50.

Growing Communities

7502 7588/www.growingcommunities.org.
Boxes £6-£12.
This social enterprise claims to have been the first organic box provider in the country. Produce is Hackney grown, and to cut down on fuel use local customers are encouraged to pick up their own boxes from points across the borough. Local growers are encouraged to bring along their own produce too. Prices start at £26 a month for a small weekly veg bag, with six varieties of seasonal produce.

Natoora

7627 1600/www.natoora.co.uk.
Boxes £15-£29.
Natoora's range of fruit and veg boxes starts with the 2kg veg box (£14.95), which might include peas, asparagus, cherry tomatoes, courgettes, fresh herbs and onions. It also stocks some 3,500 products sourced directly from farmers and producers in the UK, France and Italy, from artichoke tortellini and a wide range of cheeses to Cornish fish and veal from Auvergne.

Organic Delivery Company

7739 8181/www.organicdelivery.co.uk.
Boxes £8.95-£26.
Along with an impressive fruit and veg box selection (including a small seasonal salad box), there's also chocolate, cleaning products, booze, a range of organic pet food and more, all sourced with vigilant attention to food miles and origin.

Woodfield Organics

07847 450358/www.woodfieldorganics.com.
Boxes £4-£20.
Working with a co-operative of certified organic producers in England (and one in Italy), Woodfield does its best to deliver strictly seasonal produce from the farm to your door in 24 hours. Delivery is free, with no minimum order, but currently available only in west London.

Specialist delivery companies

A Lot of Coffee

0845 094 6498/www.alotofcoffee.co.uk.
This company roasts its coffee freshly every week and delivers beans and grounds all over London. There's a wide variety of beans, from Mexico, Columbia, Papua New Guinea, Sumatra and Ethiopia; all are organic and fairly traded, with the website providing full details of suppliers you're buying from.

Clare's Organics

01367 242077/www.claresorganics.co.uk.
Clare's Organics is a monthly organic meat box scheme, with a choice between bespoke and set boxes, poultry-only options and the facility to specify meats cuts you don't ever want to receive. The quality is excellent, justifying the prices (from £30). An £8.95 delivery charge also applies for Londoners, unless you spend over £100.

Jefferson's Seafoods

01503 269076/www.jeffersons-seafoods.co.uk.
Certificated by the Organic Food Federation and the RSPCA Freedom Foods, this Cornwall-based company supplies the likes of Locanda Locatelli and the Ritz with fillets of fresh, sustainable fish. Sign up for the flourishing home delivery service and choose from a wonderful array of fresh seafood and chunky, own-made fish cakes; for kids, there's monkfish and lemon zest nuggets.

GOING OUT

BEAUTY

FASHION

PARTIES

FOOD

HEALTH

ECO

OUTDOORS

HOME

CHILDREN

PETS

TRANSPORT

RESOURCES

GOING OUT

BEAUTY

FASHION

PARTIES

FOOD

HEALTH

ECO

OUTDOORS

HOME

CHILDREN

PETS

TRANSPORT

RESOURCES

Recycling

Someone, somewhere can use most of the stuff you chuck out, from old computers to unused paint.

General recycling

Many boroughs now run segregated box systems for garden waste, food leftovers and miscellaneous waste. For services and collection days in your borough, use the postcode finder at **Recycle for London** (www.recycleforlondon.com).

Another useful resource is **Direct Gov** (www.directgov.uk), which has details of local recycling and waste services, and a link that lets you apply for a bulky items collection. The **London Community Recycling Network** (www.lcrn.org.uk) is also a useful resource. For eco-friendly junk collection services, *see p161*.

Charity shops always welcome donations. If you don't know where to find your nearest shop, check with the **Association of Charity Shops** (www.charityshops.org.uk). Alternatively, post an ad on **Freecycle** (www.freecycle.com) or the smaller **Reuze** (www.reuze.co.uk) and give your goods away.

Specialist services

COMPUTERS & PRINTER CARTRIDGES

Computer Aid International
10 Brunswick Industrial Park, Brunswick Way, N11 1JL (8361 5540/www.computer aid.org).
Donate your old or unwanted computers to developing countries by dropping off your PC at the workshop, where it will be data-wiped and refurbished, then shipped off to a school or community project.

Each One Counts
0800 435576/www.eachonecounts.co.uk.
Inkjet cartridges, laser toners and mobiles can all be recycled here. Register and order freepost bags online, then send the item off; the proceeds go to various charities.

Eco-chip
0845 257 7249/www.ecochip.co.uk.
If your computer and peripherals are less than eight years old, Eco-chip will collect, datawipe and refurbish them for free before donating them to charity.

FURNITURE

The **Furniture Re-use Network** (www.frn.org.uk) lists local projects in need of furniture and electrical items.

Furniture Aid South Thames
7793 7787/www.furniture-aid.co.uk.
This south London company will collect large donations of furniture and working white goods from central and south London free of charge (minus congestion charges).

ReStore Community Projects
8493 0900/www.restorecommunity projects.org.
Restore will collect most bulky household goods (though not single items) for £10, in two daily time slots. Items must be in good condition as they're given to families in need.

Respond Furniture Centre
8316 1099/www.respondbank.co.uk.
Up and running since 1984, this south-east London-based charity will collect good quality furniture, restore it, and redistribute it to help those in need – from the homeless to refugees.

IPODS

Apple Recycling Programme
www.apple.com/environment.
Buy an Apple product and you can return its equivalent piece of kit to any Apple Retail Store. If you return an iPod for recycling, you'll get a 10% discount on a new one.

MOBILE PHONES

Most big charities accept mobile phones for recycling, including **Help The Aged** (7278 1114, www.helptheaged.org.uk), **Oxfam** (0300 200 1300, www.oxfam.org.uk) and **WaterAid** (0845 600 0433, www.wateraid.org/uk).

Refuge
0808 200 0247/www.refuge.org.uk.
For each phone donated to Refuge, the charity gets £3.50 from a partner group, which will reformat your phone for use in the developing world. Just post the phone in, free of charge, following online instructions.

Fonebak
01865 471900/www.fonebak.com.

If you're raising funds, register with Fonebak and you'll be sent a collection pack including 30 recycling bags (the minimum number). For each reusable phone you manage to collect, your organisation will get £4.

PAINT

Community RePaint
0113 200395/www.communityrepaint.org.uk.
Operating across the country, this inspired scheme will accept most old household paints (see the website for details), which will then be used for community projects or given to charities. The project doesn't pick up donations, but has lots of local collection points; enter your postcode at the website to find your nearest.

SPECTACLES

Vision Aid Overseas
0845 7793 4500/www.vao.org.uk.
Opticians working with Vision Aid Overseas (including the Vision Express chain) will accept donations of old frames, then pass them on to the charity for distribution in developing countries.

GREEN VOLUNTEERING

For more general volunteering, try **Do-It** (www.do-it.org.uk) or **Timebank London** (http://london.timebank.org.uk). Or consider **Guerilla Gardening** (www.guerrillagardening.org), whose laudable aim is illicitly cultivating unloved and unlovely public spaces.

Green Gym
7278 4294/www.btcv.org.uk.
Shape up without hitting the gym by volunteering to help maintain London's green spaces. Involving hands-on gardening and conservation work, the sessions kick off with a group warm-up and generally last two to three hours.

Heath Hands
8458 9102/www.wakano.org.uk.
Help keep Hampstead Heath green and litter-free. Work sessions, open to anyone over 16, run five days a week.

Thames 21
7248 7171/www.thames21.org.uk.
Thames 21 runs regular clear-ups and of London's waterways and canals.

Waterloo Green Trust
7928 4427/www.waterloogreen.org.uk.
Weed, prune and get your hands dirty protecting and creating green spaces in south-east London.

GOING OUT

BEAUTY

FASHION

PARTIES

FOOD

HEALTH

ECO

OUTDOORS

HOME

CHILDREN

PETS

TRANSPORT

RESOURCES

Shopping & services

Ways to live a greener – and more ethical – everyday life.

Banking

The excellent **Ethical Consumer** site (www.ethicalconsumer.org) suggests building societies that have some degree of ethical credibility, including Abbey, Norwich & Peterborough and Alliance & Leicester. In terms of banks, the choice is more limited.

Co-operative Bank
08457 212212/www.thecooperative bank.co.uk.
One of the first banks to adopt an ethical policy, the Co-Op encourages its customers to raise issues of concern and will not invest in areas customers vote against. A range of other ethical policies, detailed on the website, put it way ahead of other high street banks.

Ecology Building Society
0845 674 5566/www.ecology.co.uk.
This Yorkshire-based building society offers savings accounts, along with mortgages for renovations or new builds with 'an environmental benefit'. Interest rates on savings can be on the low side.

Smile
0870 843 2265/www.smile.co.uk.
The online offshoot of the Co-operative Bank shares its ethical and eco-friendly policies – sourcing 98% of its electricity from renewable sources and refusing to invest in companies involved in the arms trade, for example, or whose core activity adds to climate change.

Triodos
0117 973 9339/www.triodos.co.uk.
Triodos maintains corporate social responsibility by financing companies and projects that benefit people and the environment. No high street presence (and an unwieldy website) can mean more effort to manage your money, though.

Beauty

CONTENT beauty
14 Bulstrode Street, W1U 2JG (3075 1006/ www.beingcontent.com). Bond Street or Baker Street tube/Marylebone tube/rail. Open 10.30am-6pm Tue-Sat; 10.30am-6pm Sun.
This gorgeous little boutique, opened in 2008, houses organic beauty brands such as Laid Bare, Stemp Organics and Suki Colour, plus perfume, vegan beauty buys, men's grooming products and baby ranges.

Fashion

For organic cotton baby basics, *see p176* **Green Baby**.

Equa ★
28 Camden Passage, N1 8ED (7359 0955/ www.equaclothing.com). Angel tube. Open 10am-6.30pm Mon-Wed, Fri, Sat; 10am-7pm Thur; noon-5pm Sun.
Equa's rails are packed with beautifully cut dresses and blouses from fairtrade, fashion-forward labels like Noir and WildlifeWorks, plus a selection of innovative lines such as Green Knickers, which are made, oddly enough, from bamboo and soya.

Howies
42 Carnaby Street, W1F 7D (7287 2345/ www.howies.co.uk). Oxford Circus tube. Open 10am-7pm Mon-Wed, Fri, Sat; 10am-8pm Thur; 11am-5pm Sun.
This new casualwear store's eco policy sets it apart from its Carnaby Street neighbours.

Walls are made from reclaimed wood chippings, shelves from sustainable wood. E-receipts replace paper, and customers fill up bottles with tap water.

Loglike
New Spitalfields Traders Market, Crispin Place, Brushfield Street, E1 6EB (www.loglike.co.uk). Liverpool Street tube/rail. Open 10am-4pm Fri; 9.30am-5pm Sun.
Loglike specialises in great graphic T-shirts for men, women and children, in a nice range of styles and colours. Original artwork is screenprinted by hand on to 100% organic, fair trade cotton Ts.

Terra Plana
64 Neal Street, WC2H 9PQ (7379 5959/ www.terraplana.com). Covent Garden tube. Open 10am-7pm Mon-Fri; 11am-6pm Sun.
Shoes here are made from eco-friendly materials such as chrome-free and vegetable-tanned leathers; look out for Worn Again sneakers, fashioned from recycled rubber and canvas. Regular 'shoe amnesties' offer money off new shoes in return for donating old pairs.

Energy-saving

A number of services offer eco advice, including **Green Electricity** (www.greenelectricity.com), which locates your nearest green energy providers, and **Energy Saving Trust** (0800 512 012, www.energysavingtrust.org.uk), where a home energy check questionnaire results in advice on improving energy efficiency.

Other do-it-yourself eco audits can be found at the **London Climate Change** website (www.londonclimatechange.co.uk) or the **Carbon Calculator** at www.carboncalculator.com.

DIY Kyoto
7729 7500/www.diykyoto.com.
This company sells a nifty wireless gadget, the Wattson, which monitors your home's energy usage and changes colour accordingly; a great visual impetus to turning off the tumble drier. At £149.50 it's not cheap, but DIY Kyoto thinks you can save five to 20% on annual electricity bills, meaning recouped costs within one or two years for most homes.

GOING OUT
BEAUTY
FASHION
PARTIES
FOOD
HEALTH
ECO
OUTDOORS
HOME
CHILDREN
PETS
TRANSPORT
RESOURCES

SWAPS

What's Mine is Yours
www.whatsmineisyours.com.
Founded in 2004 by fashionista, stylist and personal shopper Judy Berger, this is a great site for browsing all manner of swaps, from glitter balls to cameras and furniture to clothing. There's lots of vintage clothing, and a buy and sell section.

Read It, Swap It
www.readitswapit.co.uk.
This online community of readers who swap their books is based on eBay-style personal ratings. It's completely free to register and partake, but you have to pay for your own postage.

Visa Swap
www.visaswap.com.
The more unwanted designer and high-street clothes, shoes and bags you donate – and the more exclusive the labels are – the more points you'll get on your Visa Swap card, which you then use to buy things at an open swap weekend. All items not swapped are donated to clothing charity Traid.

GOING OUT
BEAUTY
FASHION
PARTIES
FOOD
HEALTH
ECO
OUTDOORS
HOME
CHILDREN
PETS
TRANSPORT
RESOURCES

Green Concierge

0800 089 0098/www.greenhomes concierge.co.uk.

For £199, the Green Concierge team will visit your home and produce an energy performance report covering areas of concern, and suggest a programme for improvements.

3 Acorns

7703 8748/www.3acorns.co.uk.

Donnachadh McCarthy audits your carbon footprint, taking in energy and transport use as well as waste and shopping habits. He then suggests ways to reduce your carbon footprint. The price is around £210.

Homeware

The annual **Eco Design Fair** (www. ecodesignfair.co.uk) in Islington gathers together the best emerging talent in eco design, including suppliers who don't normally sell direct to the public.

Eco

213 Chiswick High Road, W4 2DW (8995 7611/www.eco-age.com). Turnham Green tube. Open 10am-6pm Tue-Sat; 11am-4pm Sun.

Eco is the (sunlit, solar-powered and -heated) joint project of actor Colin Firth and his wife. Stock ranges from energy-saving lightbulbs to bigger investments such as solar panels and wind turbines. The stylish furniture is worth a look even if you're not eco-minded.

Harland Organic Furnishings

07984 635726/www.organic-furnishings.co.uk.

This online company welcomes visitors (by appointment) to its west London base. Its small range is elegant and ethically minded, with an emphasis on organic soft furnishings and muted, natural tones.

Karavan Eco Shop

167 Lordship Lane, SE22 8HX (8299 2524/ www.karavan.co.uk). East Dulwich rail. Open 10.30am-5.30pm Mon-Fri; 10am-6pm Sat; noon-4pm Sun.

Karavan is packed to the brim with a great mix of beautiful and useful products for the home, all manufactured using sustainable materials and methods, or geared to making your life more environmentally friendly.

Siecle

Unit B2, St Leonards Road, Park Royal, NW10 6ST (8123 9354/www.sieclecolours. com). Park Royal tube. Open 8am-5pm Mon-Fri.

Siecle manufactures more than 200 bright, lead-free Latex-based colours, including wall paint (£30/2.5 litres), and water-soluble semi-gloss emulsion for wood, metal and plastic at £19 a litre. You can sell back unused paint.

Junk mail prevention

Stop Junk Mail

www.stopjunkmail.org.uk.

This useful site offers loads of handy tips for reducing the amount of junk mail you receive, including a suggestion to opt out of the Royal Mail's door-to-door junk mail deliveries by emailing optout@royalmail.com.

Mailing Preference Service

www.mpsonline.org.uk.

Registering with the MPS will deter companies who may have bought your details from databases.

Stop Junk Mail

www.stopjunkmail.org.

Get a 'no junk mail' sticker from this site; it's a simple but effective strategy, particularly against local taxi firms and takeaways.

Motoring

Environmental Transport Association

0845 389 1010/www.eta.co.uk.

This carbon-neutral motoring organisation offers an award-winning international rescue service, and can also help you offset the carbon emissions of your car, flights and home energy consumption.

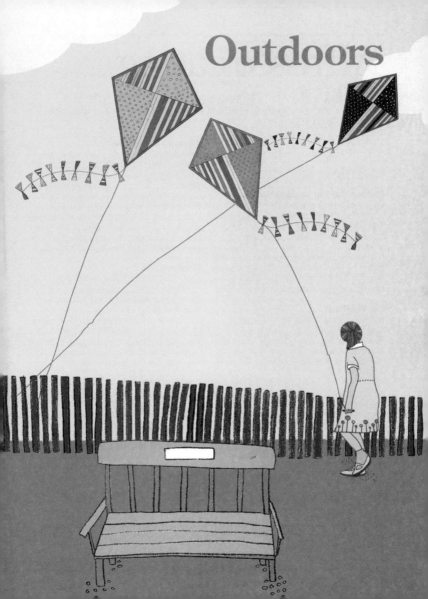

Outdoors

Alfresco eating

We've recommended our favourite park cafés, along with the best places to pick up a ready-assembled picnic – perfect for the ultimate lazy summer's afternoon.

Park cafés

CENTRAL

Garden Café at Russell Square ✈

Russell Square Gardens, WC1B 5EH (7637 5093). Russell Square tube. Open 7am-6pm Mon-Fri; 8am-5pm Sat, Sun (closed Sun Nov-Mar). No credit cards. Takeaway service. £.
Overlooking a lovely, leafy garden square, the sprawling patio at this Italian family-run café is a wonderfully relaxing spot. Tuck into a top-notch English breakfast, or tea and cakes.

Inn The Park

St James's Park, SW1A 2BJ (7451 9999/ www.innthepark.com). St James's Park or Westminster tube. Open Summer 8am-11pm Mon-Fri; 9am-11pm Sat; 9am-6pm Sun. Winter times vary; call for details. Takeaway service. ££.
Part Modern British restaurant, part café, this stylish joint is perfect for laid-back breakfasts and lunches or romantic suppers. There are splendid ice-creams, cakes and afternoon teas; if you'd rather picnic, takeaways are available.

NORTH

Brew House

Kenwood, Hampstead Lane, NW3 7JR (8341 5384). Bus 210, 214. Open Oct-Mar 9am-dusk daily. Apr-Sept 9am-6pm daily. Takeaway service. £.
In warm weather, the terrace is always buzzing at this lovely café, which occupies part of neoclassical Kenwood House. The homely (often organic and free-range) grub and own-made cakes are equally enticing.

Clissold Park Café

Clissold Park Mansions, Stoke Newington Church Street, N16 9HJ (7923 9797/ www.clissoldparkcafe.com). Finsbury Park tube/rail/73, 341, 393 bus. Open 9am-7pm daily. No credit cards. Takeaway service. £.
Housed inside a Queen Anne mansion, this unassuming little café serves snacks and simple meals (omelettes, panini). On sunny days, eating under the stripy umbrellas on the lawn and admiring the ducks is heavenly.

Garden Café

Inner Circle, Regents Park, NW1 4NU (7935 5729/www.companyofcooks.com). Baker Street or Regents Park tube. Open 9am-6pm daily. £-££.
The interior of this revamped 1960s café is surprisingly chic; the terrace, surrounded by rose beds, is glorious. Superior-quality classics (prawn cocktail or ploughman's lunches), seasonal mains and super puds are on offer.

Pavilion Café

Highgate Woods, Muswell Hill Road, N10 3JN (8444 4777). Highgate tube. Open Summer 9am-7pm daily. Winter 9am-4pm daily. Takeaway service. £.
This little treasure is deservedly popular, thanks to its tasty, well-presented global food and alcohol licence. If in doubt, plump for the free-range steak, which comes from a local butcher's and is served with fresh horseradish.

Pavilion Café Victoria Park ✈

Victoria Park, by Old Ford Road & Grove Road, E9 5DU (8980 0030/www.the-pavilion-cafe.com). Bethnal Green tube, then 8 bus. Open 9am-5pm daily. £.
The lakeside location is a treat – as is the food. Huge breakfasts (with meat and veggie

options) feature organic eggs and sensational sausages from Marylebone's Ginger Pig. Look out for the fab lemon drizzle cake too.

EAST

Eat2 @ Weavers
Weavers Fields Community Space, Kelsey Street, E2 6HD (7729 3111). Bethnal Green tube. Open 9am-3.30pm Mon-Fri. Takeaway service. £.
Part of the Weavers Restaurant Trust, Eat2 helps disabled and unemployed members of the community attain NVQ catering qualifications. A daily-rotating menu might include steak and kidney pie or African chicken stew, at great prices.

Spark Café
White Mansion Lodge, Springfield Park, E5 9EF (8806 0444/www.sparkcafe.co.uk). Stamford Hill or Stoke Newington rail. Open Apr-Oct 10am-6pm daily. Nov-Mar 10am-4pm daily. No credit cards. £.
Set in the beautiful White Lodge Mansion, Spark offers a fabulous menu: Springfield Special sandwiches, own-made soups, tasty cakes, shakes and organic juices.

SOUTH

Common Ground
Wandsworth Common, off Dorlcote Road, SW18 3RT (8874 9386). Wandsworth Common rail. Open 9am-5.15pm Mon-Fri; 10am-5.15pm Sat, Sun. Takeaway service. £.
The cosy back room of this child-friendly cafe is a heavenly retreat on a winter's day. The food is own-made, including cakes, sandwiches and children's mini meals.

Pavilion Café
Dulwich Park, off College Road, SE21 7BQ (8299 1383/www.pavilioncafedulwich.co.uk). North Dulwich or West Dulwich rail. Open Summer 9am-6.30pm daily. Winter 9am-4pm daily. Takeaway service. £.
The glass-fronted, licensed café is a lovely place to while away an hour at any time of day. There are freshly-made sandwiches, soups and specials; olive and goat's cheese

quiche, perhaps, or prawn and pea risotto. Produce is free-range and locally sourced.

Pavilion Tea House
Greenwich Park, Blackheath Gate, SE10 8QY (8858 9695). Blackheath rail/ Greenwich rail/DLR. Open 9am-5.30pm Mon-Fri; 9am-6pm Sat, Sun. £.
Tuck into huge portions of bean casserole, welsh rarebit, scrambled eggs or smoked salmon on toast in this licensed hexagonal café, while the kids eat ice-cream in a garden hedged off from the central thoroughfare.

WEST

Holland Park Café
Holland Park, Ilchester Place, W8 6LU (7602 6156). Holland Park or High Street Kensington tube. Open Summer 9.30am-9.30pm daily. Winter 9.30am-4.30pm daily. Takeaway service. £.
Hot and cold homemade food (from soups and sarnies to jacket potatoes and cod goujons), in one of the nicest – and possibly cheapest – places to eat in Kensington, set in an historic Dutch garden.

Fait Maison in Ravenscourt Park
Ravenscourt Park, Paddenswick Road, W6 0UL (no phone, www.fait-maison.co.uk). Ravenscourt Park tube. Open 9am-7pm daily. No credit cards. £.
Recently taken over by the Fait Maison mini-chain, this pleasant park stop offers cakes, salads, sandwiches and panini – all freshly made that morning.

City Secret

For hassle-free alfresco eating, drop by **Up Box** (7 Ludgate Circus, EC4M 7LF, 8968 7514, www.up-box.co.uk). Open on weekdays from 11am to 3pm, it offers five ready-packed lunchboxes a day (the initials stand for 'urban picnic'), each with a different global influence and complete with mini-dessert.

GOING OUT

BEAUTY

FASHION

PARTIES

FOOD

HEALTH

ECO

OUTDOORS

HOME

CHILDREN

PETS

TRANSPORT

RESOURCES

Picnics

If you're heading to the following parks, here are some handy spots to pick up a sumptuous picnic.

BATTERSEA PARK

Daylesford Organic

44B Pimlico Road, SW1W 8LP (7881 8060/www.daylesfordorganic.com). Sloane Square tube. Open 8am-8pm Mon-Fri; 8am-7pm Sat; 10am-4pm Sun.

If you're coming from the Chelsea side of the river, this is the place to pick up some wholesome treats on your way. Handsome, free-range meat pies, award-winning breads and pastries and artisan cheeses from Daylesford's own herd of happy Friesians are all perfect picnic fare.

CLAPHAM COMMON

Esca

160 Clapham High Street, SW4 7UG (7622 2288). Clapham Common tube. Open 8am-9pm Mon-Fri; 9am-9pm Sat, Sun.

Handily situated at the Clapham Common end of the high street, Esca has a dazzling selection of too-good-to-be-true cakes in the window, complemented by huge salads and hot specials inside, which can be packed up for your convenience in a little brown box.

GREEN PARK

Fortnum & Mason

181 Piccadilly, W1A 1ER (7734 8040/ www.fortnumandmason.com). Green Park or Piccadilly Circus tube. Open 10am-8pm Mon-Sat; noon-6pm Sun.

If it's a superior spread you're after, pitch your blanket near Fortnum's. The extravagant pre-packaged picnics start at £50 for a wicker hamper with champagne, almonds, olives and truffles: for more solid sustenance, assemble your own choice of comestibles from the food hall. Here, a dazzling profusion of cheese, charcuterie, pâtés and pies awaits.

HAMPSTEAD HEATH

Rosslyn Delicatessen

56 Rosslyn Hill, NW3 1ND (7794 9210/ www.rosslyndeli.net). Hampstead tube. Open 8.30am-8.30pm daily.

The Rosslyn has a hamper for every date of the season, from Glyndebourne to Ascot. Its Hampstead Heath Hamper (£18.50 per head) includes a smoked salmon parcel, chicken kebab, two salads and chocolate brownies.

HOLLAND PARK

Ottolenghi ★

1 Holland Street, W8 4NA (7937 0003/ www.ottolenghi.co.uk). High Street Kensington tube. Open 8am-8pm Mon-Fri; 8am-7pm Sat; 9am-6pm Sun.

Blending Mediterranean and Middle Eastern influences, this chic deli and bakery provides wonderful alfresco fare. Pick up a takeaway box and fill it with immaculately fresh, inventive salads, tarts and sandwiches – not forgetting the amazing chocolate meringues.

HYDE PARK

Theo Randall

InterContinental, 1 Hamilton Place, Park Lane, W1J 7QY (7318 8747/www.theo randall.com). Hyde Park Corner tube. Lunch served noon-3pm Mon-Fri. Dinner served 5.45-11.15pm Mon-Sat.

Theo Randall's five-course Italian feasts for two start at £65 – and are worth every penny. Dishes might include Devon crab with aioli, rocket and fennel salad, or poached langoustines with Sicilian lemon; there's a £10 children's version, packed Dick Whittington-style in a checked cloth on a stick.

PRIMROSE HILL

Melrose & Morgan

42 Gloucester Avenue, NW1 8JD (7722 0011/www.melroseandmorgan.com). Chalk Farm tube. Open 8am-8pm Mon-Fri; 8am-6pm Sat; 9am-5pm Sun.

This famed deli offers a range of ready-assembled picnics. You can opt for a simple

ploughman's picnic (£30 for two), or a more opulent spread (£65) starring mackerel pâté, bread, free range roast chicken with white bean and tomato relish, salad, Eton mess, cheese and oatcakes, and a bottle of rosé. Order 24-48 hours ahead.

QUEEN'S PARK

Baker & Spice
75 Salusbury Road, NW6 6NH (7604 3636/ www.bakerandspice.com). Queens Park tube/ rail. Open 7am-7pm Mon-Sat; 8am-5pm Sun.
Supplier of hampers to Lord's Cricket Ground, Baker & Spice rustles up delectable set-menu picnics for two (from £48), including such delights as chilled tomato soup, poached organic salmon, Valrhona chocolate brownies and a bottle of Sauvignon Blanc.

REGENT'S PARK

Villandry
170 Great Portland Street, W1W 5QB (7631 3131/www.villandry.com). Great Portland Street tube. Open 8am-10pm Mon-Sat; 10am-6pm Sun.
This superb deli and charcuterie offers the finest foie gras, *jambon* and salami, as well as vegetarian options and a salad counter.

HAMPERS

With branches across the city, **Carluccio's** (www.carluccios.com) can also rustle up splendid picnics for two, with prices from £45; order 24 hours in advance.

One Aldwych
1 Aldwych, WC2B 4RH (7300 1000/www.onealdwych.com). Covent Garden or Temple tube. Open call for details.
You don't have to be staying at this high-end hotel to order one of its glorious baskets of all-British classics, including chicken and ham pie, lobster, kilner jars of potted shrimps and pudding. It's £30 per person, but filling enough to keep you fuelled until teatime.

Paul
47 Thurloe Street, SW7 2LQ (7581 6034/www.paul-uk.com). South Kensington tube. Open 7am-9pm Mon-Fri; 8am-9pm Sat; 8am-8pm Sun.
In summer, when you spend over £20 at selected branches of Paul, you're given a sweet little *pique nique* box in which to carry your spoils to the park. Choose from delightful quiches, salads, sarnies and speciality breads such as the emmental-rich *fougasse fromage*.

Selfridges
400 Oxford Street, W1A 1AB (7318 3900/www.selfridges.com). Bond Street or Marble Arch tube. Open 9.30am-8pm Mon-Wed, Fri, Sat; 9.30am-9pm Thur; noon-6pm Sun.
With 48 hours' notice, the fabulous food hall here will put together a picnic box for you for a flat fee of £7.50 plus the price of whatever comestibles your heart desires.

GOING OUT
BEAUTY
FASHION
PARTIES
FOOD
HEALTH
ECO
OUTDOORS
HOME
CHILDREN
PETS
TRANSPORT
RESOURCES

Green spaces

Escape from the city without leaving town.

Boating lakes

Alexandra Park

Alexandra Palace Way, N22 7AY (7262 1330/www.alexandrapalace.com). Wood Green tube, then W3 bus. Boat hire Easter-July, Sept 10am-6pm Sat, Sun & school hols. Late July, Aug 10am-6pm daily. Rates £4/30 mins; £2/30mins reductions. No credit cards.
This small, man-made lake went through a rather gunky phase a few years ago, but has since been cleaned up and is home to a large number of coots, mallards, Canada geese and ducks. Pedalos and rowing boats are available for hire; under-12s must wear a life jacket.

Battersea Park

Albert Bridge Road, SW11 4NJ (7262 1330/www.batterseapark.org). Battersea Park rail. Boat hire Easter-late July, Sept 10am-6pm Sat, Sun & school hols. Late July-Aug 10am-6pm daily. Rates £4/30mins; £2/30mins reductions. No credit cards.
Built in the 1850s as part of the park's mission to encourage morally desirable leisure activities, the boating lake is surrounded by ancient trees. Two islands, forbidden to human feet, shelter herons, cormorants and grebes, while a restaurant hosts live music in summer. Under-eights must be accompanied.

Finsbury Park

Seven Sisters Road, N4 1EE (07905 924282/www.haringey.gov.uk). Manor House tube/Finsbury Park tube/rail. Boat hire Easter-Oct noon-6pm daily. Rates £6/30mins. No credit cards.
Restored to its former glory following a hefty Lottery grant, the park and its once-neglected boating lake are now looking their best. Rowing boats carry up to four people each, with life jackets available for children.

Greenwich Park

Romney Road, SE10 9NF (7262 1330/www.royalparks.org.uk). Cutty Sark DLR/Maze Hill or Greenwich rail. Boat hire Easter-mid July, Sept 10.30am-5pm Sat, Sun & school hols. Mid July-Aug 11am-5pm daily. Rates £3/20mins; £2/20mins reductions. No credit cards.
This 2ft deep concrete pond may not be as beautiful as some of its greener rivals, but remains popular. Situated near the St Mary's Gate entrance, it has pedalos and rowing boats – and often stays open late on sunny days. Under-eights must be accompanied.

Hyde Park

Serpentine Road, W2 2UH (7262 1330/www.royalparks.org.uk). Hyde Park Corner, Marble Arch or Knightsbridge tube. Boat hire Easter-Sept 10am-7pm daily. Rates £6/30mins, £8/hr; £2/30mins, £3/hr reductions; £14/30 mins, £19/hr family.
London's biggest boating lake covers 64 acres of water and has over 100 pedal boats for hire. It's also home to the Serpentine Solar Shuttle, the UK's first solar powered passenger craft, which ferries up to 40 eco-voyagers around the lake, starting at the boat house (£3, £2 reductions; noon-6pm).

Regent's Park

Outer Circle, NW1 4NR (7298 2145/www.royalparks.org.uk). Baker Street or Regent' Park tube. Boat hire Summer 9am-8pm daily. Winter 10am-4pm daily. Closed Dec-Feb. Rates £4.85/30mins, £6.50/hr; £3.35/30mins, £4.40/hr reductions; £20/hr family. No credit cards.
The boating lake near Hanover Gate is home to more than 650 waterfowl, including 260 pairs of ducks. Twenty pedalos and 30 rowing boats are available for hire, with a £5 deposit required.

City Secret

A deliciously muddy low-tide scramble can be had at Deptford's **Creekside Centre** (14 Creekside, SE8 4SA, 8692 9922, www.creeksidecentre. org.uk). Clad in fetching thigh-high waders, you'll be taken on a two-and-a-half-hour expedition exploring the area's history and wildlife. Tickets cost £8.50.

Community gardens

Discover the true meaning of a grassroots movement by visiting one of the capital's community gardens: there are now over 100. Download a map with information on each project at www.farmgarden.org.uk/london. Every June, **Open Squares Weekend** (www.opensquares.org) gives you the keys to even more secret gardens in London, as 175 private green spaces briefly go public.

Calthorpe Community Garden

258-274 Grays Inn Road, WC1X 8LH (7837 8019/www.calthorpeproject.org.uk). Russell Square tube/King's Cross tube/rail. Open Winter 9am-5pm Mon-Fri; 11am-5pm Sat-Sun. Summer 10am-6pm Mon-Fri; noon-6pm Sat-Sun.

A former dumping ground rescued from developers in 1984 by local residents, this 1.2-acre haven now features a waterfall, children's gardens, wildlife areas and a café.

Culpeper Community Garden

1 Cloudesley Road, N1 0EG (7833 3951/www.culpeper.org.uk). Angel tube. Open 8am-dusk daily.

Started up in 1982 to teach local schoolchildren how to grow vegetables, the Culpeper continues to support various community groups. Its verdant lawns, ponds, rose pergolas, ornamental beds, vegetable plots and wildlife area also soothe frazzled shoppers. Look out for seasonal events too.

The Gardens Community Garden

Doncaster Gardens, N4 1HX (8374 7721/www.gardensresidents.blogspot.com). Manor House tube/Harringay Green Lanes rail. Open 9am-dusk daily.

As much a social centre as a horticultural one, the Gardens hosts Easter egg hunts, a summer fair, a Halloween party and Christmas carols. Winner of the London in Bloom Best Community Garden award in 2007, it's an enchanting spot: features include beautifully kept beds of flowers and ferns, a community mosaic and willow sculptures.

Harleyford Road Community Garden

Entrances on Harleyford Road or by 37 Bonnington Square, SE11 5AX (7485 5001). Oval tube/Vauxhall tube/rail. Open 9am-dusk daily.

This former wasteland in the middle of traffic-choked Vauxhall now comprises a secret garden with mosaic pathways winding between trees and flower beds, a pond, picnic tables and a children's play area. Wilder areas of long grass encourage butterflies to visit.

Phoenix Garden

21 Stacey Street (entrance on St Giles Passage), WC2H 8DG (7379 3187/www.phoenixgarden.org). Tottenham Court Road tube. Open dawn-dusk daily.

In the heart of the West End, this award-winning oasis was planted by the local community on the site of a former car park. Office workers in the know see themselves here as they eat their sandwiches, in the company of frogs, beetles and woodpeckers.

Roots and Shoots

Walnut Tree Walk, SE11 6DN (7587 1131/www.rootsandshoots.org.uk). Kennington tube. Open 10am-4pm Mon-Fri. Occasional weekends, call for details.

Set up in 1982, Roots and Shoots has transformed a derelict civil defence site into an inspiring half-acre garden featuring a summer meadow, hazel coppice, beehives and two ponds. It's beautiful and slightly wild – just how the butterflies, dragonflies and grasshoppers like it. In autumn there's fresh apple juice, pressed in the barn.

GOING OUT

BEAUTY

FASHION

PARTIES

FOOD

HEALTH

ECO

OUTDOORS

HOME

CHILDREN

PETS

TRANSPORT

RESOURCES

Graveyards

The city has an abundance of wonderfully atmospheric Victorian graveyards to explore, where ivy-covered headstones lean at unlikely angles and stone angels overlook the tangled pathways. Unless otherwise stated, admission is free.

Abney Park Cemetery

Stoke Newington High Street, N16 0LN (7275 7557/www.abney-park.org.uk). Stoke Newington rail/73, 106, 149, 243, 276, 349 bus. Open dawn-dusk daily. Visitors' centre 10am-4pm Mon-Fri.

Abney Park became the first non-denominational London cemetery in Victorian times, sparking a scandal with its hieroglyphic-adorned Egyptian-style gates. The now gloriously overgrown 32-acre site has many impressive trees, remnants of what was once the largest cemetery arboretum to be found in Europe.

Brompton Cemetery

Fulham Road, SW10 9UG (7352 1201/www.royalparks.org.uk). West Brompton tube. Open Summer 8am-8pm daily. Winter 8am-4pm daily.

Laid out in formal fashion around a domed chapel, modelled on St Peter's in Rome, this well-ordered cemetery is the posthumous residence of suffragette Emmeline Pankhurst. It's a peaceful haven – except on match days at nearby Stamford Bridge.

Bunhill Fields Cemetery

38 City Road, EC1Y 1AU (7374 4127). Old Street tube/rail. Open Oct-Mar 8am-4pm Mon-Fri; 9.30am-4pm Sat-Sun; Apr-Sept 8am-dusk Mon-Fri; 9.30am-4pm Sat-Sun.

City workers in search of souls lunch in this former dissenters' burial ground, dating back to the 17th century, where the graves of William Blake, John Bunyan and Daniel Defoe can be found. A guided tour (£4) runs on Wednesdays at 12.30pm from April to September, meeting at the gardener's hut (www.citygardenswalks.com).

Hampstead Cemetery

Fortune Green Road, NW6 1DR (8883 1230). West Hampstead rail. Open Summer 9am-5pm daily. Winter 9am-4pm daily.

Opened in 1876 and now gently sliding into wonderfully photogenic decay, the 26-acre site was designed by leading landscape gardener Joseph Metson. The Llewelyn Davies boys, who were the inspiration for JM Barrie's *Peter Pan*, are buried here.

Highgate Cemetery

Swain's Lane, N6 6PJ (8340 1834/www.highgate-cemetery.org). Highgate tube. Open East cemetery Apr-Oct 10am-5pm Mon-Fri; 11am-5pm Sat-Sun; Nov-Mar 10am-4pm Mon-Fri; 11am-4pm Sat-Sun. Admission East cemetery £3. West cemetery tours £5; £1 reductions. No credit cards.

Arguably Britain's finest Victorian garden cemetery, Highgate's famous inmates include Karl Marx and George Eliot. The beautiful West Cemetery, with its decaying, ivy-covered tombs, is accessible by guided tour only.

Kensal Green Cemetery

Harrow Road, W10 4RA (8969 0152/www.kensalgreen.co.uk). Kensal Green tube/rail/18, 23, 52, 70, 295, 316 bus. Open Apr-Sept 9am-6pm Mon-Sat; 10am-6pm Sun. Oct-Mar 9am-5pm Mon-Sat; 10am-5pm Sun.

London's oldest public cemetery was a fashionable final resting place in the 19th century, and numerous noble names adorn its mausoleums. Here too are the graves of Isambard Kingdom Brunel, Wilkie Collins, Anthony Trollope and William Makepeace Thackeray. A guided tour runs on Sundays.

Nunhead Cemetery

Entrances on Limesford Road or Linden Grove, SE15 3LP (7732 9535/www.fonc.org.uk). Nunhead rail. Open Summer 8am-7pm daily. Winter 8am-4pm daily. Tours 2.15pm last Sun of month.

One of the lesser known but most attractive of London's Victorian cemeteries, this 52-acre site is now part nature reserve. Crumbling tombs stand amid ash and sycamore trees, while heroes of Trafalgar and Waterloo sleep beneath avenues of lime.

Parks

For details of London's eight **Royal Parks**, visit www.royalparks.org.uk, which provides details of forthcoming events, plus sports and leisure facilities. If you fancy a game of **tennis**, *see p118*.

Best for…
Bathing

Hampstead Heath

Men & Women's ponds, Millfield Lane, N6. (7485 4491/www.cityoflondon.gov.uk). Gospel Oak rail. Open 7am-8.30pm May-mid Aug, varies rest of year. Mixed pond, East Heath Road, NW3. Hampstead Heath rail. Open May 3-Sept 28, 7am-6.30pm.

Who needs chlorine when you can go pond dipping instead? The heath's three bathing ponds were originally dug as reservoirs to feed the capital's water supply and have been a popular place for outdoor swimming since the 19th century. Their closure was averted in 2007 after an army of bathers, hardened by years of early morning dips, faced down the local council. Concerns about the water quality have now been resolved, and lifeguards are on duty most days. A day ticket for the ponds costs £2, a one year season ticket £100. To get opening times for winter, call ahead as times are dependent to a degree on weather.

Best for…
Birdlife

St James's Park

Horse Guards Road SW1 (7930 1793/www.royal parks.org.uk). St James's Park tube. Open 5am-midnight daily.

The lake in St James's Park is home to ducks, geese, gulls, black swans and, best of all, friendly pelicans – first introduced to the park in the 15th century, as a show-stopping gift from the Russian ambassador. Daily feeding time

with the wildlife officers is at 2.30pm, if you fancy joining them for lunch. Afterwards, check out what's on at the bandstand, which has a packed summer schedule.

Best for…
Dinosaurs

Crystal Palace Park

Crystal Palace Park Road, Anerley Hill & Thicket Road, SE26 (8778 9496/www.crystalpalacepark.org). Crystal Palace or Penge West rail. Open 7.30am-dusk daily.

A Victorian vision of *Jurassic Park*, this series of life-size dinosaur sculptures were a world first when they were unveiled in 1854. Made of concrete and brick, they were based on the best available evidence at the time. They have since been proved far from scientifically accurate, but that doesn't detract from their freaky charm as they loom out of the undergrowth. After falling into disrepair, they have recently been restored and are now protected with a Grade I listing.

GOING OUT

BEAUTY

FASHION

PARTIES

FOOD

HEALTH

ECO

OUTDOORS

HOME

CHILDREN

PETS

TRANSPORT

RESOURCES

GOING OUT
BEAUTY
FASHION
PARTIES
FOOD
HEALTH
ECO
OUTDOORS
HOME
CHILDREN
PETS
TRANSPORT
RESOURCES

Best for...
Children

Kensington Gardens
Kensington Gore, W2 2UH (7298 2141/ www.royalparks.org.uk). Lancaster Gate, Queensway or Bayswater tube. Open 6am-dusk daily.
As well as the famous bronze statue depicting Peter Pan and a host of friendly animals, the park's Diana, Princess of Wales Memorial Playground is inspired by the boy who never grew up, with teepees, a tree encampment and a huge pirate ship surrounded by a sandy 'beach' (*see also p171*).

Best for...
Formal gardens

Queen Mary's Rose Garden
Regent's Park, Inner Circle, NW1 4NR (7486 7905/www.royalparks.org.uk). Baker Street or Regent's Park tube. Open dawn-dusk daily.
First laid out in the 1930s, London's largest rose garden boasts some 30,000 roses of more than 400 varieties; visit in mid June to enjoy the multitude of blooms at their fragrant best. Nearby, there's the boating lake (*see p134*); after your exertions, recover in the estimable Garden Café (*see p130*).

THE CITY'S HIDDEN GARDENS

The Square Mile might not seem the most obvious place to find tranquil green retreats, but the area harbours a wealth of hidden garden gems, many created on the sites of buildings destroyed in the Great Fire of London and during the Blitz. Before setting off to explore, download a map at www.cityoflondon.gov.uk. Alternatively, a two-hour guided tour of the City's historic green spaces leaves from the information centre at St Paul's every Saturday and Sunday from April to September at 1.30pm (£6, 8441 1926, www.citygardenswalks.com).

The best known garden is probably **Postman's Park**, just up from St Paul's tube station on King Edward Street. Featured in the film *Closer*, the small but serene memorial garden has a Victorian wall of tiles that commemorate ordinary people who sacrificed their lives for others, designed by Charles Frederic Watts.

Head down the road towards Newgate Street for **Christchurch Greyfriars**, with its lovely, box-hedge bordered rose garden, a suntrap on summer afternoons, and at its best in June and July.

East of Postman's Park, another gem is the diminutive **St Mary Aldermanbury Garden** on Love Lane, with its heady-smelling camellia, knot garden and neat box and yew hedges: a bust of Shakespeare looks down on office workers eating their lunch.

A walk along London Wall will take you to the City of London's first public park, **Finsbury Circus**, tucked behind Moorgate tube. Between May and September, bowls can be played here; rinks cost £3.50 an hour, including use of overshoes so you won't muddy your office brogues (turn up and ask the gardener, or book ahead by calling 07768 536874 between 10am and noon). The bandstand hosts jazz performances during the City of London Festival (www.colf.org).

Finally, it's impossible to talk about the City's gardens without squeezing in a mention of the impossibly romantic **St Dunstan in the East Church Garden**, a short stroll from Monument tube. Here, creepers and wisteria weave around a tower and the ruins of a Christopher Wren-designed church, while exotic shrubs flourish in the shelter of the walls.

Best for...
Kite-flying

Parliament Hill
Highgate Road, NW5 1QR (7485 4491).
Gospel Oak or Hampstead Heath rail.
Parliament Hill has acquired the nickname Kite Hill, thanks to its popularity with aficionados of this heady pastime. Standing over 300ft high, the famous mound (on the south east side of Hampstead Heath) offers unsurpassed views of Canary Wharf's distant skyscrapers, the City and the dome of St Paul's Cathedral.

See also *Richmond Park, for Kitevibe's power-kiting lessons (07866 430979/ www.kitevibe.com).*

Best for...
Sports

Hackney Marshes
Homerton Road, E9 5PF (football pitch bookings 8985 8206/www.hackney.gov.uk/ parks). Hackney Wick rail.
Hackney Marshes claims the greatest concentration of football pitches in the whole of Europe, with 87 pitches hosting hundreds of hotly-contested amateur matches every Sunda; expect a vocal crowd of supporters. Hockey and rugby fanatics are also catered for.

Best for...
Theatre

Regent's Park
Open Air Theatre, Inner Circle, NW1 4NR (0844 826 4242/www.openairtheatre.org). Baker Street or Regent's Park tube.
Britain's only permanent professional outdoor theatre, the Open Air Theatre has one of the largest auditoria in the capital. Its annual 15-week season always includes its signature piece *A Midsummer Night's Dream*, a children's play and a musical, plus various Sunday night comedy and concerts. It's a delightful place to take a picnic on a summer night; all the productions have specially long intervals. It can get chilly as the evening draws on, so take an extra jumper.

Best for...
Lounging

Green Park
Piccadilly, SW1 (79301793/www.royalparks. org.uk). Green Park or Hyde Park Corner tube. Open dawn-dusk daily.
The park's iconic green and white striped deckchairs are much sought-after on clement afternoons, so arrive early to bagsy yours, then settle down with the papers. The deckchairs are available next to the refreshment kiosk by the Green Park tube entrance from March to October, and cost £1.50 for two hours or £2 for four.

Best for...
Pastoral bliss

Richmond Park
Richmond upon Thames, Surrey, TW10 5HS (8948 3209/www.royalparks.org.uk). Richmond tube/rail, then 65 or 371 bus. Open summer 7am-dusk daily. Winter 7.30am-dusk daily.
Ancient woodlands, rolling hills, herds of roaming deer... It's easy to forget you're in a city at all when you visit London's largest royal park (save for the tower blocks encroaching from Roehampton). To feel truly countrified, survey it on horseback by hiring a steed from one of several local stables; call the park for details.

Best for...
Conkers

Bushy Park
Hampton Court Road, Hampton, Middlesex TW12 2EJ (8979 1586/www.royal parks.org.uk). Teddington or Hampton Wick or Hampton Court rail. Open Dec-Aug, Oct dawn-dusk daily; Sept, Nov 8am-10.30pm.
The Chestnut Avenue in Bushy Park is at its towering finest in late spring, when the trees' 'candles' are in bloom, providing a good excuse for an annual celebration in the park on the second Sunday of May. In the autumn, the horse chestnuts come into their own as a source of champion specimens for knuckle-bruising conker fights.

GOING OUT
BEAUTY
FASHION
PARTIES
FOOD
HEALTH
ECO
OUTDOORS
HOME
CHILDREN
PETS
TRANSPORT
RESOURCES

GOING OUT
BEAUTY
FASHION
PARTIES
FOOD
HEALTH
ECO
OUTDOORS
HOME
CHILDREN
PETS
TRANSPORT
RESOURCES

Wildlife & nature reserves

The **London Wildlife Trust** (www.wildlondon.org.uk) manages over 50 nature reserves across the capital, with habitats ranging from woodlands and meadows to grasslands and marshes.

Camley Street Natural Park

12 Camley Street, NW1 0PW (7833 2311/ www.wildlondon.org.uk). King's Cross tube/ rail. Open 10am-5pm daily.
On the banks of Regent's Canal, this two-acre reserve squeezes in wildflower meadows, marsh woodland and reed beds. Its habitats support a rich variety of birds and butterflies.

Epping Forest

Information Centre, High Beech, Loughton, Essex IG10 4AF (8508 0028/www.cityof london.gov.uk/openspaces). Wanstead tube/ Chingford rail. Open Information Centre Summer 11am-6pm daily. Winter 10am-3pm daily. Forest 24hrs daily.
Henry VIII's former hunting ground covers some 6,000 acres, from East London to just north of Epping. The majority of the forest is heavily wooded but it also encompasses meadow, parkland and ponds. And there's a grazing herd of English Longhorn cattle.

Greenwich Peninsula Ecology Park

Thames Path, John Harrison Way, SE10 0QZ (8293 1904/www.urbanecology.org.uk). North Greenwich tube/108, 161, 422, 472, 486 bus. Open 10-5pm Wed-Sun.

City Secret

The **Parkland Walk** (www.parkland-walk.org.uk) is a leafy trail and nature reserve running from Finsbury Park to Highgate Wood. The four-and-a-half-mile footpath follows a series of disused railway lines, passing atmospheric abandoned platforms and echoing tunnels en route.

Once an industrial wasteland, now returned to marshland, the park consists of an inner and outer lake – the latter open at all times. Spot cormorants and herons from the bird hides and look out for frogs, toads and newts.

Highgate Wood

Muswell Hill Road, N10 3JN (8444 6129/ www.cityoflondon.gov.uk/openspaces). Highgate tube/43, 134, 263 bus. Open 7am-dusk daily.
A 70-acre remnant of the ancient Forest of Middlesex, this oak, holly and hornbeam wood harbours foxes, bats and grey squirrels. There's a café and visitors' centre, which organises popular bat watching walks.

London Wetland Centre

Queen Elizabeth's Walk, SW13 9WT (8409 4400/www.wwt.org.uk). Barnes rail. Open Mar-Oct 9.30am-6pm daily; Nov-Feb 9.30am-5pm daily. Admission £8.95; £6.70 reductions; £4.95 4-16s; free under-4s; £25 family.
This Barnes-based 100-acre Site of Special Scientific Interest is four miles out of central London, but feels worlds away. Its rustling reeds and tranquil ponds are a haven for birds (including kingfishers and spoonbills).

Railway Fields

Green Lanes, by Umfreville Road N4 1EY (8348 6005/www.haringey.gov.uk). Manor House tube/Harringay Green Lanes rail. Open 9am-5pm Mon-Fri. Call ahead.
Mysterious wrought iron gates creak open to reveal a little-known nature reserve just off bustling Green Lanes. The two-acre site, a former railway goods yard, supports more than 200 species of wildflower.

Sydenham Hill Wood & Cox's Walk

Entrances on Crescent Wood Road & junction of Lordship Lane and Dulwich Common, SE21 (www.wildlondon.org.uk). Sydenham Hill/Forest Hill rail/P4, 176, 185, 197, 202, 363 bus. Open dawn-dusk daily.
Once part of the Great North Wood, which stretched from Deptford to Selhurst, this woodland is home to myriad wildlife, from fungi and bluebells to rare insects.

Home

Art

London has no shortage of glossy commercial galleries and fairs aimed at wealthy collectors, but there are also plenty of places to source affordable artwork.

Fairs & open studios

Unless otherwise specified, listed fairs run in late October, creating a fringe scene around the pricey **Frieze Art Fair** (www.friezeartfair.com). Look out, too, for the ad hoc annual **Keith Talent Gallery** (www.keithtalent.com) fair, where prices for a great range of work start at £200.

It's also worth subscribing to **Art Rabbit** (www.artrabbit.com) and **New Exhibitions** (www.newexhibitions.com), both of which will alert you to new names before their prices skyrocket.

Affordable Art Fair
Battersea Evolution, SW11 4NJ (8246 4848/ www.affordableartfair.com). Sloane Square tube, then free shuttle bus. Admission £12.
Over 120 galleries exhibit a dizzying selection of original prints, photography, sculpture and paintings, priced from £50-£3,000. The fair takes place in March and October.

Art Car Boot Fair ★
Old Truman Brewery, 91 Brick Lane, E1 6RU (7770 6100/www.artcarbootfair.com). Liverpool Street tube/rail. Admission £3.
With past stallholders including the likes of Gavin Turk and Peter Blake, this day-long summer knees-up is a great place to pick up quirky small-scale offerings (jewellery, prints, T-shirts) from seriously collectable artists.

artLONDON
Royal Hospital Chelsea, Royal Hospital Road, SW3 4SR (7259 9399/www.artlondon.net). Sloane Square tube. Admission £9-£12.
Held the week before Frieze, this lively four-day art fair attracts galleries from around the world and sells 'a little bit of everything'. Prices range from £100 to £100,000.

Chocolate Factory Open Studios
Chocolate Factory, 1 Clarendon Road, N22 6XJ (8365 7500/www.collage-arts.org). Wood Green tube. Admission free.
Over 100 artists open their studios for this annual event, held over a weekend in autumn. Pieces run the gamut from screenprints to sculpture, with plenty of items under £500.

Free Range
Old Truman Brewery, 91 Brick Lane, E1 6QL (7770 6100/www.free-range.org.uk). Liverpool Street tube/rail. Admission free. No credit cards.
June and July sees the Truman Brewery overrun with new artistic talent, as weekly-changing exhibitions showcase the work of more than 3,000 graduate artists. With prices starting at £5 for prints, it's a great chance to scout future stars. It's open Friday to Monday: go on a Friday to nab the newest stock.

Great Western Studios Open Studios
The Lost Goods Building, Great Western Road, W9 3NY (7221 0100/www.great westernstudios.com). Westbourne Park tube. Admission free. No credit cards.
Seventy studios are opened to the public for the first weekend in December, then one weekend in early June, selling new painting, sculpture, illustration, photography and crafts. Gift items sell for as little as £30-£50, while more serious artworks cost from £300.

London Art Fair
58 White Lion Street, N1 9PP (7288 6736/ www.londonartfair.co.uk). Angel tube. Admission call for details.

This mammoth art fair has been going strong for more than two decades, exhibiting work from over 100 galleries. All art forms are represented, with prices from £160-£200 for screenprints and photographic prints. Held in January, it's London's first art fair of the year.

Secret Sale

Royal College of Art, Kensington Gore, SW7 2EU (7590 4186/www.rca.ac.uk/secret). South Kensington tube. Admission free.
Anonymous artworks by world-famous artists are mixed with works by the RCA's graduates at this hugely popular November sale, where 2,500 postcard-sized works are sold off for £40 each on a first come, first served basis. Be prepared for long queues and an almighty scrum on sale day.

Framing

Alec Drew

5-7 Cale Street, SW3 3QT (7352 8716/www. alec-drew.co.uk). Sloane Square tube. Open 9.15am-6pm Mon-Fri; 9.30am-1pm Sat.
Expect a wide choice of frames and museum-quality glass from a company that's just as happy framing the kids' doodles as that attic find that might be an original Turner. Staff can also recommend related services, such as restretching, cleaning, removing old backing and providing linen backing for posters.

Art & Soul ⭐

Unit G14, Belgravia Workshops, 157 Marlborough Road, N19 4NF (7263 0421/ www.artandsoulframes.com). Archway tube. Open 9am-5pm Tue-Fri; by appointment Sat.
Rebecca Bramwell aims to provide a service for customers on a budget who want quality framing. She's happy to advise on what suits the work, and her prices are very reasonable. Readymade small frames made from offcuts cost as little as £3.50.

John Jones

4 Morris Place, off Stroud Green Road, N4 3JG (7281 5439/www.johnjones.co.uk). Finsbury Park tube/rail. Open 9.30am-6pm Mon-Fri by appointment.

Clients at this well-known framing workshop include Tate and Christie's; if you want to be in such luminary company, it'll cost you. The average framing costs over £250, but for that you get impeccable quality, skilled craftsmen and the knowledge that your work has been framed by the best in the business. Note that it's open by appointment only.

Pendragon Fine Art Frames

1-3 Yorkton Street, E2 8NH (7729 0608/ www.pendragonframes.com). Old Street tube/rail. Open 9am-5pm Mon-Fri; by appointment Sat.
Keith Andrews has been running Pendragon for almost a decade, offering advice, suggestions and patience in equal measure from his Hackney workshop, where he and a genial team of craftsmen make excellent frames at affordable prices. Galleries like the Serpentine recommend this place, and with good reason.

Ray's Glass & Frames

120 Hackney Road, E2 7QF (7729 4727). Open 9am-3pm Mon-Fri; 7am-noon Sat; 8am-2pm Sun. No credit cards.
Framing is eminently affordable at Ray's: simply pick out a frame moulding from D&J Simons & Sons next door (122-150 Hackney Road, E2 7QS, 7739 3744, www.djsimons. co.uk), then take it in to Ray's to be cut to size and joined – at a fraction of the cost of most picture framers. The minimum charge for the service is £10.

City Secret

As well as offering an excellent range of contemporary photography, **55 Max** (6 Lonsdale Road, NW6 6RD, 7625 3774, www.55max.com) can transfer your own images on to a canvas, acrylic or magnetic board, wallpaper or roller blinds. Prices start at £40 for an 8 x 10in canvas. If you want to go all out, there's even a bespoke wallpaper service.

GOING OUT
BEAUTY
FASHION
PARTIES
FOOD
HEALTH
ECO
OUTDOORS
HOME
CHILDREN
PETS
TRANSPORT
RESOURCES

Anthony Hossack
M: 07957 158 003
Clive Gray
M: 07910 199 037

Design
Build
Restore

Hossack & Gray

Studio 10, 9e Queens Yard,
White Post Lane, London E9 5EN
www.hossackandgray.co.uk
T: 020 8986 3345

Antique Clock Restoration and Repair
Robert Loomes (MBHI,FRSA)
LONDON
68 Hatton Garden EC1N 8JY
0207 4772224
(strictly by appointment)
House calls a pleasure
Member of the British Horological Institute & LAPADA approved
www.clockrepairer.co.uk

COME TO THE COUNTRYSIDE
Mudchute
PARK & FARM
EAST LONDON'S GREEN HEART
Events throughout the summer and City farm with British rare breeds
Mudchute DLR, just nine stops from Bank DLR
t: 020 7515 5901; w: www.mudchute.org

Shops & galleries

A&D
*51 Chiltern Street, W1U 6LY (7486 0534/
www.aanddgallery.com). Baker Street tube.
Open 10.30am-7pm Mon-Sat.*
Kitsch and witty works by new artists (from
£30) plus more costly limited-edition prints.

Cosh
*69 Berwick Street, W1F 8SZ (7287 7758/
www.coshuk.com). Oxford Circus tube. Open
11am-6pm Mon-Sat.*
Cosh offers a wide range of prints from hip
young illustrators and graphic artists.

Degree Art
*30 Vyner Street, E2 9DQ (8980 0395/
www.degreeart.com). Bethnal Green tube/
rail. Open by appointment Mon-Wed;
noon-6pm Wed-Sun.*
Work by young artists, in a converted chapel.

Flow
*1-5 Needham Road, W11 2RP (7243 0782/
www.flowgallery.co.uk). Notting Hill Gate
tube. Open 11am-6pm Mon-Sat.*

This sophisticated gallery houses the work
of more than 100 artists, specialising in
applied art, including ceramics, glass, metal,
textiles and jewellery.

Greenwich Printmakers
*1A Greenwich Market, SE10 9HZ (8858
1569/www.greenwich-printmakers.org.uk).
Greenwich rail/DLR. Open 10.30am-5.30pm
daily.*
Limited-edition lithographs, etchings and
prints, with prices from £40 to £300.

Transition Gallery
*Unit 25A, Regent Studios, 8 Andrews
Road, E8 4QN (7254 4202/www.transition
gallery.co.uk). Bethnal Green tube. Open
noon-6pm Fri-Sun.*
Group shows by emerging and established
artists, with prices rarely rising above £1,000.

Will's Art Warehouse
*Sadler's House, 180 Lower Richmond Road,
SW15 1LY (8246 4840/www.wills-art.com).
Putney Bridge tube, then 22 bus. Open
10.30am-6pm daily.*
Contemporary art at keen prices (£50-
£3,000), with an emphasis on friendly service.

CRAFT COLLECTIVES

Cockpit Arts
7419 1959/www.cockpitarts.com.
Cockpit Arts' studios in Holborn and
Deptford hold regular open days where
you can buy direct from the designers.
Expect everything from exquisite hand-
woven textiles to cascading silver and
glass necklaces, funky furniture and
screen-printed notebooks – plus the
chance to be nosy, meet the artists
and have a poke around the studios.

Hidden Art London
*7729 3800/www.hiddenartlondon.
co.uk.*
The Hidden Art organisation holds
two annual open studio weekends,

usually in November and December.
Around 50 studios take part, offering
craft workshops and pieces for sale
– from ceramics and glass to textiles
and jewellery. The website features
a useful searchable directory too.

Made in Clerkenwell
7251 0276/www.craftcentral.org.uk.
Twice a year, over 70 Clerkenwell-
based designer-makers throw open
their studios to the public. Snap up
necklaces for £15 or inexpensive
letterpress-printed cards and
stationery, or invest in cutting-edge
furniture designs or bespoke
commissions from rising talents.

GOING OUT

BEAUTY

FASHION

PARTIES

FOOD

HEALTH

ECO

OUTDOORS

HOME

CHILDREN

PETS

TRANSPORT

RESOURCES

GOING OUT

BEAUTY

FASHION

PARTIES

FOOD

HEALTH

ECO

OUTDOORS

HOME

CHILDREN

PETS

TRANSPORT

RESOURCES

Address Book Secrets
Rob Ryan
Artist, illustrator & shopkeeper

Too many design shops are identikit indie boutiques that look the same. I prefer places that only stock a handful of things but do it really well, like **Franklin Alvarez** (53 Columbia Road, E2 7RG, 07737 517252). It sells kids' clothes and cushions made using old fabrics, all handmade by Bev Alvarez. There's also a selection of lovely illustrations and jewellery by Jen Franklin, who uses old notebooks, frames and paper in her work. That's all they do: a tiny range of beautiful things you won't find anywhere else.

One of my favourite oddities is **Gardners** (149 Commercial Street, E1 6BJ, 7247 5119). It's a shop for shopkeepers, with every kind of paper and plastic bag you can imagine, and those fluorescent star-shaped price tickets – but it sells lots of great household things too.

I also really like **Shelf** (40 Cheshire Street, E2 6EH, 7739 9444, www.help yourshelf.co.uk). It stocks unusual bits and pieces for the home, as well as lots of nice stationery and art, most of it made by local designers and artists.

The owners of **Prick Your Finger** (260 Globe Road, E2 0JD, 8981 2560, www.prickyourfinger.com), Racheal Matthews and Louise Harries, call it a 'modern haberdashery', but it's so much more than that – it hosts exhibitions and has amazing things like knitted coral reefs and jewellery. A lot of the wool is from a flock of sheep in Wales that they own, and some even comes from a pet angora rabbit.

There used to be loads of indoor markets in central London and now there are hardly any, but **Queenway Market** (23-25 Queensway, W2 4QJ, 7221 8049, www.queenswaymarket. co.uk) is still going strong. It feels like it goes on forever, but wander round it for long enough and you'll find Psychic Mews – a kind of real-life Diagon Alley from *Harry Potter*. It's a row of little cottages with a gypsy caravan at the end of it, selling stuff relating to clairvoyancy; the whole place just defies belief.

If you're a woman there's a world of incredible shoes out there, but if you're a bloke there's a world of incredible shit. But the **Olde Curiosity Shop** (13-14 Portsmouth Street, WC2A 2ES, 7405 9891, www.curiosityuk.com) redresses the balance. It looks like a faux 16th-century building, all sloping roof, wonky floors and wooden beams, but it's all genuine. Daita Kimura has been selling the most fantastic men's shoes there since 1992, including handmade shoes designed by John Moore, a hugely talented contemporary of Judy Blame's back in the 1980s.

I love visiting the **Talking Bookshop** (11 Wigmore Street, W1U 1PE, 7491 4117, www.talkingbooks.co.uk). I like listening to stories in the car, and for a long journey the books they sell are great – particularly the unabridged ones.

My shop **Ryantown** (126 Columbia Road, E2 7RG, 7613 1510) is open noon-5pm Saturday, 9am-5pm Sunday.

Interiors

From collectable classics to cutting-edge modern design.

Architectural salvage

Although its premises are just outside London, honourable mention must be made of the splendid **Antique Church Furnishings** (Rivernook Farm, Sunnyside, Walton-on-Thames, Surrey KT12 2ET, 01932 252736, www.church antiques.com), which specialises in prewar church fixtures and furniture (the pews and chapel chairs are of more interest to most buyers than the fonts and pulpits). Prices are a steal, and they'll deliver anywhere.

Architectural Forum
312-314 Essex Road, N1 3AX (7704 0982/ www.thearchitecturalforum.com). Angel tube/38, 56, 73, 341 bus. Open 10am-5pm Mon-Sat.
The shop sells polished-up fireplaces and interesting antiques (Victorian cell doors from Clerkenwell prison and a lovely mahogany till, on our last visit) at reasonable prices. There's also a small but vertiginously stacked outdoor yard, dominated by Belfast sinks and cast-iron radiators in various states of repair; for access, ask in the shop.

D&A Binder ✦
101 Holloway Road, N7 8LT (7609 6300/ www.dandabinder.co.uk). Highbury & Islington tube/rail. Open 10am-6pm Mon-Sat.
It's not strictly a salvage yard, but the wonderful D&A Binder specialises in vintage shop fittings. There are treasure to be found amid its dusty recesses: a 1920s mahogany shirt cabinet would be perfect for many-shirted modern-day dandies, while smaller but just as enticing pieces include mirrors, mannequins, hooks, hatstands and old advertising paraphernalia.

LASSCo
Brunswick House, 30 Wandsworth Road, SW8 2LG (7394 2100/www.lassco.co.uk). Vauxhall tube/rail. Open 10am-5pm Mon-Sat.
LASSCo has three outlets displaying its vast range of architectural salvage, with items running from £2.50 for a bar of soap to £25,000 for a mirror when we last popped in (and a rather nice library table from the British Museum). The main site in Vauxhall is the one to head for if you fancy a good root around. Should you prefer to hunt from the comfort of your chair, the website is excellent, with great search criteria and good navigation.

Park Royal Salvage
Lower Place Wharf, Acton Lane, NW10 7AB (8961 3627/www.parkroyalsalvage. co.uk). Harlesden tube. Open 7.30am-4.30pm Mon-Fri. No credit cards.
A relative newcomer to the salvage scene, in five years Park Royal has built up an impressive collection of pieces – from reclaimed bricks, beams, flooring and railway sleepers to fireplaces, sash and stained glass windows, elaborate garden statuary and antique baths and sinks.

Retrouvius
2A Ravensworth Road, NW10 5NR (8960 6060/www.retrouvius.com). Kensal Green tube. Open 10am-6pm Mon-Sat.
Former architects Adam Hills and Maria Speake like to 'bridge the gap between destruction and construction' in their smart west London salvage business, where the emphasis is on 20th-century salvage and modern antiques, such as a lovely Ercol side table for £65 and reissued Ernest Race rockers (£465), manufactured exclusively for Retrouvius to the original specifications. There's a great range of artwork too.

GOING OUT
BEAUTY
FASHION
PARTIES
FOOD
HEALTH
ECO
OUTDOORS
HOME
CHILDREN
PETS
TRANSPORT
RESOURCES

Interior & design boutiques

Aria

Barnsbury Hall, Barnsbury Street, N1 1PN (7704 6222/www.aria-shop.co.uk). Highbury & Islington tube/rail. Open 10am-6.30pm Mon-Wed, Fri, Sat; 10am-7pm Thur; noon-5pm Sun.

One of London's oldest independent design stores, Aria stocks all the big names (Alessi, Verner Panton, Kartell, Philippe Starck et al) in its bright and spacious shop, a former music hall.

Atelier Abigail Ahern

137 Upper Street, N1 1QP (7354 8181/ www.atelierabigailahern.com). Angel tube/ Highbury & Islington tube/rail. Open 10.30am-6pm Mon-Sat; noon-5pm Sun.

An inventive selection of work, from neon chandeliers to hand-thrown, ceramic-topped tables, creates a delightful departure from the clean, sparse lines of many modern interiors stores. Price tags tend to be substantial.

Form London

39 Park Road, N8 8TE (8348 7070/www. formlondon.co.uk). Hornsey rail. Open 10am-6.30pm Mon-Sat; noon-5.30pm Sun.

This Crouch End gem ensures a constantly fresh look by supplementing a well-chosen range of contemporary furniture, lighting and accessories with vintage finds.

Graham & Green

4 Elgin Crescent, W11 2HX (7243 8908/ www.grahamandgreen.co.uk). Ladbroke Grove tube. Open 10am-6pm Mon-Sat; 11.30am-5.30pm Sun.

The Graham & Green chain sells an enticing mix of furniture and accessories, ranging from sweet 1950s-inspired oak chairs (£150) to more opulent pieces, such as the embossed-brass Darjeeling chest-of-drawers (£875).
Other locations *across the city.*

Lifestyle Bazaar

10 Newburgh Street, W1F7RN (7734 9970/ www.lifestylebazaar.com). Oxford Circus

tube. Open 11am-7pm Mon-Wed, Sat; 11am-8pm Thur; noon-5pm Sun.*

Bright, fresh colours and quirky modern designs in a light-filled space make this little shop a delight to explore. The French ownership ensures a strong Gallic presence, but there's much to admire from globally sourced designers too.

Mint

70 Wigmore Street, W1U 2SF (7224 4406/ www.mintshop.co.uk). Bond Street tube. Open 10.30am-6.30pm Mon-Wed, Fri, Sat; 10.30am-7.30pm Thur.

Mint's owner Lina Kanafani has an unerring instinct for good design and a great eye for the unusual and unexpected – which means the tiny, two-level premises are packed with exciting furniture, clocks, ceramics and lighting from both established designers and recent graduates.

Places & Spaces

30 Old Town, SW4 0LB (7498 0998/www. placesandspaces.com). Clapham Common tube. Open 10.30am-6pm Tue, Wed, Fri, Sat; 10.30am-7pm Thur; noon-4pm Sun.

Laura Slack's small Clapham store is chock-full of classic and contemporary designs, from Hans Wegner's sleek oak-framed chairs to Tom Dixon's elegantly understated brass Beat Lights (£125). The shop offers an impressive sourcing service, as well as exclusive contracts with a number of European manufacturers.

City Secret

The annual price-slashing one-day showroom sale at design store **Vitra** (30 Clerkenwell Road, EC1M 5PG, 7608 6200, www.vitra.com) is the stuff of legend. Design aficionados queue for days in the hope of taking home an Eames chair, RRP £3,194, for under £100. If you want to join in the fun, make straight for the piece you want and grab the slip attached to it to bag the sale.

Pop UK

278 Upper Richmond Road, SW15 6TQ (8788 8811/www.popuk.com). East Putney tube/Putney rail. Open 10am-6pm Mon-Sat; noon-5pm Sun.

High-end wares from top European brands and designers feature in an airy boutique that shows off pieces like Philippe Starck's dramatic gun lighting range to great effect.

Russell Roberts

8 Cheshire Street, E2 6EH (7613 3355/ www.8cheshirestreet.com). Liverpool Street tube/rail. Open noon-6pm Thur, Fri, Sat; 10am-4pm Sun.

Mid-century classics sit happily alongside more contemporary creations at this Cheshire Street shop: last time we looked, stock ranged from a mounted stag's head (£450) to a curvy 1930s Bruno Mathsson Eva chair (£425).

SCP

135-139 Curtain Road, EC2A 3BX (7739 1869/www.scp.co.uk). Old Street tube/rail. Open 9.30am-6pm Mon-Sat; 11am-5pm Sun.

SCP is known for its beautiful yet functional pieces, with timeless classics from the likes of Jasper Morrison, Matthew Hilton and Robin Day. Smaller buys include Donna Wilson's hip knitted toys (from £20) and Rob Brandt's crumpled ceramic beakers (from £4.95).

Other location *87 Westbourne Grove, W2 4UL (7229 3612).*

Skandium

86 Marylebone High Street, W1U 4QS (7935 2077/www.skandium.com). Open 10am-6.30pm Mon-Wed, Fri, Sat; 10am-7pm Thur; 11am-5pm Sun.

Skandium is one of those shops that takes your breath away when you walk in, thanks to its quirky owl-print Iittala tableware (from £6.50), strokably smooth Artek chairs and jewel-like lighting from the likes of Unique Interieur, Le Klint and Louis Poulsen.

Other location *247 Brompton Road, SW3 2EP (7584 2066).*

Suzy Hoodless

10 Clarendon Cross, W11 4AP (7221 8844/ www.suzyhoodless.com). Holland Park tube.

Open 9.30am-6.30pm Mon-Fri; by appointment Sat, Sun. No credit cards.

Design consultant and former *Wallpaper** interiors editor Suzy Hoodless stocks her own chic, distinctive furniture, rug and wallpaper designs alongside a finely edited selection of antiques and 20th-century homeware. The quality is high, as are the prices.

Twentytwentyone

274 Upper Street, N1 2UA (7288 1996/ www.twentytwentyone.com). Angel tube/ Highbury & Islington tube/rail. Open 10am-6pm Mon-Fri; 10am-5.30pm Sat; 11am-5pm Sun.

Voted *Time Out* magazine's top independent interiors store in 2008, Twentytwentyone stocks an alluring mix of vintage originals, reissued classics and contemporary designs. The River Street store houses furniture, while the shoebox-sized Upper Street shop is great for gifts and accessories.

Other location *18C River Street, EC1R 1XN (7837 1900).*

Unto This Last

230 Brick Lane, E2 7EB (7613 0882/ www.untothislast.co.uk). Liverpool Street or Old Street tube/rail. Open 9am-6pm Mon-Fri; 10am-6pm Sat, Sun.

This unpretentious Brick Lane workshop is dedicated to the small-scale manufacturing of birch plywood and laminate bookcases, cabinets, slatted chairs and beds, all at very reasonable prices. A curved coffee table, for example, costs from £95, though the intricate, undulating Nurbs table is £580.

Viaduct

1-10 Summers Street, EC1R 5BD (7278 8456/www.viaduct.co.uk). Farringdon tube/ rail. Open 9.30am-6pm Mon-Fri; 10.30am-4pm Sat.

Viaduct's galleried premises showcase the finest contemporary design, with a particular focus on the work of leading European manufacturers such as Driade, xO and Droog. You don't have to spend a fortune to pick up a design icon, with affordable pieces such as Marcel Wanders' Sponge Vase (£106) or Azumi's angular Edge Clock (from £90).

GOING OUT

BEAUTY

FASHION

PARTIES

FOOD

HEALTH

ECO

OUTDOORS

HOME

CHILDREN

PETS

TRANSPORT

RESOURCES

GOING OUT

BEAUTY

FASHION

PARTIES

FOOD

HEALTH

ECO

OUTDOORS

HOME

CHILDREN

PETS

TRANSPORT

RESOURCES

Flowers & gardens

Blooming bouquets, inspiring garden centres and recommended garden designers.

Florists

Most of the major chains will send flowers abroad, including **Interflora** (0870 366 6555, www.interflora.co.uk) and **Teleflorist** (0800 083 0930, www. teleflorist.co.uk).

More and more florists now offer fairtrade flowers. Order online from the **Organic Flower Company** (0845 226 0608, www.tofc.co.uk); **John Lewis** (0845 604 9049, www.johnlewis.com) also sells selected fairtrade bunches.

Columbia Road Market (Columbia Road, Bethnal Green, E2) is a must for cut flowers, shrubs and bedding plants. It runs from 8am to 2pm every Sunday, with cut-price bargains towards the end.

Angel Flowers
60 Upper Street, N1 0NY (7704 6312/ www.angel-flowers.co.uk). Angel tube. Open 9am-7pm Mon-Sat; 11am-5pm Sun.
The premises may be small, but the range of bouquets is impressive, ranging from hand-tied posies (from £20) to enormous, show-stopping arrangements of hot tropicals and orchids. They're a favourite for weddings, but equally obliging if you call for a bouquet. The shop delivers to north, north-west and central London, with prices from £30.

Bloomsbury Flowers

*29 Great Queen Street, WC2B 5BB
(7242 2840/www.bloomsburyflowers.co.uk).
Covent Garden tube. Open 9.30am-5pm
Mon; 9.30am-5.30pm Tue-Fri.*
Personal service is the focus here, so instead
of ready-assembled bouquets, staff talk you
through the options to create tailor-made
seasonal bunches. Good-quality standards
like roses and peonies bloom alongside more
unusual choices such as scented herbs.
Deliveries are in pretty, tissue-lined boxes.
Other location *21A Highbury Park,
N5 1QJ (7704 0480).*

Jane Packer Flowers

*32-34 New Cavendish Street, W1G 8UE
(shop 7935 2673/delivery 0845 074 6000/
www.janepacker.com). Bond Street tube.
Open 9am-6pm Mon-Sat.*
This sleek Marylebone store offers a gorgeous
range of flowers at reasonable prices, with
chic but quirky arrangements from around
£40. Nationwide next-day delivery is offered,
with a same-day service for addresses within
a five-mile radius of the shop, while the
website offers an array of seasonal bouquets.

Jennie Mann Floral Designs

*63A Church Lane, N2 8DR (8365 2284/
www.jenniemann.com). East Finchley tube.
Open 9am-5pm Mon; 9am-5.30pm Tue-Fri;
9am-4pm Sat.*
This talented north London florist works
with seasonal and English flowers whenever
possible, with the average bouquet costing
around £35. Particularly lovely arrangements
feature old-fashioned blooms like ranunculus,
hyacinths, phlox and stocks, while nationwide
and international delivery is offered.

La Maison des Roses

*48 Webbs Road, SW11 6SF (7228 5700/
www.maison-des-roses.com). Clapham South
tube/Clapham Junction rail. Open 10am-6pm
Tue-Sat.*
For sheer romance it's hard to top this
deliciously pretty florist, devoted exclusively
to roses, among them headily perfumed
garden roses, unusual pink-tipped dolce vita
blooms and green Ecuadorian roses. Same-

day London orders arrive in smart pistachio
green packaging, and there's a next-day
nationwide service: delivery costs £5-£15.

Rebel Rebel

*5 Broadway Market, E8 4PH (7254 4487/
www.rebelrebel.co.uk). Liverpool Street tube/
rail, then 26, 48, 55 bus/London Fields rail.
Open 10am-6pm Tue-Fri; 10am-5pm Sat.*
The proprietor of this fragrant Hackney haven
is passionate about seasonal English blooms:
last time we dropped in, the heady scent of
stocks and lilac filled the shop. A delivery
service (from £30 a bouquet, plus delivery)
covers east, north and central London.

Robbie Honey

*7720 3777/www.robbiehoney.com. Open
for phone enquiries 9am-5pm Mon-Fri.*
Operating out of London's flower market
means hot young florist Robbie Honey can
select the freshest blooms for his bouquets,
starting at £55. The striking arrangements
are made up wholly from flowers rather than
padded out with foliage, and generally feature
just one variety. The team will deliver to any
London postcode, with charges from £12.50.

Scarlet & Violet ⭐

*76 Chamberlayne Road, NW10 3JJ (8969
9446/www.scarletandviolet.co.uk). Queens
Park tube. Open 9am-6pm Mon-Sat.*
The signature style at this Kensal Green
florist is beautifully simple, romantic
bouquets. We love the enamel jugs (£45-£50),
artfully filled with sweet peas, hydrangeas,
peonies and ornamental dill. Staff are happy
to make up tiny posies (£5) or bouquets (from
£15), though there are ready-assembled
bunches. Delivery is £5-£27.

Wild Bunch

*17-22 Earlham Street, WC2H 9LL (7497
1200). Covent Garden or Leicester Square
tube. Open 9.30am-7pm Mon-Sat.*
Close to Seven Dials, this sprawling flower
stall's strategic position and bundles of
exotica, such as celosia, calla and strelitzia,
earn it a good deal of attention. A mixed
bunch in water costs about £35, but you can
put together a seasonal spray for much less.

GOING OUT
BEAUTY
FASHION
PARTIES
FOOD
HEALTH
ECO
OUTDOORS
HOME
CHILDREN
PETS
TRANSPORT
RESOURCES

Garden centres

NORTH

Camden Garden Centre

2 Barker Drive, St Pancras Way, NW1 0JW (7387 7080/www.camdengardencentre.co.uk). Camden Town tube. Open Apr-Sept 9am-5.30pm Mon, Tue, Fri, Sat; 9am-7pm Wed, Thur; 11am-5pm Sun. Oct-Mar 9am-5pm Mon-Sat; 10am-4pm Sun.

Pick up a rejected perennial in need of some TLC from the bargain section by the entrance, or venture further in for a sterling selection of bedding shrubs, old-fashioned and hybrid tea roses, herbs and climbers. The maintenance and design team can be called in for anything from once-a-month upkeep to turfing, trellising and complete redesigns.

Capital Gardens

Alexandra Palace, Alexandra Palace Way, N22 7BB (8444 2555/www.capitalgardens. co.uk). Wood Green tube or Finsbury Park tube/rail, then W3 bus/Alexandra Palace rail. Open 9am-6pm Mon-Sat; 10.30am-4.30pm Sun.

London's biggest garden centre sticks to tried-and-tested favourites: plenty of bedding standards, plus verdant shrubs and climbers for those too impatient to train their own from scratch. There are plenty of accessories too, from barbecues to children's gardening kits.

Clock House Nursery

Forty Hill, Enfield, Middlesex EN2 9EU (8363 1016/www.clockhousenursery.co.uk). Enfield Town rail, then 191 bus. Open 9am-5pm daily.

From the profusion of garden centres dotted around Enfield, Clock House is one of the biggest and best. Its high-quality flowers and shrubs are sold almost at wholesale prices, as most are grown on site – a godsend if you're planning a major overhaul.

North One Garden Centre

The Old Button Factory, 25A Englefield Road, N1 4EU (7923 3553/www.n1gc.co.uk). Essex Road rail/76, 141 bus. Open Apr-Dec 9.30am-6pm Mon-Wed, Fri-Sun; 9.30am-7pm Thur. Jan-Mar 9.30am-5pm Mon-Wed, Fri-Sun; 9.30am-6pm Thur.

With its chic garden accessories and furniture, this diminutive, award-winning garden centre is pitched at style-savvy urbanites. Plants are displayed in artfully-assembled displays, making it easy to see what will work together.

EAST

Growing Concerns

2 Wick Lane, at Cadogan Terrace, E3 2NA (8985 3222/www.growingconcerns.org). Bow Road tube/DLR, then 8, S2 bus. Open Summer 10am-6pm Tue-Sun. Winter 8am-4pm Tue-Sun.

Tucked between the Hertford Union Canal and Victoria Park, this tranquil, prettily laid-out community garden centre is staffed by an enthusiastic team. Prices are competitive, with perennials from £4.50 and enormous shrubs for around £60. Teas and home-made carrot cake are a welcome sideline.

SOUTH

Dulwich Garden Centre

20-22 Grove Vale, SE22 8EF (8299 1089/ www.dulwichgardencentre.co.uk). East Dulwich rail. Open 9am-5.30pm Mon-Sat; 10am-2pm Sun.

Stock ranges from showy climbers and shrubs to seeds, planters and perennials. Herbs are a speciality, with plenty of unusual offerings (bergamot, hyssop, marsh mallow) and numerous varieties of better-known herbs: 20 species of thyme, ten mints and ten lavenders at the last count. At £14.99 for ten, they're superb value. In summer, look out for boxes of lettuce, chilli and corn seedlings.

Fulham Palace Garden Centre

Bishop's Avenue, SW6 6EE (7736 2640/ www.fulhamgardencentre.com). Putney Bridge tube. Open 9.30am-5.30pm Mon-Thur; 9.30am-6pm Fri, Sat; 10am-5pm Sun.

Profits at this friendly, countrified garden centre go to the charity that runs it, Fairbridge, which supports socially and economically alienated young people. There's a flourishing array of bedding plants and shrubs, and helpful staff.

WEST

Clifton Nurseries
5A Clifton Villas, W9 2PH (7289 6851/ www.clifton.co.uk). Warwick Avenue tube. Open Apr-Oct 8.30am-6pm Mon, Tue, Thur-Sat; 8.30am-8pm Wed; 10.30am-4.30pm Sun. Nov-Mar 8.30am-5.30pm Mon-Sat; 10.30am-4.30pm Sun.
Founded in 1851, Clifton Nurseries boast a sophisticated palm house stocked with exotic specimens and an impressive topiary-dotted outdoor space. Along with a comprehensive array of high-quality indoor and outdoor plants, the nursery offers garden design and maintenance services, including useful one-off 'garden tidies'.

C Rassell ★
80 Earl's Court Road, W8 6EQ (7937 0481). Earl's Court or High Street Kensington tube. Open Jan-Mar, mid July-Sept 9am-5.30pm Mon-Wed, Fri, Sat; 9am-6.30pm Thur. Apr-mid July, Oct-Dec 9am-5.30pm Mon-Wed, Fri, Sat; 9am-6.30pm Thur; 11am-5.30pm Sun.
The deliciously old-fashioned Rassell's is ideal for novices. A board outside suggests what to plant in the month ahead, while each species in the beautiful garden has an informative, handwritten label. There are bedding plants of every hue, as well as plenty of specimens for shady spots and terraces.

GARDEN DESIGNERS

The Royal Horticultural Society-affiliated **Society of Garden Designers** (01989 566695, www.sgd.org.uk) can provide a list of accredited members.

Creative Garden Design
07788 962735.
Stoke Newington-based Rafael Duran offers landscaping, clearance and garden maintenance. Former clients are full of praise for his work.

Lucy Sommers
07813 500327/www.lucysommers gardens.com.
Capel Manor-trained Sommers offers a full design spectrum, from lush sub-tropical to minimalist gravel and stone; her website is a great showcase.

Origin Landscapes
07815 465445/www.origin landscapes.com.
Jay Osman handles construction, maintenance and full garden design, and is 'a consumate professional', according to previous customers.

Rob Bratby Gardens
07811 472799/www.robertbratby gardens.co.uk.
Rob Bratby offers landscaping, design and planting to suit any style of garden, traditional or contemporary, with particular attention paid to ecological concerns. Prices range from around £5,000 to £50,000.

Sybil Caines
07986 542868.
This Stoke Newington designer trained at Capel Manor and focuses on design and planting plans rather than the build. Design services, including a final plan, average around £500.

Will Nash
8365 3656/07961 171406.
Garden enthusiast Nash will take on any size of garden in north London, and any size of job, from fencing to full landscaping, patios and ponds. He likes to realise ideas with clients, encouraging them to visit his past projects and talk to previous clients.

GOING OUT
BEAUTY
FASHION
PARTIES
FOOD
HEALTH
ECO
OUTDOORS
HOME
CHILDREN
PETS
TRANSPORT
RESOURCES

Jennie Mann
FLOWERS

◆ Hand tied bouquets ◆ Planted arrangements ◆ Orchids ◆ Vases and Containers
◆ Scented Candles ◆ Gifts ◆ Homewares ◆ Events ◆ Corporate
◆ Deliveries throughout northwest London and beyond

63a Church Lane, East Finchley. London N2 8DR
tel: 020 8365 2284   email: info@jenniemann.co.uk

w w w . j e n n i e m a n n . c o m

REBEL REBEL

Glamorous, inventive, stylish flowers
for your friends, parties, events, weddings,
offices and homes.

Come visit us at our shop in the heart of
Hackney, or let us deliver to you.

5 Broadway Market, London E8 4PH.

020 7254 4487

www.rebelrebel.co.uk

Bedroom walls need a freshen up?

Bathroom crying out for a make over?

Home Jane provide professional tradeswomen
for large and small jobs including:

- Plumbing
- Electrics
- Painting & Decorating
- *And much more*

Call to discuss your requirements or
visit our website for more information.

0845 832 36 39

www.home-jane.co.uk   info@home-jane.co.uk

Restoration

Make do and mend – with a little expert assistance.

CLOCKS

The Clock Clinic
*85 Lower Richmond Road, SW15 1EU
(8788 1407/www.clockclinic.com). Putney
Bridge rail/tube. Open 9am-6pm Tue-Fri;
9am-1pm Sat.*
Clocks, barometers and musical boxes will be
returned to their former glory at this south-
west London godsend.

Robert Loomes Clock Repair
*68 Hatton Garden, EC1N 8JY (7477
2224/www.dialrestorer.co.uk). Open
by appointment only.*
This antique watch and clock repairers and
restorers offers quality workmanship, with a
12-month guarantee on work undertaken.

FABRICS & UPHOLSTERY

Consult the **Association of Master
Upholsterers** (029 2077 8918, www.
upholsterers.co.uk) for a directory of
members, a list of upholstery courses
and lots of information and advice.

Atomic Antiques
*125 Shoreditch High Street E1 6JE (7739
5923/www.atomica.me.uk). Liverpool Street
tube/rail. Open 11.30am-5.30pm Tue-Fri;
11am-5pm Sat; 11am-4pm Sun.*
This Mid-century Modern furniture shop
specialises in re-upholstering chairs and
sofas from the same period.

Austrian Bedding Company
*205 Belsize Road, NW6 4AA (7372 3121).
Kilburn Park tube. Open 10am-5pm Mon-Sat.*
This duvet specialist will turn your old lumpy
duvet into a thing of beauty, cleaning and
topping up the down, then packing it into a
brand new cover.

JE Norris
*7A Tranquil Passage, SE3 0BJ (8852 8725).
Blackheath rail. Open 10am-1pm Mon-Sat.*
Upholstering East End furniture since 1945,
this reliable family business offers on-site
consultations and free estimates.

John Lewis
*300 Oxford Street, W1A 1EX (7629 7711/
www.johnlewis.com). Oxford Circus tube. Open
9.30am-8pm Mon-Wed, Fri; 9.30am-9pm
Thur; 9.30am-7pm Sat; noon-6pm Sun.*
If a much loved piece of furniture needs a
good stuffing, a gentle reshaping or a whole
new look, John Lewis can help. On selection
of an appropriate fabric, they will come to you
and give you a free estimate for the job.

Keys
*Stephenson Road, Clacton on Sea, Essex
CO1 4XA (01255 432518/www.bedlinen
centre.co.uk). Open 9am-4.30pm Mon-Sat.*
If your favourite eiderdown or duvet is
looking a bit down, Keys will supply a bag
into which you pack it off to them for
restuffing – they can even turn two skinny
ones into one fat one. Duvets cost from £135,
eiderdowns from £306.

Textile Services Association
8863 7755/www.tsa-uk.org.
The trade association for launderers and
dry-cleaners can suggest specialist cleaners
in your area for everything from antique
fabrics to continental quilts.

William Fountain & Co
*68A Cobden Road, E11 3PE (8558 3464/
www.williamfountain.com). Lytonstone tube.
Open 8am-6pm Mon-Fri. No credit cards.*
This east London family business offers
upholstery and re-upholstery, loose covers,
and furniture and antique repairs.

GOING OUT
BEAUTY
FASHION
PARTIES
FOOD
HEALTH
ECO
OUTDOORS
HOME
CHILDREN
PETS
TRANSPORT
RESOURCES

GLASS & TABLEWARE

Blue Crystal
7278 0142/www.bluecrystalglass.co.uk.
Chipped glasses, damaged chandeliers and even cloudy glasses can be repaired. Hourly rates vary, but range from £25-£45.

Bouke De Vries
8960 8010.
Specialist in repairing chipped and broken ceramic pieces, whether it be replacing the handle of a favourite teapot or repairing a broken vase; rates start at £40 per hour.

Chinasearch
01926 512402/www.chinasearch.co.uk.
Chinasearch holds thousands of patterns from over 40 glass, cutlery and dinnerware manfacturers, so if you've broken a favourite cup, there's a good chance you'll find it here.

Facets
107 Boundary Road, E17 8NQ (8520 3392/www.facetsglass.co.uk). Leyton tube. Open by appointment only.
If it has glass in it, Facets can probably fix it or restore it. The range of services is mind-boggling; antique and modern glass can be restored, hair and clothes brushes rebristled, silver cutlery replated and hourglasses refilled with sand.

Tablewhere?
8361 6111/www.tablewhere.com.
Tablewhere? keeps more than a million pieces of discontinued china, so finding vintage crockery, sourcing missing pieces or extending a dinner service should be a doddle. Prices are reasonable, and a wish list enables the company to contact you when a piece you've requested comes in.

Wilkinson's
5 Catford Hill, SE6 4NU (8314 1080/www.wilkinson-plc.com). Catford Bridge rail. Open 9am-5pm Mon-Fri.
Wilkinson's still cuts chandelier pieces using 19th-century methods, and has been at its business for almost a century, so knows its stuff. Chandelier-cleaning is also offered.

SPECIALIST SERVICES

If you're looking to restore a treasured antique to its former glory, a good starting point is the **Conservation Register** (www.conservationregister.com). The database allows you to search through hundreds of categories and will provide the names of relevant experts.

Hossack & Gray
Studio 10, 9E Queensyard, White Post Lane, E9 5EN (8986 3345/www.hossackandgray.co.uk). Hackney Wick rail. Open 9.30am-6.30pm Mon-Fri; by appointment Sat.
Antique restoration, expert leather-staining, wood-turning and gilding.

W Sitch & Co
48 Berwick Street, W1F 8JD (7437 3776/www.wsitch.co.uk). Oxford Circus tube. Open 8am-6pm Mon-Fri; 8am-1pm Sat. No credit cards.
W Sitch has occupied this Soho townhouse for more than 100 years, restoring antique lights and chandeliers. Staff will repair and rewire period lighting, or convert a favourite vase into a lamp.

TILE RESTORATION

Mosaic Restoration Company
Verwood House, High Street, West Haddon, Northamptonshire NN6 7AP (01788 510000/www.mosaicrestoration.co.uk). Open 8.30am-5.30pm Mon-Fri.
Gary Bricknell and his team will travel anywhere to deal with large- and small-scale tile cleaning, polishing or restoration projects. They also offer a bespoke service for Victorian and Edwardian-style geometric floors, pre-fabricated in their workshop.

Tiled Perfection
01920 871555/www.tiledperfection.com.
Established in the 1990s, Tiled Perfection specialise in laying and restoring Victorian tiled floors. Past customers include the V&A, but mere mortals looking to get their garden path spruced up or their entrance hall retiled are also welcomed.

Useful services

Essential services, tradesmen and contacts.

GOING OUT

BEAUTY

FASHION

PARTIES

FOOD

HEALTH

ECO

OUTDOORS

HOME

CHILDREN

PETS

TRANSPORT

RESOURCES

Cleaning

If you need a serious spring clean or end of tenancy clean-up, or can't face the post-party carnage, a specialist cleaning company could be your salvation.

For carpets and windows, the best starting points are the **National Carpet Cleaners Association** (0116 271 9550, www.ncca.co.uk) and the **Window Cleaners' Federation** (0161 432 8754, www.nfmwgc.com), both of which will direct you to members in your area.

Jeeves of Belgravia (*see p67*) also offers rug, carpet and curtain cleaning.

Absolutely Spotless
8932 7360/www.absolutelyspotless.co.uk.
Absolutely Spotless specialises in house-moving and spring cleans. Armed with an industrial hoover, its teams of cleaners guarantee a gleaming finish – and will come back if they've missed anything. Prices start from £90 for a studio apartment. Window cleaning is also offered (£20-£30 for a two-bedroom property), while carpet cleaning is good value at a pound per square yard.

Anyclean
0800 195 1215/ www.anyclean.co.uk.
Anyclean undertakes almost any kind of cleaning, including rugs, house-moving cleans and domestic cleaning. The latter starts at £9 an hour for a vetted, insured cleaner; contracts are flexible, ranging from weekly three-hour cleans to monthly visits.

Cadogan Company
8960 8020.
Cadogan will collect, clean and rehang curtains and fabric blinds (£6.50 per square yard). It also steam-cleans carpets, rugs and upholstery (from £30 for an armchair).

Clean'N'Gone
0800 075 7800/www.cleanngone.co.uk.
Clean'N'Gone specialises in cleaning rugs, upholstery and mattresses (£22 for a bedroom carpet), along with regular and one-off domestic cleaning. It charges by the job, so can give you costs upfront; a two-bedroom end of tenancy clean, for example, is £143.

The Oven Cleaning Company
01428 717174/www.theovencleaningco.com.
This company tackles one of the nastiest of chores: restoring your encrusted oven to shiny perfection. Non-caustic, non-toxic products are used, with prices from £28 (ex VAT) for a built-in single oven; the average spend is £60.

Perfect Clean
0800 195 7848/ www.perfectclean.co.uk.
Post-party blitzes, spring cleans and regular contracts are undertaken, along with carpet and upholstery cleaning. Hourly rates are reasonable: £10 for the spring clean or £11 for the after-party service, say, with a minimum of four hours per visit. You'll pay extra if you don't provide cleaning products.

GOING OUT
BEAUTY
FASHION
PARTIES
FOOD
HEALTH
ECO
OUTDOORS
HOME
CHILDREN
PETS
TRANSPORT
RESOURCES

Computer repair

If you've got an Apple laptop, it's worth knowing about the free one-on-one **Genius Bar** sessions at the Regent's Street flagship – call 0800 048 0408 to book an appointment.

Geeks On Wheels

0800 107 4110/www.geeks-on-wheels.com. Appointments 8am-9pm Mon-Fri; 9am-5pm Sat, Sun.
Guaranteeing a no fix, no fee service, the 20 technicians who make up Geeks on Wheels aren't cheap at £75 for the first hour, then £37.50 per half hour, but they are British-Standard accredited and get glowing reviews from previous customers. There's a 10% discount for pensioners, nurses and students.

Geek Squad

0800 049 4335/www.geeksquad.co.uk. Appointments 7.30am-8pm Mon-Fri; 9am-5pm Sat, Sun.
We like the *Men In Black* nature of Geek Squad, whose techs dress like FBI agents and solve some problems remotely, taking control of your PC via the net. Home visits start at £100 to fix one problem, regardless of how long it takes; charges for dealing with extra problems then range from £25-£80. The Geeks also have a no fix, no fee guarantee.

Honeylight

54 Moreton Street, SW1V 2PB (7821 0670/ www.honeylight.co.uk). Pimlico tube. Open 9am-5.30pm Mon-Fri.
Dealing with PCs and Macs, Honeylight offers free estimates for data recovery and repairs if you take your computer into the shop (it takes a week) and a while-you-wait emergency service, plus call-out engineers who'll come anywhere within the M25 (from £85/hr plus VAT). It's accredited by both Apple and ISO 9002 quality systems, so you're in safe hands.

Mac Daddy

Unit 10, ZLR Studios, West Heath Yard, 174 Mill Lane, NW6 1TB (7431 2408/ www.mac-daddy.co.uk). West Hampstead
tube. *Open by appointment 10am-5pm Mon-Fri. No credit cards.*
Mac Daddy's Apple-certified engineers run a West Hampstead-based Mac Clinic and offer a range of services, including an annual freelance contract (£375) that includes a yearly check-up, priority in the workshop, telephone support and a discounted call-out rate. The pay-as-you-go rate is £55 per hour, with a sliding call-out fee based on London zones, and there's a same-day repair/upgrade rate of £90 per hour. Prices are exclusive of VAT.

Mike Will Fix It

0776 264 7547/www.mikewillfixit.com. Appointments 8am-7pm Mon-Sat. No credit cards.
The first port of call for any PC owner should be Mike. At just £15 per hour for labour, capped at £90 (for home users) irrespective of job, time or distance, his prices beat most bigger companies hands down. He'll travel to any part of London and can usually be there within 24 hours. As a certified Windows support service with years of experience, he should be able to solve any problem. And if he can't, he won't charge you.

PureMackintosh

07956 288958/www.puremackintosh.com. Open 10am-6pm. Mon-Fri. No credit cards.
Specialising in Macs and covering all of London, Chris Essex-Hill and Alan Drew have 35 years' combined experience of Macs, dealing with software, hardware, networking, buying advice, upgrades and maintenance. Call-outs cost £75 an hour, though they're happy to discuss full- and half-day rates.

Scooter Computer

1 Putney Bridge Approach, SW6 3JD (7384 5949/scootercomputer.co.uk). Putney Bridge tube. Open 9am-5pm Mon-Fri; by appointment Sat. No credit cards.
Happy dealing with both Macs and PCs, Scooter Computer charges an hourly rate (£69 plus VAT for the first hour, then a half-hourly rate) or a range of fixed fees (installation of wireless broadband, say, for £89 plus VAT) for services to small businesses and home users in central and south-west London.

CONCIERGE SERVICES

You don't need a six-figure salary to use a concierge service these days, thanks to a new breed of companies aimed at Londoners on less lavish budgets. Instead of demanding eye-wateringly expensive yearly membership, they charge by the hour – and the range of services is also broader that you might think. While they can sort out parties, holidays and other delicious frivolities, they can also step in to tackle more tedious everyday tasks, like waiting in for a delivery on your behalf, or organising your paperwork and bills.

Busy People
8981 8972/www.busy-people.co.uk.
Busy People offers both hourly and fixed-fee rates. Waiting in for a delivery, for example, is charged at £40 for four hours (ex VAT), cat-sitting at £9.50 per visit and moving house cleans at £12 per hour, while party help can be had at £14 per hour, or a weekend nanny for £10 per hour. References are scrupulously checked.

Buy:time
0870 486 2624/www.buy-time.co.uk.
Want to organise a surprise party, sort out your bills and long-neglected admin or get the errands you never have time for done in one fell swoop? Buy:time promises to organise your life by the hour, by the day, or via a bespoke plan. There are no joining fees, just an hourly rate of £39, which is reduced if you buy blocks of time; 20 hours, for example, is charged at £29 per hour (ex VAT).

Cushion the Impact
7704 6922/www.cushionthe impact.co.uk.
If it's legal, moral and feasible, Cushion the Impact will be happy to help. Whether it's organising unpaid bills and unfilled tax returns or tackling time-consuming chores, they'll take it off your hands. The hourly fee is £40, although the more hours you buy, the cheaper the rates then become.

Life's Too Short
0800 066 5373/www.lifes2short.co.uk.
Lifestyle management comes in at just £29 an hour for regular users of Life's Too Short, or £40 for one-off projects, whether it be finding and booking tradesmen, researching a holiday, getting your filing up to date or helping you move house.

Electricians

See also **Home Jane** and **020 Handyman**, *p160*.

Electrical Contractors' Association
7313 4800/www.eca.co.uk.
This nationwide trade association can provide you with a list of contractors.

National Inspection Council for Electrical Installation Contracting
0870 013 0382/www.niceic.org.uk.

The NICEIC is a regulatory body issuing strict rules to its members; use the online Find an Electrician feature to locate your nearest registered electrician. It also offers an independent complaints procedure, if work doesn't meet its standards.

RJ Electrical
8599 2841/mobile 07836 677836.
Richard James is a general electrician who knows his stuff, returns your calls, and is warmly recommended by former clients. He does rewiring, call-outs and cooker repairs, and is based in north-east London.

Glaziers

The **Glass & Glazing Federation** (0870 042 4255, www.ggf.org.uk) provides a directory of local glaziers.

In addition to the companies listed below, **Ray's Glass & Frames** (*see p143*) takes on domestic glazing jobs and repairs broken windows, charging a £60 call-out fee, plus glass and labour costs.

Absolute Glass
7394 9324/24hr emergency line 0800 298 1488/www.absoluteglass.net. Open 24hrs.
Undertakes emergency window repair, and installs all types of glass and windows.

Classic Window Company
8275 0770/www.classicwindow.co.uk. Open 9am-5pm Mon-Fri.
The Classic Window Company specialises in overhauling and repairing sash windows.

Sash Window Workshop
0800 597 2598/www.sashwindow.com. Open 8.30am-5pm Mon-Thur; 8.30am-4.30pm Fri.
A team of joiners, craftsmen and painters can restore, replace, draught-seal, double-glaze and soundproof sash or casement windows.

Handymen

Online forums such as **Rated People** (*see p164*) are a good place to find reliable handymen; the Federation of Master Builders' online **Find a Builder** service (*see p164*) is also useful, but geared more towards specific building projects.

A Woman's Touch ★
7167 2124/www.awomanstouch.org.uk.
Kerrie Keeling and her team are highly recommended for their decorating work, but also take on construction and renovation jobs, from electrical and plumbing jobs through to extensions and loft conversions. The team are accredited by both the Federation of Master Builders and the Guild of Master Craftsmen.

Handymen for Hire
07980 178150/www.handymanforhire.co.uk.
All kinds of DIY is offered (bar working with gas appliances, or major electrical works), from hanging paintings to custom-building furniture. Most work is costed by the half-day (£175) or day (£275), but there are also hourly rates (£60/first hour, then £25/30mins) and fixed quotes for larger jobs.

Home Jane
0845 832 3639/www.home-jane.co.uk.
From handywomen to plasterers, painters and plumbers, Home Jane offers vetted, fully qualified and insured female home helpers. Jobs tackled range from replacing door locks to rewiring and furniture restoration.

Johnny Cashman
07776 231949.
As well as being a fantastic general handyman, Johnny Cashman is a CORGI-registered plumber who can handle both gas central heating and plumbing work.

Kensington Maintenance Company
0845 838 2928/www.k-m-c.co.uk.
Owen Muir at KMC specialises in odd jobs, whether it be getting you into your house when you've locked yourself out, painting and decorating or fixing a leaking tap.

0800 handyman
0800 426396/www.0800handyman.co.uk. Open 8am-6pm Mon-Fri; 10am-2pm Sat.
The team at 0800 can take on everything from sash window cord replacement to plumbing in sinks, all for a half-hourly rate of £20, plus a £20 call-out charge (ex VAT). 'Prompt, unpatronising and trustworthy', enthuses one regular user.

020 Handyman
8358 3847/mobile 07881 524592/ www.020handyman.com.
020 Handyman charges £40 for the first half hour, then £40 for each subsequent hour, up to a maximum daily rate of £240 (labour costs only, ex VAT). All staff handling plumbing and gas jobs are CORGI registered and all electricians fully accredited.

Junk collection

In addition to the services listed below, think about donating unwanted items to charity or find out if they can be recycled (*see p124*); another option is giving them away on **Freecycle** (www.freecycle.org).

Most local councils offer a collection service for bulky goods such as fridges, ovens and furniture – it's often free, or costs around £15-£20 for a pick-up.

Any Junk?

0800 043 1007/www.anyjunk.co.uk.
Any Junk? will pretty much anything you want to get rid of – and promises to recycle or reuse over a third of it. Prices are based on load size and start at around £58, which includes the services of a two-man team. There's an extra charge for disposing of computer monitors and fridges.

Clutter Clinic

07834 338568/www.clutterclinic.co.uk.
If you're swamped with clutter and need impartial advice on what to get rid of and how to maximise storage space, the Clutter Clinic can help. An initial consultation costs £50 per hour, then it's £60 an hour for the clearing. The company can also help streamline and reorganise your wardrobe, or help you unpack after moving house.

Ecojunk

0800 043 0432/www.ecojunk.com.
Ecojunk collects junk and garden waste, then recycles as much of it as possible. Prices start at £51, though extra charges are levied for collections made outside business hours and disposing of fridges and computer monitors.

Eco Rubbish Clearance Company

0800 988 3061/www.ecorubbish clearance.co.uk.
Another eco-aware operation, which sends a two-strong team and van to collect your junk – and promises to sweep up afterwards. Prices start at £45, with labour included for the first two hours. There's also a free scrap car collection service.

Locksmiths & keyholding companies

The **Master Locksmiths Association** (0800 783 1498, non-emergencies 01327 262255, www.locksmiths.co.uk) can also help you to find a qualified locksmith in your area.

Delta Security

181 Dalston Lane, E8 1AL (8985 1855/ www.deltasecurity.net). Hackney Downs rail. Open 8am-5pm Mon-Fri.
As well as offering all manner of locks and security systems, Delta will get you into your house if you're locked out. The call-out and labour charge is around £60, not including the cost of a new lock, if required.

Farringdon Locksmith & Tool Supplies

29 Exmouth Market, EC1R 4QL (7837 5179). Angel tube. Open 8am-5.30pm Mon-Sat.
This helpful locksmith offers emergency lock services across London, with charges starting at around £65, plus the cost of a replacement lock.

SpareKeys

0870 069 5397/www.sparekeys.com.
SpareKeys will hold on to a set of your car, office and house keys; if you then lock yourself out, you can call them 24/7 and they'll get you back in. The annual membership fee is £39, with a £20-£30 charge for each call out: more expensive than relying on neighbours, but more reliable too.

Tony Andrews

299 Muswell Hill Broadway, N10 1BY (8444 7300/www.tonyandrews.net). Open 8.30am-6pm Mon-Sat; 11am-5pm Sun.
This long-established local locksmiths provides an emergency call-out service within half an hour in the Muswell Hill area (though they'll cover most of north London). Lock opening, replacement and post-burglary repairs are also swiftly undertaken. Highly recommended by in-the-know locals.

GOING OUT
BEAUTY
FASHION
PARTIES
FOOD
HEALTH
ECO
OUTDOORS
HOME
CHILDREN
PETS
TRANSPORT
RESOURCES

Plumbers

Two trade bodies cover plumbing, the **Association of Plumbing & Heating Contractors** (7647 0626, www.aphc.co.uk) and the **Institute of Plumbing & Heating Contractors** (024 7647 0626, www.plumbers.org.uk). Both can provide lists of contractors. *See also p160* **Home Jane** and **Johnny Cashman**.

All Go Plumbing
0800 083 2215/www.allgoplumbing.co.uk.
Alan Good and his team cover a wide range of plumbing jobs, from bespoke bathrooms to humble blocked loos.

Aqua-Care
0800 389 2238/www.24hrlondonplumber. co.uk.
This CORGI-registered emergency specialist offers a one-hour service with no call-out fee.

Dyno
0800 000999/www.dyno.com.
Part of British Gas, Dyno offers a fast, reliable service and friendly staff who don't try to blind you with science.

Imperial Plumbing
0845 351 0440/www.imperialbuildand plumb.com.
The website features simple instructions on how to turn off your water supply, while the company offers a 24-hour call-out service.

Kate Churchill
07733 333727.
Covering selected areas of north London, Kate Churchill offers a dependable, fairly-priced service and has 20 years' experience.

Leakbusters
0800 328 8125/www.leakbusters.net.
Plumbers whose work comes in under the original quote due to unexpected savings are hard to find: this is a north London gem.

Mainbreak Plumbing
07917 108876.

Craig and Simon are CORGI-registered to carry out gas boiler work, but also take on tiling jobs and complete bathroom refits.

Rosie Riley
8692 3375/07932 566039.
Rosie Riley covers south-east London for all types of plumbing work, but will travel further afield for major work.

Removals

The **British Association of Removers** (01923 699480, www.bar.co.uk) represents over 500 removal and storage companies, all of them covered by its Office of Fair Trading-approved code of practice; search online for London-based firms.

It's always best to get a range of estimates, and read the insurance policy small print very carefully.

Register with the excellent (and free) **www.iammoving.com**, who will inform a personalised list of companies, such as utilities, of your new address. The **Post Office** (0845 722 3344, www.post office.co.uk) can redirect mail to your new address, charging from £7.10 for a month.

Cadogan Tate Moving & Storage
0800 988 6011/www.cadogantate.com.
This long-established firm is one of London's smartest. Personal move planners and special crates for delicate items such as chandeliers ensure peace of mind for its well-heeled clients.

Dulwich Removals
8678 1774.
Still going strong after 20 years, Dulwich Removals are happy to undertake moves of all sizes, generally in south London (though they will consider moves further afield). As a guide price, a one-bedroom move within south London is around £300.

Fast Forward
8888 1050/www.ffg123.com.
Fast Forward will move anything anywhere in the UK, whether it be hauling your old fridge to a friend across town or shifting the

FLATPACK ASSEMBLY

Em FlatPack
8861 0889/www.emflatpack.co.uk.
The 23-strong team offers a set rate for most jobs and reasonable hourly rates; £35 for the first hour, then £20 for each subsequent hour.

Fearless Mike
01273 711166/www.fearless mike.com.
Can't bear the thought of queuing for that IKEA wardrobe, never mind assembling it? IKEA specialists Mike Ear and his team will buy, deliver and assemble it for you. Delivery costs from £25, assembly from £30 per hour for a one-man job.

Put 'Em Up
8427 0054/www.putemup.co.uk.
This Harrow-based company is a dab hand at assembling everything from kitchens to garden sheds. A telephone quote is available for most items: a chest of drawers, for example, is £40.

Screwdriver
0800 454828/www.screwdriver-flatpack.co.uk.
Screwdriver charges a fixed rate if the item you need assembling is in its database, so you know exactly what you'll pay. Other items are charged by the hour (£42), then £9 per 15 minutes. If you're moving house, staff can dismantle furniture too.

Unflatpack Company
7460 2600/www.unflatpack.com.
John Griffin's company happily assembles pretty much any piece of furniture that comes in a box. The rate is £15 per half hour: a basic wardrobe, which takes about 45 minutes to assemble, would cost £30, plus a £20 call-out fee.

---

entire contents of your Mayfair mansion to a remote corner of Scotland.

Movers Not Shakers
7630 9005/www.moversnotshakers.co.uk.
Movers Not Shakers caters for all sizes of job, from a simple 'man-with-a-van' service (from £35/hr) to big international moves.

Nifty Shifty ★
0800 1777 213/www.niftyshifty.co.uk.
Nifty Shifty's team is brilliant, say past users: professional, organised, reliable and calm.

Roger's Removals
8953 6777/www.rogersremovals.co.uk.
This reliable Finchley firm has been in the removals business for almost 40 years.

Shirley's Removals
7254 5580.
Originally specialising in moving house for the gay community, this small but well-run removals firm promises to treat your possessions with care and move them swiftly.

Tool hire

Tool Chest
68 Iffley Rd, W6 0PB (8748 7912/www.tool chesthire.co.uk). Hammersmith tube. Open 8am-5pm Mon-Fri; 9am-2pm Sat.
This Hammersmith-based tool and plant hire company will deliver, or you can go along to the shop. Prices are competitive: a cordless drill costs a tenner to use for a 24-hour period.

HSS Hire
95 Tower Bridge Road, SE1 4TW (7357 9207/www.hss.com). London Bridge tube/rail. Open 7am-5.30pm Mon-Fri; 8am-1pm Sat.
This fairly-priced tool-hire company has outlets across London.
Other locations *across the city.*

GOING OUT

BEAUTY

FASHION

PARTIES

FOOD

HEALTH

ECO

OUTDOORS

HOME

CHILDREN

PETS

TRANSPORT

RESOURCES

Trade associations & useful contacts

A number of websites offer directories of tradesmen with user-generated reviews, allowing you to read previous customers' comments on all kinds of companies, from plumbers to interior designers. Sites include **Problem Solved** (www.problem solved.co.uk) and **HomePro** (0870 734 4344, www.homepro.com). At **Rated People** (0870 220 8810, www.rated people.co.uk), you're asked to submit a description of the job, then tradespeople submit quotes – but you can still check comments from former customers.

It's best to employ a member of a trade association that demands adherence to a strict code of practice. If you have legal concerns, contact the **Office of Fair Trading** (0845 722 4499, www.oft.gov.uk), or consult its *Shoppers' Rights,* which explains your legal rights as a consumer.

Association of Building Engineers
01604 404121/www.abe.org.uk.
ABE can connect you to builders, surveyors and structural designers.

British Woodworking Federation
0870 458 6939/www.bwf.org.uk.
Search online to locate a joiner in your area.

Design For Homes
08704 163378/www.designforhomes.org.
Offers an architects search for specific projects, as well as lots of sound advice.

Federation of Master Builders
7242 7583/www.findabuilder.co.uk.
Small and medium-sized building companies registered with the FMB are carefully vetted before they are allowed to join, and must adhere to a strict code of practice.

Guild of Master Craftsmen
01273 478449/www.findacraftsman.com.
The Guild covers all kinds of specialist areas, such as stained glass and roof-thatching, as well as plumbing and general building work.

EMERGENCIES

Council for Registered Gas Installers
0800 915 0480/ www.trustcorgi.com.
All contractors should be registered with CORGI by law; call to check if you're in doubt, or to find a CORGI-registered installer. The website also provides advice on gas safety.

National Grid
0800 111999/ www.transco.uk.com.
The National Grid (formerly Transco) operates a free, 24/7 emergency service. If you smell gas, call the helpline – though if you're calling from a mobile, go outside first.

Thames Water
0800 714614/non-emergencies 0845 920 0800/www.thames-water.com.
Call to report water leaks.

Painting & Decorating Association
02476 353776/www.paintingdecorating association.co.uk.
The association lists 2,500 approved painters and decorators, and offers an arbitration service if problems arise within six months.

RIBA
7580 5533/www.architecture.com.
To find a registered architect near you, search online or call client services on 7307 3700.

Royal Institution of Chartered Surveyors
0870 333 1600/www.rics.org.
Advisers can help you locate a surveyor or a professional in a related field.

Women & Manual Trades
7251 9192/www.wamt.org.
WAMT publishes an annual directory of recommended London tradeswomen.

Children

Activities

The following activities and venues have all been recommended, used and abused by real parents. We've scoured London – and covered most of it with jammy fingerprints.

Drop-in activities

There are hundreds of drop-in activities in London, and most museums offer crafts at weekends. For under-fives there's also an extensive network of one o'clock clubs, many with structured activities; check with your local council. And on public holidays, all sorts of unlikely venues teem with workshops.

ARTS & CRAFTS

Art 4 Fun
172 West End Lane, NW6 1SD (7794 0800/www.art4fun.com). West Hampstead tube/rail. Open 10am-6pm Mon, Wed-Sun; 10am-8pm Tue. Fees £5.95/day plus materials; workshops call for details.
Kids can learn how to make a mosaic, or decorate various wood, glass, fabric or ceramic items (from £3.50) with non-toxic paints; if you've opted for ceramics, staff will glaze and fire your masterpiece. Workshops for six- to ten-year-olds, covering all kinds of art techniques, run in school holidays.

Artsdepot ✶
5 Nether Street, N12 0GA (8369 5454/ www.artsdepot.co.uk). West Finchley or Woodside Park tube. Open 9am-5.30pm Mon-Fri; 10am-5.30pm Sat; noon-5.30pm Sun. Session times vary; call for details. Fees from £7/session.
The glorious Messy Play sessions at this stylish community arts centre allow pre-schoolers (six months to four years) the chance to get down and dirty with tubs full of paint. Attendees at the Mini Moves dance classes can be as young as four weeks old.

There are also term-long art, dance and drama courses for kids aged three or over, plus children's shows every Sunday in the theatre.

Geffrye Museum
136 Kingsland Road, E2 8EA (7739 9893/ www.geffrye-museum.org.uk). Liverpool Street tube/rail, then 149 bus/Old Street tube/rail, then 243 bus. Open 10am-5pm Tue-Sat; noon-5pm Sun. Fees free.
The first Saturday of the month brings workshops for five- to 16-year-olds, including wig-making, lotion-mixing (using lavender from the beautiful herb garden), silhouetting and more. The museum also runs family-friendly Summer Sunday events and free half-term workshops covering everything from trifle-making to puppet design.

V&A Museum Of Childhood
Cambridge Heath Road, E2 9PA (8983 5200/www.vam.ac.uk/moc). Bethnal Green tube/rail. Open 10am-5.45pm daily. Fees free.
Art activities at the V&A are well thought out and substantial, with parent and toddler workshops most Fridays and special holiday activities for over-fives. The art cart arrives every day from 2pm, and is open to all ages: when its appeal wanes, kids can follow a gallery trail through the museum's awesome collection of toys, filling in the clues to track down a missing toy.

COOKING

Brilliant Kids Café & Arts Centre
7-8 Station Terrace, NW10 5RT (8964 4120/www.brilliantkids.co.uk). Kensal Green tube/Kensal Rise rail. Open 8am-6pm Mon-Fri; 9am-5pm Sat; 10am-4pm Sun. Fees £5-£7/session.

This bright, airy café hosts everything from Popcorn Club film screenings to collage-making classes – but the cookery lessons are our favourite. Attendees whip up a culinary delight then proudly bear it home, along with a recipe card. Classes are held every day except Sunday, and open to childen aged over 14 months; call for class times and to reserve a place, as sessions fill up fast.

Hob
The Brunswick, WC1N 1AY (7837 8843/ www.hobstore.co.uk). Russell Square tube. Classes 12.30-5pm Sun. Fees free.
This smart kitchenware shop in Bloomsbury runs free Sunday cookery sessions for two-and-overs, led by chef Thierry. The focus is simple, healthy recipes that are easy enough to repeat at home. Happily, cookies and gingerbread do make the occasional appearance on the menu.

CREATIVE WRITING

Children's Writers & Illustrators in South London
cwislenquiries@hotmail.com.
Send this enterprising group of authors an email and they will reply with regular newsletters, advertising everything from poster illustration workshops (threes to 12s) to intensive writing courses for over-eights. The activities are Lambeth-based and held on an ad hoc basis, but are well worth looking out for; the writers involved have a real talent for inspiring youngsters.

AFTER-HOURS ADVENTURES

Book your place and pack your toothbrush: a whole host of London's most famous attractions now offer children (and their parents) the rare opportunity to stay the night.

First off, **Kew Gardens** (Richmond, Surrey TW9 3AB, 8332 5655, www.kew.org). Aimed at eight- to 11-year-olds, the Midnight Ramble involves searching for badgers, owls and bats and exploring the tropical houses, before gathering round the campfire to toast marshmallows, then sleeping in the Climbers & Creepers play zone. Tickets cost £40 and sell out fast: the ideal group size is one adult to four or five kids.

Monthly Science Night Sleepovers at the **Science Museum** (Exhibition Road, SW7 2DD, 7942 4747, www.sciencemuseum.org.uk) are equally action-packed. For £30 per person (the smallest group size is one adult and five children), you can take part in an evening of science shows, hands-on workshops and an IMAX 3D film. Next morning it's up bright and early for breakfast, a drawing contest and, finally, prize-giving. Phew.

History buffs might prefer to sleep among the statues in the **British Museum** (Great Russell Street, WC1B 3DG, 7323 8000, www.british museum.org) – a rare treat held three or four times a year for Young Friends of the BM and guests of existing members. Sign up for membership (£20/yr) and book well in advance. Pitching camp in the Egyptian sculpture galleries is an unforgettable experience, and there's a different theme at each event (emperors, pre-history, the Olympics).

Would-be pirates, meanwhile, can enlist as crew members aboard the **Golden Hinde** (Pickfords Wharf, Clink Street, SE1 9DG, 0870 011 8700, www.goldenhinde.org). Dressed as sailors, children aged six to 12 take part in actor-led workshops on barber surgery, navigation, and anchor-raising, scoff stew from pewter plates and round off the night with a mock battle before kipping on the gun deck.

GOING OUT

BEAUTY

FASHION

PARTIES

FOOD

HEALTH

ECO

OUTDOORS

HOME

CHILDREN

PETS

TRANSPORT

RESOURCES

DANCE & MUSIC

East London Dance
*Stratford Circus, Theatre Square, E15 1BX
(8279 1050/www.eastlondondance.org).
Stratford tube/rail. Classes times vary;
phone for details. Fees free.*
This East End dance centre runs free hip hop
and street dance classes for children aged
eight and above. Led by professionals,
sessions are exhilarating (and exhausting).

Handel House Museum
*25 Brook Street, W1K 4HB (7495 1685/
www.handelhouse.org). Bond Street tube.
Open 10am-6pm Tue, Wed, Fri, Sat; 10am-
8pm Thur; noon-6pm Sun. Admission £5;
£2-£4.50 reductions, free under-5s.*
Family-friendly musical events take place on
selected weekends, from the Composer
Surgery (for budding maestros) to dressing-
up and storytelling sessions. Although the
workshops are aimed at older kids, toddlers
are allowed. The museum's curators are
passionate about spreading a love of classical
music to children.

Jackson's Lane
*269A Archway Road, N6 5AA (8341 4421/
www.jacksonslane.org.uk). Highgate tube.
Open 10am-10pm Tue-Sat; 10am-5pm Sun.
Fees from £5/session.*
The studios in this arts centre are always
buzzing with some kind of workshop. The
star attraction for under-fives is Mabel's
Monster Music: structured sessions with
singing and storytelling, run by the lovely
Cate. For older kids, street dance (nine to 15s)
is popular. The venue is also home to a good
café, a toddler group and children's theatre
productions. Classes change sporadically, so
check the website.

NATURE

Oasis Children's Nature Garden ⭐
*Larkhall Lane, SW4 2SP (7498 2329/
www.oasisplay.org.uk). Stockwell tube.
Open Term time 3.30-5.30pm Tue-Fri;
10am-3.30pm Sat. School hols 10am-
3.30pm Mon-Fri. Admission 25p-50p.*

A riotous little patch of the countryside in
inner London, Oasis runs a Saturday Nature
Club, charging 50p per child. Children of all
ages are welcome, though under-fives must
be supervised. The digging pit (a patch of
mud that kids are allowed to dig and water
without bothering seedlings) and the heavily
populated frog pond are the big draws.

SPORT & YOGA

Albert & Friends' Instant Circus
*St Alban's Church Hall, Margravine Road,
W6 8HJ (8237 1170/www.albertandfriends
instantcircus.co.uk). Classes times vary;
phone for details. Fees £8.50/session.*
These Saturday morning sessions are great
fun, with general circus skills classes for three
to sevens and eight to 16s kicking off the day,
then more specialised lessons such as static
trapeze and corde lisse in the afternoon.

It's A Kid's Thing
*279 Magdalen Road, SW18 3NZ (8739
0909/www.itsakidsthing.co.uk). Earlsfield
rail. Open 9am-6pm daily. Fees £2-£5.
Soca Tots £8/session.*
Our favourite class at this activity centre is
Soca Tots football training, where children as
young as six months can practise their
dribbling. Soca Tots is a franchise, so you can
find your local class at www.socatots.com;
we've picked out this family-run venue
because parents love its healthy café, party
rooms and indoor play zone. Other activities
include baby massage, music and messy art –
often included in the entry fee. Book ahead.

Sitaram Partnership
*Brockwell Lido, Dulwich Road, SE24 0PA
(8678 0054/www.sitaram.org). Herne Hill
rail. Classes Family yoga 4.30-5.15pm Wed.
Fees £5/session (per family).*
Sitaram specialises in yoga for families, with
pregnancy yoga, classes for parents with
babies in special care, and baby yoga. Our
favourite is family yoga, where three- to nine-
year-olds and their parents work through a
yoga-based story, with meditation at the end.
Places are limited, so call ahead. The toddler
and parent yoga class is another rare find.

City farms & zoos

Admission to the following farms and zoos is free, unless otherwise specified, but donations are always appreciated.

Battersea Park Children's Zoo

Queenstown Road, Battersea Park, SW11 4NJ (7924 5826/www.batterseazoo.co.uk). Sloane Square tube, then 19, 137 bus/ Battersea Park or Queenstown Road rail/ 156, 345 bus. Open Summer 10am-6pm daily. Winter 10am-dusk. Admission £6.50; £4.95 reductions; free under-2s; £20.50 family.

Tiny things for tiny tots are the order of the day at Battersea's zoo, as playful otters, lively meerkats, a mouse doll's house and a wide range of other friendly critters keep the little ones delighted for hours.

Freightliners City Farm

Paradise Park, Sheringham Road, off Liverpool Road, N7 8PF (7609 0467/www. freightlinersfarm.org.uk). Caledonian Road or Holloway Road tube/Highbury & Islington tube/rail. Open Summer 10am-4.45pm Tue-Sun. Winter 10am-4pm Tue-Sun. No credit cards.

In the heart of Islington, this farm teems with a wide variety of animal activity. The inhabitants range from cows, sheep, geese, cockerels and bees to impressively sized rare breeds, like the super-sized giant Flemish rabbits. You can buy hen and duck eggs of all hues in the shop, along with own-grown fruit and veg for tea.

Hackney City Farm

1A Goldsmiths Row, E2 8QA (7729 6381/ www.hackneycityfarm.co.uk). Cambridge Heath Road rail, then 26, 48, 55 bus. Open 10am-4.30pm Tue-Sun, bank hol Mon.

Set against the urban backdrop of Hackney Road, this ever-popular farm is a genuine urban oasis. A wide array of animals, including rare-breed pig Bella the saddleback, delight the throngs. The award-winning Frizzante Café is another draw, along with regular pottery and craft classes for adults and children.

Kentish Town City Farm

1 Cressfield Close, off Grafton Road, NW5 4BN (7916 5421/www.ktcityfarm.org.uk). Chalk Farm tube/Kentish Town tube/rail/ Gospel Oak rail. Open 9am-5.30pm daily.
London's oldest city farm stretches into pasture and well-tended vegetable gardens by the railway line. A pond with a dipping platform is full of frogs, and a riding school is the scene of weekend pound-a-go pony rides.

London Zoo

Regent's Park, NW1 4RY (7722 3333/ www.zsl.org). Baker Street or Camden Town tube, then 274 or C2 bus. Open Mar-late Oct 10am-5.30pm daily. Late Oct-Feb 10am- 4pm daily. Admission £17; £13.50-£15.50 reductions; free under-3s; £55.50 family.
The biggest and arguably the best of the capital's animal encounters, where you can meet uncaged monkeys, feed the penguins, watch dramatic birds of prey displays and learn all about buglife. Don't miss the steamy, tropical Blackburn Pavilion bird house.

Mudchute City Farm ★

Pier Street, E14 3HP (7515 5901/ www.mudchute.org). Crossharbour, Mudchute or Island Gardens DLR. Open 9am-5pm daily.

City Secret

The crowning glory at the **Horniman Museum** (100 London Road, SE23 3PQ (8699 1872, www.horniman. ac.uk) is its magnificent aquarium, refurbished in 2006. It houses over 200 species of aquatic life in 14,000 litres of water, divided into seven distinct zones, but it's the superb interactive displays and wonderful live exhibits – including mesmerising jellyfish and British seahorses – that make this place such a treat. When he died, the museum's eponymous Victorian founder bequeathed it to the people of London, so entrance is absolutely free.

London's biggest city farm offers a surreal experience: standing in a meadow full of sheep while taking in the skyscrapers of Canary Wharf. You're allowed to feed many of the animals (goats, geese and horses).

Stepping Stones Farm

Stepney Way, at junction with Stepney High Street, E1 3DG (7790 8204/www.stepping stonesfarm.org.uk). Stepney Green tube. Open 10am-4pm Tue-Sun.
A full complement of farmyard creatures hunker down next to old railway carriages full of straw bales, all rubbing along together very nicely in the shadow of St Dunstan's Church.

Spitalfields City Farm

Buxton Street, off Brick Lane, E1 5AR (7247 8762/www.spitalfieldscityfarm.org). Whitechapel tube. Open Summer 10am- 4.30pm Tue-Sun. Winter 10am-4pm Tue-Sun.
This spick-and-span community farm features geese honking about in a lovely space, where poultry, gardeners and livestock produce free-range eggs, seasonal vegetables and manure (respectively).

Surrey Docks Farm

South Wharf, Rotherhithe Street, SE16 5ET (7231 1010). Canada Water tube, then 381, C10 bus. Open 10am-5pm Tue-Sun.
The riverside location, a yard patrolled by naughty goats (it pays to keep your chocolate out of sight), paddocks filled with farmyard animals and a resident blacksmith all combine to make Surrey Docks Farm a firm favourite.

Vauxhall City Farm

165 Tyers Street, SE11 5HS (7582 4204/ www.vauxhallcityfarm.info). Vauxhall tube/ rail/2, 36, 44, 77 bus. Open 10.30am-4pm Wed-Sun. Closed 1wk in late summer, phone to check.
You can't miss this charming, community- staffed farm as you get off the train, as your senses are assailed by the unmistakeable farmyard byre aroma. Inhabitants include chickens, rabbits, goats, horses and some very friendly pigs.

Playgrounds

On sunny days, you can't beat **Coram's Fields** (*see p177*); if the weather's too wet for its petting zoo, sandpits and swings, great indoor alternatives include **It's A Kid's Thing** (*see p168*) and **Zoomaround** (*see p177*).

Diana, Princess of Wales' Memorial Playground

Black Lion Gate, Broad Walk, Kensington Gardens, W8 2UH (7298 2117/www.royalparks.gov.uk). Bayswater tube/70, 94, 148, 390 bus. Open Summer 10am-7.45pm daily. Winter 10am-4pm daily. Over-12s must be accompanied by a child.

Dominated by a huge pirate ship surrounded by white sand, this is a wonderland for tinies. Other attractions include a tepee camp, treehouse encampment and the swingiest baby swings in town. In summer, there's a paddling pool with plugs, so children can change the water flow, plus free school holiday entertainment. Much of the equipment is accessible to children with special needs.

Glamis Adventure Playground

Glamis Road, E1W 3DQ (7702 8301/www.glamisadventure.org.uk). Shadwell DLR. Open Term-time 3.15-7pm Mon-Fri; 10am-4pm Sat. School hols 10am-5.30pm Mon-Fri.

As well as massive play structures, swings and slides, this award-winning adventure playground has a vegetable garden and den-building area. Designed for children aged eight and over, it also runs summer sleepovers and barbecues.

Highgate Wood & Queen's Wood

Muswell Hill Road, N10 3JN (8444 6129/www.cityoflondon.gov.uk/openspaces). Highgate tube. Open 7.30am-dusk daily.

This under-12s playground is well equipped for wheelchair users, with accessible swings and a sensory bridge. Old favourites include the sandpit, rope slides and pyramid, while the adjoining Queen's Wood has swings strung from the trees.

Kidspace

Colonnades, 619 Purley Way, Croydon, Surrey CR0 4RQ (8686 0040/www.kidspaceadventures.com). Waddon rail/119, 289 bus. Open 9.30am-7pm Mon-Thur; 9.30am-8pm Fri; 9am-8pm Sat; 9am-7pm Sun. School hols 9am-7pm Mon-Thur, Sun; 9am-8pm Fri, Sat. Admission Adults £2.50-£3.50; children £5.50-£8.50; free under-1s.

Rather than the usual indoor soft play structures, Kidspace's giant climbing frames are made from sustainable timber, with parents encouraged to climb in too. The resulting atmosphere is joyous. A soft play area for toddlers, go-karts, mini-golf and a 27-foot climbing wall make this kid (and dad) heaven. It's for under-13s only.

Parsloes Park

Parsloes Avenue/Gale Street, Dagenham, Essex RM9 5QP (8595 4155/www.lbbd.gov.uk). Becontree tube. Open dawn-dusk daily.

A new teen area joins the established children's playground, with tubular slides, a two-person skyway and rodeo board. Natural rock seating, mounds and 29 newly planted trees keep this playground green.

Queens Park

Kingswood Avenue, NW6 6SG (8969 5661). Queens Park tube/rail. Open Park 7.30am-dusk daily. Zoo 11am-5pm Mon-Fri; 1-5pm Sat, Sun.

This north London playground has a colossal sandpit, a paddling pool (filled in May, which is earlier than most pools) and a small children's zoo. There are separate areas for under-fives and fives to 12s.

St Giles-in-the-Fields

60 St Giles High Street, WC2H 8LG (7240 2532/www.stgilesonline.org). Open Summer 7am-dusk daily. Winter 8.30am-dusk daily.

Tucked behind Shaftesbury Avenue Odeon, this West End playground is an essential piece of London parent knowledge. It's a basic affair with swings, a roundabout and two slides – nothing groundbreaking, but fantastic for your kids to let off some steam after a hard morning spent trawling the shops of Covent Garden or Oxford Street.

GOING OUT
BEAUTY
FASHION
PARTIES
FOOD
HEALTH
ECO
OUTDOORS
HOME
CHILDREN
PETS
TRANSPORT
RESOURCES

Address Book Secrets
Jasmine Guinness & Honey Bowdrey
Owners, Honeyjam toy shop

Lucky 7 (127 Westbourne Park Road, 7727 6771, www.lucky7london.co.uk) is a classic all-American diner that serves organic burgers and fries, and delicious malt shakes. It's wonderfully laid-back, and staff are very patient with children. If your children love the big fast-food chains and you're not so keen, this is a happy compromise.

The **Sir John Soane's Museum** (13 Lincoln's Inn Fields, WC2A 3BP, 7405 2107, www.soane.org) is wonderful for older kids. It has amazing Egyptian and Roman remains, crammed into an incredible building.

Honey's six-year-old son was thrilled by the **Puppet Theatre Barge** (opposite 35 Blomfield Road, W9 2PF, 7249 6876, www.puppetbarge.com) – the fact it was on a boat amazed him. The shows are sophisticated enough for adults to enjoy, and it's lovely that a traditional puppet show can still keep children utterly spellbound.

Children who are into knights will be enthralled by the **Wallace Collection** (Hertford House, Manchester Square, W1U 3BN, 7563 9500, www.wallacecollection.org). It's best known for its wonderful paintings, but boys will head straight for the huge array of armour.

Essenza (210 Kensington Park Road, W11 1NR, 7792 1066, www.essenza.co.uk) serves wonderful Italian food and looks very grown-up and modern, but is very child-friendly. The staff adore children, in true Italian fashion, and happily dispense crayons and paper.

The adventure playground at **Holland Park** (Ilchester Place, W8 6LU, 7471 9813, www.rbkc.gov.uk) is great. It's got all sorts of equipment, but our kids' favourite is a sit-on zip wire, which they've christened the death slide. Afterwards, you can spot koy carp in the Japanese Kyoto Garden.

Queen's Ice Rink and Bowl (see p114) is great. It's not particularly posh, but then it's not particularly expensive either. You can skate for as long as you want, there's bowling next door, and they serve tremendous Belgian waffles, slathered with chocolate sauce. It's perfect for kids' parties.

The **Westway Sports Centre** (see p113) is another fail-safe party venue; kids can do football training or even learn rock climbing. But the nicest summer party is a picnic in the park, with water pistols for the kids. If you're going to Queen's Park, pick up marvellous pizza by the quarter-of-a-metre from **Pizza Teca** (53-55 Salusbury Road, NW6 6NJ, 7624 5518) and lovely cupcakes and brownies from the **Hummingbird Bakery** (see p70) on Portobello Road.

Finally, our toyshop **Honeyjam** (267 Portobello Road, W11 1LR, 7243 0449, www.honeyjam.co.uk) is a treasure trove of traditional and unusual toys and books – some retro, some modern; some silly, some educational. There are lots of pocket money bits and bobs too, so a child can come in with a pound to spend and leave happy.

Eating out

With children's menus of nuggets and chips all too often a depressing reality, good food for kids can be hard to find. We've picked out some eateries that not only have excellent menus, but are places where families can happily hang out for an afternoon.

Restaurants & cafés

In addition to the cafés listed below, check out the **Brilliant Kids Café** (*see p166*), which offers locally sourced ingredients, free-range (and often organic) meat, and superlative chocolate brownies. For **park cafés**, *see p130*.

From the big chains, our favourites are **Wagamama** (noodles, rice dishes and fresh juices), **Pizza Express** (the Piccolo menu offers three courses for £5.95) and **Carluccio's** (exceedingly tot-friendly).

CENTRAL

Tate Modern Café: Level 2 ★
2nd floor, Tate Modern, Sumner Street, SE1 9TG (7401 5014/www.tate.org.uk). Southwark tube/Blackfriars or London Bridge tube/rail. Meals served 10am-6pm Mon-Thur, Sat, Sun; 10am-10pm Fri. £-££.
This winner of *Time Out* Best Family Restaurant 2007 prides itself on the sourcing of its menu; catch of the day from Newlyn boats, real Lancashire cheesecake and fresh Dorset crab might feature. Children are given crayons and activity sheets, and can pick mini portions from the adult menu for £6.95.

Rainforest Café
20 Shaftesbury Avenue, W1D 7EU (7434 3111/www.therainforestcafe.co.uk). Piccadilly Circus tube. Meals served noon-10pm Mon-Thur; noon-8pm Fri; 11.30am-8pm Sat; 11.30am-10pm Sun. ££.
Children are thrilled by the animatronic animals, jungle noises and waterfalls, but what we like about this restaurant is that its

menu has been approved both by the Soil Association and Allergy UK. Items are marked for their absence of gluten, dairy or egg – so you can order gluten-free sausage and mash, or egg-free pasta with organic salmon and veg. At £10.99 for two courses it isn't cheap, but that's par for the course round here.

NORTH

Camden Arts Centre Café
Arkwright Road, NW3 6DG (7472 5516/ www.camdenartscentre.org). Finchley Road or Hampstead tube/Finchley Road & Frognal rail. Meals served 10am-5.30pm Tue, Thur-Sun; 10am-8.30pm Wed. £.
This serene café is one of the loveliest spots to lunch in north London, especially if you bag a table on the lavender-planted terrace. There's plenty of room for buggies, plus books and puzzles to keep children busy. The menu ranges from sourdough and granary sandwiches to child-friendly light bites (own-made houmous with pitta, bruschetta) and mini portions of the daily special.

Pick More Daisies
12 Crouch End Hill, N8 8AA (8340 2288/ www.pickmoredaisies.com). Finsbury Park tube/rail, then W7 bus/Crouch Hill rail. Open 9am-10pm Mon-Fri; 10am-10.30pm Sat, Sun. £.
This 'Californian-style' Crouch End café is famed for its gourmet burgers (beef, veggie and bison) and fine combo breakfasts (fruit with champagne sorbet, followed by poached eggs on granary toast, say). Children are made very welcome, with a £4.50 kids' menu of US classics (peanut butter and jelly sandwiches, pancakes, baked macaroni).

GOING OUT

BEAUTY

FASHION

PARTIES

FOOD

HEALTH

ECO

OUTDOORS

HOME

CHILDREN

PETS

TRANSPORT

RESOURCES

GOING OUT
BEAUTY
FASHION
PARTIES
FOOD
HEALTH
ECO
OUTDOORS
HOME
CHILDREN
PETS
TRANSPORT
RESOURCES

EAST

Mudchute Kitchen

Mudchute Park & Farm, Pier Street, E14 3HP (7515 5901/www.mudchute kitchen.org). Crossharbour, Mudchute or Island Gardens DLR. Open 9am-5pm Tue-Sun. Meals served 9am-4pm Tue-Sun. £.
Overlooking the stables and open from breakfast until teatime, the café at London's largest city farm is a wonderfully homespun affair. Almost everything on the seasonal, daily-changing menu is sourced on the farm, including goose smoked in the on-site smokehouse. Kids can pick half portions from the main menu or tuck into nursery favourites.

SOUTH

Bodean's

169 Clapham High Street, SW4 7SS (7622 0408/www.bodeansbbq.com). Clapham Common tube. Meals served noon-3pm, 5-11pm Mon-Fri; noon-11pm Sat; noon-10.30pm Sun. £.
Ice hockey on the TV and plastic cows gazing down keep juniors occupied while waiting for their meal of chicken, burger or ribs with mash or fries at this cheery barbecue joint. At this branch (and the Fulham outpost) kids eat free with a paying adult every day between noon and 5pm.
Other locations *across the city.*

ICE-CREAM PARLOURS

Gelateria Danieli

16 Brewers Lane, Richmond, Surrey TW9 1HH (8439 9807/www.gelateria danieli.com). Richmond tube/rail. Open Summer 10am-10pm daily. Winter 10am-6pm daily. Times may vary; call to check.
Connoisseurs of all ages flock to this Richmond hole-in-the-wall to sample the superlative ice-creams and sorbets, made with fresh fruit and minimum additives. Flavours range from cinnamon and plum or *dulce de leche* to classic raspberry ripple; scoops are a steal at £1.95 each.
Other locations *across the city.*

Marine Ices

8 Haverstock Hill, NW3 2BL (7482 9003/www.marineices.co.uk). Chalk Farm tube. Open noon-11pm Tue-Sat; noon-10pm Sun.
Generations of children have scoffed chocolate sauce-slathered banana splits, peach melbas and sundaes at this sweetly old-fashioned geletaria, opened by the Mansi family in 1930. If you're en route to Primrose Hill, order a cone at the takeaway hatch.

Morelli's at Harrods

Harrods Food Halls, 87-135 Brompton Road, SW1 7XL (7893 8959/www. morellisgelato.com). Knightsbridge tube. Open 9am-8.45pm Mon-Sat; noon-5.45pm Sun.
For truly show-stopping sundaes, this is the place to come. With 24 hours' notice you can commission your own bespoke flavour to take home, for £13.55 per litre plus the cost of your chosen ingredients.

Oddono's

14 Bute Street, SW7 3EX (7052 0732/ www.oddonos.com). South Kensington tube. Open 11am-11pm Mon-Thur, Sun; 11am-midnight Fri, Sat.
Truly top-notch ingredients (Valrhona chocolate, Piedmont hazelnuts, Madagascan vanilla pods) mean even the simplest gelati taste sublime here, though grown-ups may be tempted by more sophisticated combinations such as chocolate and cognac.

Parlour Restaurant

Fortnum & Mason, 181 Piccadilly, W1A 1ER (7734 8040/www.fortnumand

Munchkin Lane

83 Nightingale Lane, SW12 8NX (8772 6800). Wandsworth Common rail. Meals served 8am-6pm Mon-Fri; 9.30am-4.30pm Sat. £.

Children love the toys, blackboards, play den and video screen; adults love the creamy cappuccinos and tuna melt bagels. Kids can chow down on massive (and modestly priced) plates of organic macaroni cheese and fish pie.

WEST

Le Cercle

1 Wilbraham Place, SW1X 9AE (7901 9999/www.lecercle.co.uk). Sloane Square

mason.co.uk). Green Park or Piccadilly Circus tube. Open 10am-7.30pm daily.

For sheer indulgence, Fortnum's first-floor ice-cream parlour is hard to beat. The children's menu offers sumptuous sundaes for £6 or dual scoops for £4, while adult options include fantastic bellini sorbets and wonderfully innovative sundaes, starring unusual ingredients such as stem ginger and honeycomb or marmalade and lemon curd.

Scoop

40 Shorts Gardens, WC2H 9AB (7240 7086/www.scoopgelato. com). Covent Garden tube. Open 11am-9pm daily. Times may vary; call to check.

Opened in 2007, this Italian-run *gelataria* offers a sublime array of flavours: kids will love the creamy, hazelnut-studded *bacio*, while the other 23 flavours include heady amaretto or ricotta and caramelised figs. Gluten- and sugar-free ices are available, as are nifty takeaway coolboxes.

tube. Lunch served noon-3pm, tea served 3-6pm, dinner served 6-11pm Tue-Sat. £££.

All credit to this smart Sloane Square establishment for reaching out to families with its 'Petits Gourmets' dégustation menu. At lunchtimes, the five-course menu is free for under-12s accompanied by an adult eating à la carte. Beleaguered parents might be amazed, but dishes such as pumpkin with star anise slip down remarkably well.

Deep Blue

Science Museum, Exhibition Road, SW7 2DD (7942 4488/www.sciencemuseum. org.uk). South Kensington tube. Open 10am-6pm, lunch served 11.30am-3pm daily. £.

You don't have to be visiting the Science Museum to take advantage of the wonderful restaurant – but beware long queues at weekends. The kids' menu is fantastic value at £4.50 for two courses, offering spaghetti, chicken and chips or any dish from the main menu, followed by ice-cream.

Giraffe

270 Chiswick High Road, W4 1PD (8995 2100/www.giraffe.net). Turnham Green tube. Meals served 8am-11pm Mon-Fri; 9am-11pm Sat; 9am-10.30pm Sun. £.

Numerous parents recommended Giraffe to us – and this branch, adjacent to Chiswick Common, was singled out for particular praise. Staff fuss over youngsters, presenting them with a balloon at the door, while the well-balanced kids' menu (£1.95-£5.50) includes grilled chicken, mash and veggies or egg and beans on toast.

Other locations *across the city.*

Gracelands

118 College Road, NW10 5HD (8964 9161/ www.gracelandscafe.com). Kensal Green tube. Meals served 8.30am-6pm Mon-Fri; 9am-5pm Sat; 9.30am-3pm Sun. £.

The regularly changing kids' menu at Gracelands features the likes of pasta with own-made pesto or bolognese and sausage and mash. Main menu options run from splendid quiches to salads and ciabatta, but many parents pop in just to chat over coffee while toddlers investigate the play corner.

GOING OUT

BEAUTY

FASHION

PARTIES

FOOD

HEALTH

ECO

OUTDOORS

HOME

CHILDREN

PETS

TRANSPORT

RESOURCES

GOING OUT
BEAUTY
FASHION
PARTIES
FOOD
HEALTH
ECO
OUTDOORS
HOME
CHILDREN
PETS
TRANSPORT
RESOURCES

Parties

The following entertainers and venues have been recommended by parents (and children) who have used them. Relax and enjoy.

Entertainers

Jigsaw
8447 4530/www.jigsaw-arts.co.uk.
For smooth-running themed parties, call in this north London stage school's teachers, who moonlight as entertainers. Spellbinding takes the children through wizard school, while would-be pirates can go treasure hunting. Prices start at £120 for an hour.

Juggling John
8938 3218/0845 644 6659/ www.jugglingjohn.com.
Circus skills (with a fair amount of juggling, naturally), magic, escapology and edge-of-the-seat storytelling keep even fidgety guests enraptured. Prices start at £125 for an hour.

Karma Drama
07956 932561/www.karmadrama.co.uk.
Karma Drama can arrange anything from simple singalongs for toddlers (£120/90mins) to all-singing, all-dancing 'MTV Star' parties, or fashion parties (creating customised T-shirts then parading on the catwalk) for pre-teens. Drama and West End musical-themed events (*Grease*, *High School Musical*) are also tremendous fun. A two-hour extravaganza with props and costumes, led by four staff, costs around £500.

Mad Science
0845 330 1881/www.madscience.org.uk.
White-coated scientists bring the experiments to you, along with indoor fireworks, green slime and an optional candy floss machine. Parties cost from £195 for an hour, with an extra charge for the fab party bags, and cater for up to 20 children; 'Mega Parties' are available for bigger groups.

Mini Makeovers
8398 0107/www.minimakeovers.com.
Girls aged five to 15 are treated to manicures, makeovers and a disco, with parties for the younger ones focused on being glittery rather than pouty. It costs from £160 for eight kids, with limousine hire as an optional extra.

Oranges & Lemons
07900 447218/www.orangesandlemons parties.co.uk.
Juliet keeps rooms full of kids entertained for two hours with traditional party games, crafts and her dynamic personality, charging from £190. During the final story, which stars the birthday boy or girl, party bags are given out.

Venues

Ask your child where their favourite place is, and you're 98 per cent sure to find a party package there.

Chislehurst Caves
Old Hill, Chislehurst, Kent BR7 5NB (8467 3264/www.chislehurstcaves.co.uk). Chislehurst rail. Open times vary; call for details.
Little gremlins can enjoy a spooky tour of the caves, with ghost stories and a bat-shaped cake. Packages cost from from £60 (for a maximum of 20 children and four adults), plus £4.50 a head for food.

Colour House Children's Theatre
Merton Abbey Mills, Watermill Way, SW19 2RD (8542 5511/www.colourhousetheatre. co.uk). Colliers Wood tube. Open times vary; call for details.
Your party get front seats for the show at this delightful children's theatre, ending with the

cast singing *Happy Birthday* to the blushing birthday boy or girl. Once the rest of the audience has left, the empty theatre is yours. Prices for the show and venue hire, with no extras, start at £145 for ten guests.

Coram's Fields 🪁
93 Guilford Street, WC1N 1DN (7837 6138/ www.coramsfields.org). Russell Square tube. Open May-Aug 9am-7pm daily. Sept-Apr 9am-dusk daily.
Holding a party at this lovely, centrally located playground is a steal: you can hire a room, complete with kitchen, for £40 an afternoon. You need to provide your own food – but with the fantastic playground, sandpits, lawns and petting zoo outside, the entertainment's sorted.

Discover
1 Bridge Terrace, E15 4BG (8536 5555/ www.discover.org.uk). Stratford tube/rail/DLR. Open times vary; call for details.
Dedicated to creating stories, this is a perfect party venue. A Story Builder accompanies your guests along the story trail, followed by mask-making in a special birthday party room. You bring the food, so prices come in at a bargain £6.50-£8.50 per guest.

Fulham Palace
Bishop's Avenue, SW6 6EA (7610 7164/ www.fulhampalace.org). Hammersmith or Putney Bridge tube. Open times vary; call for details.
Parties in the lovely grounds or schoolroom can be historically themed, and include a tour in which kids get to handle real and replica artefacts. Costumed staff tell stories or lead craft sessions; making giant poppies, perhaps, or animal masks. Prices start from £200.

Mystical Fairies
12 Flask Walk, NW3 1HE (7431 1888/ www.mysticalfairies.co.uk). Hampstead tube. Open 10am-6pm Mon-Sat; 11am-6pm Sun.
Little girls (or boys) in love with all things pretty and pink will adore Mystical Fairies' parties, held in the fairy-lit Enchanted Garden basement or at your home; pirate and wizard-themed events are also available. Prices start at £375 for a two-hour, at-home party.

GOING OUT
BEAUTY
FASHION
PARTIES
FOOD
HEALTH
ECO
OUTDOORS
HOME
CHILDREN
PETS
TRANSPORT
RESOURCES

PARTY BAGS

Happy Green Earth
0845 388 0931/www.happygreen earth.com.
Heart- or robot-shaped organic chocolate lollies and wooden toys and puzzles prove going green needn't be dull and worthy: the racing cars (£1.35) and wool purses (£2.50) are particularly sweet.

Letterbox
0844 888 5000/www.letterbox parties.co.uk.
Letterbox's website offers almost 100 party bag gems, from parent-friendly french knitting sets and paper aeroplane kits to child-pleasing noisy putty and rocket balloons. Many cost under £2.

Little Cherry
01753 857003/www.little cherry.co.uk.
Little Cherry's eco ethos means its party bags are filled with lovely wooden toys (from spinning tops or skipping ropes to chunky beads). Pre-filled bags start at under £4.

Party Party
For listings, see p74.
Most of Party Party's traditional party bag fillers cost under a pound. Fortune-telling fish can be yours for 10p a throw, while whoopee cushions are a mere 60p.

Zoomaround
46 Milton Grove, N16 8QY (7254 2220/www. zoomaround.co.uk). Highbury & Islington tube/rail, then 393 bus/73, 141, 236, 341, 476 bus. Open times vary; call for details.
Beloved by local parents, this cheery indoor play centre offers bargain party packages. A two-hour shindig for 12 children costs from £126, which includes 90 minutes of play, plus food, balloons, invites and a birthday gift.

Shopping

For the complete lowdown on children's shops in London, consult the annually updated Time Out's *Shops & Services* guide: the following are a few of our favourite smaller boutiques.

All-rounders & gifts

Bob & Blossom
140 Columbia Road, E2 7RG (7739 4737/ www.bobandblossom.com). Old Street tube/ rail/55 bus. Open 9am-3pm Sun.
Despite restricted opening hours (coinciding with Sunday's flower market), Bob & Blossom does a roaring trade, selling retro knitted toys and rattles, guitars, spinning tops, and its own-label stripey Ts and cheeky slogan hats.

Green Baby
345 Upper Street, N1 0PD (7359 7037/ www.greenbaby.co.uk). Angel tube/Highbury & Islington tube/rail. Open 10am-5pm Mon-Fri; 9.30am-5.30pm Sat; 11am-5pm Sun.
Founded in 1999, Green Baby remains a first port of call for eco-conscious parents, selling organic cotton baby basics (from £4.50 for a short-sleeved bodysuit) and a sterling selection of washable nappies, along with Tushies gel-free disposables, nursery equipment and strokably soft sheepskins.
Other locations *across the city.*

Igloo
300 Upper Street, N1 2TU (7354 7300/ www.iglookids.co.uk). Angel tube/Highbury & Islington tube/rail. Open 10am-6.30pm Mon-Wed; 10am-7pm Thur; 9.30am-6.30pm Fri, Sat; 11am-5.30pm Sun.
A one-stop shop for everything from sweet melamine tableware and hobby horses to Anne Claire Petit's quirky crocheted toys. The clothes (newborn to eights) include Mini-A-Ture's delicate dresses and smocks and No Added Sugar's bold, slogan-print Ts.
Other locations *80 St John's Wood High Street, NW8 7SH (7483 2332).*

JoJo Maman Bébé
68 Northcote Road, SW11 6QL (7228 0322/www.jojomamanbebe.co.uk). Clapham Junction rail. Open 9.30am-5.30pm Mon-Sat; 11am-5pm Sun.
Best-known as a catalogue retailer of all things child-related, JoJo's also has a mini-chain of stores in London's nappy valleys (Putney, Turnham Green, Finchley and Dulwich). Friendly staff and a strong ethical trading ethos add to the appeal of this reliable outfit, up and running for more than 15 years.
Other locations *across the city.*

Lilliput
255-259 Queenstown Road, SW8 3NP (7720 5554/0800 783 0886/www.lilliput. com). Queenstown Road rail. Open 9.30am-5.30pm Mon, Tue, Thur, Fri; 9.30am-7pm Wed; 9am-6pm Sat; 11am-4pm Sun.
Tucked away under Battersea's railway arches, Lilliput's vast showroom holds an enormous range of stock. There are slick sets of wheels from all the big names (Phil & Teds, Stokke, Bugaboo, Silver Cross) at discounted prices, plus feeding, changing, sleeping and bathing gear galore.

Mini Kin
22 Broadway Parade, N8 9DE (8341 6898). Finsbury Park tube/rail, then 41, W7 bus. Open 9.30am-5.30pm Mon-Sat; 10.30am-5.10pm Sun.
As well as Aviva and Burt's Bees toiletries, accessories and clothes from the likes of Imps & Elfs, Their Nibs and Mitty James, Mini Kin has a hairdressing salon out back. Animal chairs, colourful decor and friendly staff help coax reluctant tots into the hot seat; cuts cost from £10.95.

Trotters

34 King's Road, SW3 4UD (7259 9620/ www.trotters.co.uk). Sloane Square tube. Open 9am-7pm Mon-Sat; 10.30pm-6.30pm Sun.

A shop of many parts, Trotters sells clothes, books, toys and accessories, as well as incorporating a hairdressing station (cunningly kitted out with an aquarium to distract recalcitrant tots). The shoe concession, staffed by expert fitters, runs a loyalty card scheme for regulars.

Other locations *127 Kensington High Street, W8 5SF (7937 9373); 86 Northcote Road, SW11 6QN (7585 0572).*

Clothes & shoes

Biff

41-43 Dulwich Village, SE21 7BN (8299 0911/www.biffkids.co.uk). North Dulwich rail/P4 bus. Open 9.30am-5.30pm Mon-Fri; 10am-6pm Sat.

With separate areas devoted to footwear, childrenswear and babies' clothes, Biff makes head-to-toe shopping pleasantly painless for harassed parents and their offspring. The labels stocked are diverse enough to accommodate most tastes, ranging from Kenzo and Catamini to Pepe, Quiksilver and O'Neil.

Olive Loves Alfie

84 Stoke Newington Church Street, N16 0AP (7241 4212/www. olivelovesalfie.co.uk). Finsbury Park tube/rail, then 106 bus/73, 393, 476 bus. Open 9am-5.30pm Mon-Fri; 10am-6pm Sat; noon-5pm Sun.

Gorgeous prints and colourful stripes dominate this sweet boutique, which steers clear of anything pink and frilly or plastered in logos.

Rails of beautifully made clothes from the likes of Marimekko, Katvig and I Love Gorgeous fill the diminutive premises.

One Small Step One Giant Leap ★

3 Blenheim Crescent, W11 2EE (7243 0535/www.onesmallsteponegiantleap.com). Ladbroke Grove or Notting Hill tube. Open 10am-6pm Mon-Fri; 9am-6pm Sat; 11am-5pm Sun.

Part of an ever-expanding mini-chain, this airy, attractive shoe shop and its cheery staff offer top-notch British and European brands, covering everything from back-to-school sensibles to delicate ballet pumps.

Other locations *across the city.*

Petit Aimé

34 Ledbury Road, W11 2AB (7221 3123/ www.aimelondon.com). Notting Hill Gate tube. Open 10am-6.30pm Mon-Sat.

Launched in summer 2008, the children's offshoot of French womenswear boutique Aimé (next door at no.32) is the epitome of Gallic chic, with understated, deliciously stylish dresses and separates from France's finest (including Isabel Marant, Bon Ton, Makié and Antik Batik) for newborn to ten-year-olds.

Showroom 64

64 Great Titchfield Street, W1W 7QH (7636 2501/www. showroom64.com). Oxford Circus tube. Open 10.30am-5.30pm Mon-Fri.

A great source of presents for new babies, Showroom 64 stocks a small but well-edited array of labels (newborn to tens, though the emphasis is on younger children). We love Dandy's retro T-shirts, Maria Collins' old-fashioned bonnets and Bonnie Baby's cashmere and cotton knits.

GOING OUT

BEAUTY

FASHION

PARTIES

FOOD

HEALTH

ECO

OUTDOORS

HOME

CHILDREN

PETS

TRANSPORT

RESOURCES

Soup Dragon

27 Topsfield Parade, Tottenham Lane, N8 8PT (8348 0224/www.soup-dragon.co.uk). Finsbury Park tube/rail, then W7 bus. Open 9.30am-6pm Mon-Sat; 11am-5pm Sun.
Children can cook up a storm in the dinky mini-kitchen play area, while parents browse through the gorgeous – and affordable – clothes. Expect lesser-known labels and contemporary styles – we love Holly's clover-print PJs (from £9.50) and Katvig's jaunty stripey swimsuits and bird-print romper suits (both £15.90)
Other locations *106 Lordship Lane, SE22 8HF (8693 5575).*

Their Nibs

215 Kensington Park Road, W11 1NR (7221 4263/www.theirnibs.com). Ladbroke Grove or Notting Hill Gate tube. Open 10am-6pm Mon-Sat; noon-5pm Sun.
Vintage-style attire and quirky prints are the order of the day at this Notting Hill boutique, founded five years ago. From cowboy-print pyjamas (£25) to demure floral sundresses (£38), every item is a classic – charming but never twee. Their Nibs also does an own-label range of homeware using the shop's distinctive floral prints.
Other locations *79 Chamberlayne Road, NW10 3ND (8964 8444).*

CHIC MATERNITY SHOPS

It's impossible to cover maternity wear without a mention of the mighty **Topshop** (214 Oxford Street, W1W 8LG, 7636 7700, www.topshop.com), whose ground-floor maternity department offers chic, affordable styles, plus a small, adorable range of baby togs (girls only – sorry, chaps).

Blossom Mother & Child
164 Walton Street, SW3 2JL (7589 7500/www.blossommotherandchild. com). South Kensington tube. Open 10am-6pm Mon-Sat; noon-5pm Sun.
Blossom's owners have a gift for sourcing pregnancy-friendly pieces from the hottest designers; the Clements Ribeiro range is exclusive to the store. The own-brand line includes lovely cocktail frocks (£325) and perfectly cut trousers (£149). It also sells specially adapted jeans from hip names like J Brand.

Crave Maternity
207 Kings Road, SW3 5ED (7349 9822/www.cravematernity.co.uk). Sloane Square tube. Open 10am-6pm Mon, Tue, Thur-Sat; 10am-7pm Wed; noon-5pm Sun.

Filling a much-needed niche between high street and high fashion, Crave's designs range from boyfriend jeans (£75) to sweet summer dresses and elegant black frocks (from £65).

Elias & Grace
158 Regent's Park Road, NW1 8XN (7449 0574/www.eliasandgrace. com). Chalk Farm tube. Open 10am-6pm Mon-Sat; noon-6pm Sun.
Luxurious, top-of-the-range pieces for well-heeled mothers-to-be are this Primrose Hill boutique's forte: labels (tested for fit on a prosthetic bump) include Matthew Williamson, Jenny Dyer and See by Chloé. Adorable baby clothes are upstairs.

9 London
8 Hollywood Road, SW10 9HY (7352 7600/www.9london.co.uk). Earl's Court tube. Open 10am-6pm Mon-Sat; noon-6pm Sun.
Head here for amazingly flattering day and evening dresses: you're following in the footsteps of a whole host of celebrities. You'll pay around £130 for a deliciously pretty sundress; more for opulent silk evening attire.

Pets

GOING OUT

BEAUTY

FASHION

PARTIES

FOOD

HEALTH

ECO

OUTDOORS

HOME

CHILDREN

PETS

TRANSPORT

RESOURCES

Pets

Vets, rescue centres, pet shops and grooming parlours – plus mutt-friendly pubs to drop by for a pint.

Dog-friendly pubs

Brown Dog
28 Cross Street, SW13 0AP (8392 2200/ www.thebrowndog.co.uk). Barnes Bridge rail. Open noon-11pm Mon-Sat; noon-10pm Sun.
Aptly, the logo at this laid-back local is a chap walking his dog: well-behaved pets are welcome in the cosy bar and dining area, or pretty beer garden. The gastropub fare is accomplished and, this being Barnes, even the dog treats are a cut above: pigs' ears and bones are generally available (some free, some not), while resident mutt Mr Bojangles looks on from his basket.

Grapes
76 Narrow Street, E14 8BP (7987 4396). Westferry DLR. Open noon-3pm, 5.30-11pm Mon-Thur; noon-11pm Fri, Sat; noon-10.30pm Sun.
The Grapes' german shepherd Max has passed away, but this ancient, beam-filled riverside pub retains its popularity with east London pet owners. After a pint of ale, and an equally refreshing bowl of water or ice cubes for your dog, head across the road for a walk in Ropemakers' Field.

Hope
1 Bellevue Road, SW17 7EG (8672 8717/ www.thehopepub.co.uk). Wandsworth Common rail. Open noon-11pm Mon-Wed; noon-midnight Thur-Sat; noon-10.30pm Sun.
The smartly turned-out Hope is well placed to cater for dog-walkers heading to the common, and has made a virtue of doing so. A nearby pottery has been commissioned to cast personalised bowls for the pub's regulars, while jars of treats await in the doggy snack area. It's a pleasant spot to while away an afternoon, with an impressive range of international beers and obscure draught ales on tap.

Mucky Pup ★
39 Queen's Head Street, N1 8NQ (7226 2572/www.myspace.com/muckypupn1). Angel tube. Open 4pm-1am Mon-Sat; 1pm-midnight Sun.
A sign on the door reading 'strictly no under-18s unless they've got four legs' sets the tone at this earthy, unpretentious boozer, which won the Dog Trust's award for most dog-friendly pub in Britain a few years back. Staff are happy to provide dogs with bowls of water and free snacks, while Wi-Fi and a free jukebox add to the appeal for their owners.

Prince's Head
28 The Green, Richmond, Surrey TW9 1LX (8940 1572). Richmond tube/rail. Open 11am-11pm Mon-Sat; noon-10.30pm Sun.
The management at this Fuller's pub stock up on chews and biscuits on a weekly basis – offered free of charge, along with water – and dogs are warmly welcomed. Choose from the sterling range of real ales (ESB, Chiswick, London Pride) that can be enjoyed at one of the outdoor tables overlooking Richmond Green.

Spaniards Inn
Spaniards Road, NW3 7JJ (8731 6571). Hampstead tube/210 bus. Open 11am-11pm Mon-Fri; 10am-11pm Sat, Sun.
Conveniently located for walks on the heath, the Spaniards is the only pub we know with its own semi-automated dog wash on the premises; buy a token from the bar for a shampoo, rinse and dry. Dog biscuits are on sale and pooches are allowed anywhere on the premises – although there's a strict leads policy because of the cats in the garden.

Grooming parlours

A good groomer should be happy to let you see the salon's facilities, and talk you through procedures. He or she should be able to carry out scissor and clipper work, plus hand stripping (plucking out the dead coat) and anal gland, teeth, nail and skin care. Cats should be groomed in a calm, peaceful environment, away from dogs.

In addition to the salons listed below, **Primrose Hill Pets** (see p186) also offers an excellent grooming service, charging from £28 for dogs and £30 for cats; book at least a week in advance.

Dog About Town
196 Bellenden Road, SE15 4BW (7358 9709). Peckham Rye rail. Open 9.30am-5pm Tue-Sat. No credit cards.
Dog About Town is a no-nonsense cat and dog grooming parlour of 40 years' standing. Small dogs are clipped for £30; larger varieties cost from around £50.

Dogs Delight
4 Station Parade, Burlington Lane, W4 3HD (8995 4040/www.dogs-delight.net). Chiswick rail. Open 10.30am-5pm Mon-Fri; Sat by appointment.
Run by a mother-and-daughter team, Dogs Delight offers a doggy day crèche and boarding, dog walking and cat sitting, in addition to professional grooming services. Prices for cats start at £40, while dogs depend on the size and breed. Pre-book, unless it's for a quick walk-in treatment (from £8).

City Secret

Freebie magazine **London Dog Tails** (www.londondogtails.com) is a mine of information for canine owners in the capital, from product and pub reviews to tried-and-tested walks and details of upcoming events; pick up a copy from vets and pet shops around town, or check it out online.

Pet Pavilion
Chelsea Farmers' Market, 125 Sydney Street, SW3 6NR (7376 8800/www.petpavilion. co.uk). South Kensington or Sloane Square tube. Open 9.30am-6pm Mon-Sat; 11am-6pm Sun.
The largest of this smart London mini-chain's outlets, the Chelsea flagship shop offers clipping from £31, baths from £16 and hand stripping (for long-haired dogs) from £45. Other treatments include deep coat conditioning, de-matting and dental care.
Other locations 60 Gloucester Road, SW7 4QT (7584 8848); 174 Kensington Church Street, W8 4DP (7221 1888).

Pugs & Kisses
183 New King's Road, SW6 4SW (7731 0098/www.pugsandkisses.com). Parsons Green tube. Open 10am-6pm Mon-Sat.
This stylish pet boutique also has an expert team of trained groomers. Quick treatments for cats and dogs include nail clipping (£10), ear cleaning and trimming (£7) and 15-minute de-matting sessions (£15). Staff try to keep full grooming sessions down to two hours to minimise distress, and charge from £35-£100 depending on the breed.

Top Dog Grooming
598 Kingston Road, SW20 8DN (8542 9449). Raynes Park rail. Open 9am-4pm Mon-Fri; 9am-1pm Sat. No credit cards.
Bathing costs from £20, grooming and clipping from £30, while prices for a quick nail-trim or ear-clean start at £6. Top Dog also caters for sensitive skins, and can treat for fleas and various skin conditions.

Waggin' Tails
366 Fulham Road, SW10 9UU (7823 3111/www.waggintailsonline.com). Fulham Broadway tube. Open 10am-5pm Mon; 10am-6pm Tue, Wed, Fri; 10am-7pm Thur; 10am-5pm Sat.
This friendly Fulham cat and dog grooming salon offers everything from pedicures to reflexology and aromatherapy baths (treatments cost from £7, clips from £30). Cats' 'bed and breakfast' is available at £10 a night, while doggy day care costs from £8.

GOING OUT
BEAUTY
FASHION
PARTIES
FOOD
HEALTH
ECO
OUTDOORS
HOME
CHILDREN
PETS
TRANSPORT
RESOURCES

1000 ways to change your life

TIME OUT GUIDES
Visit timeout.com/shop

Pet shops

Animal Fair of Kensington

17 Abingdon Road, W8 6AH (7937 0011). High Street Kensington tube. Open 9.30am-6pm Mon-Sat; 11am-5pm Sun.

This deceptively large Kensington outlet has been a local institution for more than 50 years, selling fish, hamsters, gerbils, rats, guinea pigs and rabbits. There's a wide selection of food and accessories for pets of all kinds, including radio-controlled and battery-powered mice for frustrated felines. The shop also offers a dog grooming service (from £24).

Aquatic Design Centre

109 Great Portland Street, W1W 6QG (7580 6764/www.aquaticdesign.co.uk). Portland Street tube. Open 10am-8pm Mon-Thur; 10am-7pm Fri; 10am-6pm Sat; 11am-5pm Sun.

One of the world's leading bespoke fish tank designers, with clients including Harrods and Selfridges, Aquatic Design promises to turn your underwater dreams into reality. Its central London store also stocks a good range of more standard equipment, as well as more than 300 tanks full of an astonishing array of marine, tropical and coldwater fish, starting from just 95p.

Canonbury Veterinary Practice

226-228 Essex Road, N1 3AP (7359 3888/ www.canvet.com). Essex Road rail. Open 8am-7pm Mon-Fri; 9am-5pm Sat; 10am-2pm Sun.

This small but well-stocked pet shop sells treats, toys, food, litter, bedding and assorted pet paraphernalia. It's attached to a vet's surgery, which checks and approves all of the products that are stocked, so quality is high and there's nothing gimmicky. Puppy socialisation and basic training classes run on Tuesday evenings, costing £15 for the first two sessions, then £5 a time.

Chiswick Pets

32-34 Devonshire Road, W4 2HD (8747 0715). Turnham Green tube. Open 9am-6pm Mon-Sat; 11am-4pm Sun.

Husband-and-wife team Eileen and Raymond have been serving the local community for

MISSING PETS

If your pet goes missing, contact local police stations, vets and animal rescue centres (*see p187*); to find your local police station, visit www.met.police.uk. The **RSPCA** also recommends ringing its cruelty and advice line (0300 123 4999) – open 24 hours a day, seven days a week. You should also call the animal warden at your local council (normally within the environmental health division), who has responsibility for registering strays.

Battersea Dogs & Cats Home (*see p187*) also has a lost dogs and cats line (0901 477 8477) for Londoners, while the **Missing Pets Bureau** (0870 199 9999) operates a national

missing pets register and has links to over 12,000 rescue centres and other organisations. You should also make your own posters and put them up in the local area.

To safeguard your pet, register it with the **UK National Missing Pets Register** (www.nationalpetregister.org), who'll provide you with a unique ID that can be engraved on your pet's collar. You should also get your pet microchipped, so that if found, it can be identified; it costs £15-£30. This generally includes membership of **Petlog** (0870 606 6751, www.petlog.org.uk), which holds your address details alongside the ID number and runs a 24-hour reunification service.

GOING OUT

BEAUTY

FASHION

PARTIES

FOOD

HEALTH

ECO

OUTDOORS

HOME

CHILDREN

PETS

TRANSPORT

RESOURCES

more than 20 years and pride themselves on offering customers personalised, expert advice. As well as a full range of foods and accessories for all pets, including birds, the shop stocks small mammals such as rabbits, guinea pigs, hamsters and rats, along with reptiles (including lizards and tortoises) and coldwater and tropical fish. They're also very careful about selling to responsible owners – so staff won't sell fish without ensuring that their new tanks will have filters, for example.

Holly & Lil

103 Bermondsey Street, SE1 3XB (07836 592415/www.hollyandlil.co.uk). London Bridge tube/rail. Open by appointment Mon-Wed; 11.30am-7pm Thur; 10.30am-5pm Fri, Sat.
Friends Elaine and Sarah invented the concept of dog collar couture while walking their pooches on Primrose Hill six years ago, and their boutique now stocks a dazzling array of handmade leather accessories for the fashion-conscious canine. Your dog can embrace boho chic with a flower power charm collar, dazzle the park set with Swarovski pearls (from £72) or assert his individual sense of style with a bespoke collar. Cats are also catered for, with a variety of feline couture accessories, though the emphasis is on wacky and wonderful collars, some kitted out with colourful keepsakes.

Kings Aquatic & Reptile World

26 Camden High Street, NW1 0JH (7387 5553/www.kingsreptileworld.co.uk). Mornington Crescent tube. Open 10am-6pm Mon-Sat.
At this specialist fish, reptile and creepy crawly retailer, potential purchases include giant millipedes (£4-£20), tarantulas as big as dinner plates (£5-£200) and an army of lizards. Bigger snakes, such as Burmese pythons and anacondas, cost from £200 upwards and must be pre-ordered. Upstairs rooms are devoted to freshwater, tropical and coldwater fish, and there's everything you need to cater for your new pet, from cages and lighting to food – some of it not even dead yet.

Mungo & Maud

79 Elizabeth Street, SW1W 9PJ (7952 4570/www.mungoandmaud.com). Sloane Square tube. Open 10am-6pm Mon-Sat.
Belgravia's designer pet store is where the beautiful people and their beautiful animals shop. With an emphasis on minimalist design and natural fabrics, stock includes hand-stitched leather collars, cashmere dog sweaters, feather-filled dog and cat beds and dog tags by jewellery designer Vinnie Day. There's also the Petite Amande shampoo and fragrance range (from £15.95), which can be used by dogs and humans alike, and organic granola, carrot and pumpkin treats.

Mutz Nutz

221 Westbourne Park Road, W11 1EA (7243 3333/www.themutznutz.com). Westbourne Park tube. Open 10am-6pm Mon-Sat; noon-5pm Sun.
This Notting Hill pet emporium ranges from the workaday to the wacky, with faux lizard skin dog beds, fancy dress dog and cat outfits, birthday party kits (including a bone shaped cake tin and, of course, doggy bags) and a personalised dog bowl service making up the latter. Across the road, a doggy deli specialises in natural dog treats and food, while the spa – complete with illuminated grooming tables – is guaranteed to spoil your pooch rotten.
Other locations *Mutz Nutz Dog Spa, 22 Powis Terrace, W11 1JH (7243 3399).*

Primrose Hill Pets

132 Regents Park Road, NW1 8XL (7483 2023/www.primrosehillpets.co.uk). Chalk Farm tube. Open 9am-6pm Mon-Sat; Sun 11am-5pm.
A mere stick's throw from Regent's Park, this cat- and dog-focused outlet has a wide range of coats, beds, leads, collars and grooming equipment for pampered pets, plus a small grooming salon. Knowledgeable staff are happy to advise on such delicate subjects as the right shampoo for dogs with sensitive skin, or the best variety of dietary supplements to make your moggy's eyes twinkle. No pets are sold on the premises, but breeders' contact details can be provided.

Rescue centres

All of the organisations below require an interview and home visit before you adopt an animal. The **RSPCA** (0300 123 4555, www.rspca.org.uk) also runs rescue centres across London. For your nearest, check the website. If you're looking for a specific breed of rescue dog, the **Kennel Club** (0870 606 6750, www.the-kennel-club.org.uk) publishes a directory of different dog breed rescue centres.

Battersea Dogs & Cats Home

4 Battersea Park Road, SW8 4AA (7622 3626/www.dogshome.org). Battersea Park rail.
Battersea Dogs & Cats Home is the largest dogs' home in the UK, with up to 500 animals on site, around a fifth of which are cats. Rescue dogs cost £85, cats £50; a waiting list may apply for puppies and kittens.

Cats Protection

North London Adoption Centre, 135 Junction Road, N19 5PX (7272 6048/www.north london.cats.org.uk). Archway tube.
The UK's leading feline welfare charity has up to 7,000 cats available for re-homing at any one time through its nationwide network of local adoption centres, such as this one in Archway.

Celia Hammond Animal Trust

151-153 Barking Road, E16 4HQ (7474 8811/www.celiahammond.org). Canning Town tube/rail.
Founded by '60s model Celia Hammond, the trust runs two London clinics. Each operates a 24-hour rescue service, with website photos of recently rescued dogs, cats and kittens (re-homed in pairs, or with their mother).
Other locations *233-235 Lewisham Way, SE4 1UY (8694 6545).*

Dogs Trust West London

Highway Farm, Harvil Road, Harefield, Uxbridge UB9 6JW (0845 076 3647/ www.dogstrust.org.uk).
The West London branch of this national charity has 75 kennels, and cares for around 1,600 dogs a year. The website features a photo gallery of dogs currently needing a home.

Mayhew Animal Home

Trenmar Gardens, NW10 6BJ (8969 0178/www.mayhewanimalhome.org). Kensal Green tube.
The Mayhew was set up over 100 years ago as a home for 'the lost and starving dogs and cats of London', and now cares for up to 175 moggies, 50 dogs and 15 rabbits. There's a set fee of £120 to buy dogs, £75 for cats, £40 for rabbits and £20 for guinea pigs, which includes vaccinations.

Wood Green Animal Shelters

601 Lordship Lane, N22 5LG (0870 190 4440/www.woodgreen.org.uk). Wood Green tube.
Cats adopted from this North London shelter, first opened in 1924, come with six weeks' free pet insurance. A £55 donation is suggested.

GOING OUT

BEAUTY

FASHION

PARTIES

FOOD

HEALTH

ECO

OUTDOORS

HOME

CHILDREN

PETS

TRANSPORT

RESOURCES

Vets

To locate your nearest vet, use the postcode finder on the **Royal College of Veterinary Surgeon's** website at www.rcvs.org.uk; the RCVS also investigates complaints against vets.

If you're on a low income or receiving benefits, your pet may qualify for reduced-price neutering and other subsidised clinics. **Cats Protection** and the **RSPCA** (see p187) both offer voucher schemes for low-cost neutering, as do most rescue centres. The **Beaumont Animals' Hospital** (see below) also offers a subsidised neuter clinic for cats and dogs, while the **Blue Cross Animal Hospital** (Sheppard House, 1-5 Hugh Street, SW1V 1QQ, 7932 2370, www.bluecross.org.uk) runs an appointments-only service offering low-cost veterinary care and vaccinations to low-income south and east Londoners.

The **Mayhew Animal Home** (see p187) also offers cheap neutering to all pet owners, charging from £22-£25 for cats and £50-£85 for dogs, along with a low-cost vaccinations clinic on Wednesday, Thursday and Saturday mornings. Call for details.

Abbey Veterinary Clinic
84 Dalston Lane, E8 3AH (7254 1362). Dalston Kingsland rail. Open 9-10am, 1-2pm, 5-7pm Mon-Thur; 1-2pm, 5-7pm Fri; 2-5pm Sat.
Sparklingly clean, and sandwiched in a row of shops on Dalston Lane, Abbey has a loyal local following. The staff are unfailingly efficient, and can usually offer a same-day appointment with the vet. The consultation fee is £30.

Beaumont Animals' Hospital
The Royal Veterinary College, Royal College Street, NW1 0TU (7387 8134/www.rvc. ac.uk). Mornington Crescent tube/Camden Road rail. Open 9am-7.30pm Mon-Fri; 9am-12.45pm Sat.
Opened in 1932, the Beaumont is the Royal Veterinary College's practice. Nurses' clinics

offer everything from nail-clipping to microchipping, and puppy-training courses are held on Thursday afternoons – just £10 for four hour-long sessions with the excellent Alan Menzies.

Brockwell Veterinary Surgery
224-228 Railton Road, SE24 0JT (7737 2526/www.brockwellvets.co.uk). Herne Hill rail. Open 8am-7pm Mon, Tue, Thur, Fri; 8am-8pm Wed; 8.30am-4pm Sat.
A relaxed local that offers reliable service at fair prices: regulars praise the friendly staff. The surgery also runs an out of hours advisory line and a cat boarding service.

Dragon Veterinary Clinic
496 Hornsey Road, N19 4EF (7272 3354/ www.dragonvets.co.uk). Archway tube or Finsbury Park tube/rail. Open 9am-7pm Mon-Fri; 9am-4pm Sat.
Cats are a particular area of expertise at this cheery local practice, headed by partners Mary Nicoll and James Caspar, and represent a major chunk of the team's caseload (though they see a fair few dogs too). An onsite laboratory means fast test results, and there's a popular cattery at the back; book well ahead.

Portman Veterinary Clinic
86 York Street, W1H 1QS (7723 2068/ www.portmanvetclinic.co.uk). Marylebone tube/rail. Open 9am-noon, 3pm-5.45pm Mon-Fri.
Run by Bruce Fogle, a bestselling author and former vet at London Zoo, the Portman is a smart establishment of some 30 years' standing. It's not the cheapest, but your pet is in safe hands. The clinic is affiliated with the Emergency Veterinary Clinic (55 Elizabeth Street, SW1W 9PP, 7730 9102), which deals with out-of-hours emergencies.

Westside Veterinary Clinic ★
2 Burland Road, SW11 6SA (7223 7003/ www.westsidevets.co.uk). Clapham Junction rail. Open 9am-7pm Mon-Fri; 9am-noon Sat.
Family pets are the mainstay at this supremely friendly clinic. Staff take time to get to know your pet – and remember their names, according to one local.

Transport

GOING OUT

BEAUTY

FASHION

PARTIES

FOOD

HEALTH

ECO

OUTDOORS

HOME

CHILDREN

PETS

TRANSPORT

RESOURCES

Airports

The fastest – and cheapest – ways to reach London's closest airports, by coach, rail and car.

By coach & rail

We've given standard adult fares for rail and coach services: ask for details of railcard reductions and child fares.

Gatwick Airport
0870 000 2468/www.gatwickairport.com.
About 30 miles south of central London, off the M23.
From Victoria, the Gatwick Express (0845 850 1530, www.gatwickexpress.co.uk) takes 30 minutes and runs 3.30am to 12.30am daily. Tickets cost £17.90 for a single, £30.80 for an open return. Far cheaper (and only five to ten minutes slower) is the Southern service (0845 748 4950, www.southernrailway.com), with trains every five to ten minutes (or every 25 minutes between 1am and 4am); a single costs £10.90, an open return £19.80. Alternatively, take the Thameslink (0845 748 4950, www.firstcapitalconnect.co.uk) from London Bridge, Blackfriars, Farringdon or King's Cross for £8.90 single, £18.60 open return. With National Express (0845 013 0130, www.nationalexpress.com), the coach takes 80-90 minutes; tickets cost from £6.60 for a single. Cheaper still is the easyBus (www.easybus.co.uk) to/from Victoria, with advance tickets from £2, taking 65-80 minutes. A taxi costs around £80-£100 and takes just over an hour.

Heathrow Airport
0870 000 0123/www.heathrowairport.com.
About 15 miles west of central London, off the M4.
The Heathrow Express (0845 600 1515, www.heathrowexpress.co.uk) runs from Paddington 5.10am to 11.12pm daily, and takes 15-20 minutes. Tickets cost £15.50 single, £29 return (£1 cheaper if you book

online). The Heathrow Connect (0845 678 6975, www.heathrowconnect.com) runs from Paddington via Ealing Broadway, West Ealing, Hanwell, Southhall and Hayes. It serves terminals 1, 2, 3, and 4, with a free transfer service from Heathrow Central to Terminal 5. The journey from Paddington takes 25-30 minutes and costs £6.90; an open return is £12.90. At £4, the tube (7222 1234, www.tfl.gov.uk) is cheaper, but takes around an hour into central London on the Piccadilly Line. Tubes run from 5am until 11.57pm daily (6am to 11pm on Sundays); at night, the half-hourly N9 bus takes over. National Express (0870 580 8080, www.nationalexpress.com) coaches take 90 minutes and run half-hourly from Victoria, between 5am and 9.35pm daily: a single costs £6. A taxi into town costs £40-£80 and takes from 40 minutes to an hour, depending on traffic.

London City Airport
7646 0000/www.londoncityairport.com.
About 9 miles east of central London.
On the Docklands Light Railway (DLR), the journey from Bank to London City Airport takes around 20 minutes; trains run from 5.30am to 12.30am Monday to Saturday and 7am to 11.30pm Sunday. A taxi into central London costs around £25.

Luton Airport
01582 405100/www.london-luton.com.
About 30 miles north of central London, J10 off the M1.
Luton Airport Parkway Station is close to the airport, but not in it: there's a five-minute shuttle-bus ride. The Thameslink service (0845 748 4950, www.firstcapitalconnect.co.uk), calling at five central London stations (including St Pancras and London Bridge), takes 35-45 minutes. Tickets cost £11.90

single, £21.50 return, and trains run at least hourly through the night. Luton to Victoria takes 60-90 minutes by coach: Green Line (0870 608 7261, www.greenline. co.uk) also runs a 24-hour service, with singles at £13, returns £18. With easyBus (www.easybus. co.uk), advance singles start at £2. A taxi costs upwards of £60, and should take around 90 minutes.

Stansted Airport

0870 000 0303/www.stanstedairport.com. About 35 miles north-east of central London, J8 off the M11.

The Stansted Express (0845 748 4950, www. stansteadexpress.com) from Liverpool Street Station takes 40-45 minutes. Trains leave every 15-45 minutes; tickets cost £15 single, £25 return. The half-hourly Airbus (0870 580 8080, www.nationalexpress.com) coach from Victoria takes at least 80 minutes and runs 24 hours; a single is £10, a return £17. EasyBus (www.easybus.co.uk) also runs services from Victoria and Baker Street, and takes a similar length of time; singles cost from £2-£8. Terravision (01279 680028, www.terravision. eu) runs shuttle services to Victoria (around 75 minutes) and Liverpool Street (around 55 minutes) at £8 one way, £13 return. A taxi is £70-£90, and takes an hour.

Motorbike taxis

For speedy journeys or airport dashes, weave through packed-solid traffic perched on the back of a motorbike.

All of the companies listed have a minimum £25 charge, and offer fixed airport rates; the bikes are equipped with panniers, and can carry a small to medium suitcase. You pay a premium for the thrill though: central London to Gatwick currently costs £110-£120.

Passenger Bikes *0700 596 3292/ www.passengerbikes.com.*

Taxybikes *7255 4269/ www.addisonlee.com/services/taxybikes.*

Virgin Limobike *7930 0814/ www.virginlimobike.com.*

City Secret

Early-morning flight from Heathrow or Gatwick? Forget a dawn dash to the airport, and book into a **Yotel** (7100 1100, www.yotel.com) capsule hotel. Cabins are well-equipped but not for the claustrophobic: 7sq m standard rooms (£26/4 hrs, £57 overnight) feature a couch that turns into a bed, plus a desk, free Wi-Fi, a 60-channel flatscreen TV and a bathroom with monsoon shower.

Parking

Rates for airport parking vary depending on your length of stay, but booking ahead is invariably far cheaper than turning up on the day. For details, contact:

Gatwick *0870 850 2825/ www.gatwickairport.com.*

Heathrow *0870 850 2825/ www.heathrowairport.com.*

London City Airport *7646 0000/ www.londoncityairport.com.*

Luton *0870 608 8788/ www.london-luton.com.*

Stansted *0870 850 2825/ www.stanstedairport.com.*

VALET PARKING

For minimum stress, and to avoid carting heavy luggage and tired children from the car park to the terminal, book valet parking. After meeting you at departures, the driver takes your car to a secure car park, then delivers it back to the terminal when you land. It costs around £20-£40 on top of standard parking fees: book ahead for the best deals. Check www. baa.com for prices at Gatwick, Heathrow and Stansted, or try **BCP** (0870 013 4535, www.parkbcp.co.uk) or **Purple Parking** (0845 450 0808, www.purpleparking.com).

GOING OUT

BEAUTY

FASHION

PARTIES

FOOD

HEALTH

ECO

OUTDOORS

HOME

CHILDREN

PETS

TRANSPORT

RESOURCES

Address Book Secrets
Erol Alkan
DJ and producer

Rough Trade West (130 Talbot Road, W11 1JA, 7229 8541) is my favourite alternative record store. There aren't many places that stock noisy guitar music from Portugal. Nigel who works there is a hero to me: he's introduced me to so many great records. I love the special relationship you have with people behind the counter – it's so much better than buying online.

My first choice for a recording venue is always the **Miloco Studios**, which are dotted around London (7232 0008, www.miloco.co.uk). I produced 'Two Doors Down' for the Mystery Jets at the Square. It's a really cool, vibey room and very laid-back; everyone being at ease in the studio is really important to me.

I've been DJing for 16 years and don't play at many small venues anymore, but I love **Catch Bar** (22 Kingsland Road, E2 8DA, 7729 6097), where we run a night called Beyond the Wizard's Sleeve. We play eight hours of psychedelia to about 100 people, for free. We put on the unlistenable stuff early to make sure we only keep the people who are willing to stick it out.

Most of the new releases I want can be found at **Phonica Records** (51 Poland Street, W1F 7LZ, 7025 6070), where the staff are all DJs. They know what their customers are into, but also introduce you to new things. I've been buying records for as long as I can remember – I used to bug my dad to take me to Woolies for the latest releases.

All my broken musical equipment gets fixed at **Blue Audio** (44 Duncan Street, N1 8BW, 7713 6865). It's run by a bunch of geeky blokes who are really into their instruments, and sell new and used equipment. It's always exciting when they're getting new kit in – a dozen guys descend on the store.

I've lived in north London all my life; the last three years I've spent just off Holloway Road. **Peking Palace** (669 Holloway Road, N19 5SE, 7281 8989) does great, meat-free Chinese food: I'd recommend barbecue tofu with ginger.

Everything feels homemade at the **Amazon Café** (512 Holloway Road, N7 6JD, 7281 7452). It looks like a normal caff, but the food is really imaginative; it's quite Greek-influenced, and they do a wonderful taramasalata. There's a back garden too, and there aren't many cafés in London where you don't have to sit next to the main road, eating with the traffic.

For fast food, I head to an amazing vegetarian store called **Health Food Centre** (11 Warren Street, W1T 5LG, 7387 9289). Meat-free burgers are often like cardboard, but theirs are made with soya and are really tasty. Not eating meat, you sometimes draw the short straw, but not there.

I de-stress by going for acupuncture. Every few weeks I see Dr Phun at **JC Holistic** (2nd floor, 80 Shaftesbury Avenue, W1D 6NF, 7287 0501). I began going out of curiosity, and have been a regular for a couple of years.

Cabs & taxis

Black cabs, green cabs and more.

Black cabs

To book a black cab, call the 24-hour **Taxi One-Number** (0871 871 8710). A £2 booking fee applies, along with a 12.5% administration charge if you're paying by credit card.

Any complaints regarding black cabs should be made to the **Public Carriage Office** (0845 602 7000, www.tfl.gov.uk); note the cab's five-digit number, shown in the passenger compartment and on the back bumper.

Not sure how much a cab journey might cost? Type your starting point and destination postcodes into the ingenious **www.worldtaximeter.com**, which will calculate a rough estimate of the journey time and price.

Eco-friendly cabs

The following minicab firms use hybrid petrol and electric-powered Toyota Prius cars, and offset their carbon emissions. **Radio Taxis** (7272 0272, www.radio taxis.co.uk) also offsets carbon emissions from its black cab fleet and offers its drivers the option of using biofuel.

Climatecars
8968 0440/www.climatecars.com.
Newspapers, magazines and Belu mineral water come as standard, while bike racks allow cyclists who've had a tipple or got caught out by the rain to hitch a ride home.

Ecoigo ★
0800 032 6446/www.ecoigo.com.
Ecoigo offers a 24-hour service; carbon emissions are offset by the World Land Trust.

Green Tomato Cars
8568 0022/www.greentomatocars.com.
Green Tomato's fleet of sleek silver Priuses operates across town, offering competitive prices and a reliable service.

Minicabs

You can check if a cab company or driver is licensed at www.tfl.gov.uk. To find a licensed minicab, call the 24-hour information line (7222 1234) or use the **Cabwise** service: text the word HOME to 60835 and you'll be sent telephone numbers for two licensed minicab operators in the area, along with a taxi operator. It costs 35p, plus your standard text message rate.

The following minicab companies have female drivers:

Ladybirds *8295 0101.*

Ladycabs *7254 3501.*

Ladycars *8981 7111.*

Ladycars Ltd *8655 1918.*

City Secret

To arrive in style, call a **Karma Kar** (8964 0700, 07770 693979, www.karmakabs.com). Available to hire by the hour (£50), Tobias Moss's imported Indian Ambassador cars are wonderfully opulent: think shiny, bejewelled interiors, liberally studded with sequins and suffused with incense and raga music. They're particularly popular for weddings and Fashion Week events.

GOING OUT
BEAUTY
FASHION
PARTIES
FOOD
HEALTH
ECO
OUTDOORS
HOME
CHILDREN
PETS
TRANSPORT
RESOURCES

GOING OUT

BEAUTY

FASHION

PARTIES

FOOD

HEALTH

ECO

OUTDOORS

HOME

CHILDREN

PETS

TRANSPORT

RESOURCES

Cycling

Beat the traffic on a bike.

Bike hire

We've given daily rates, but cheaper deals are often available for longer hire periods.

Action Bikes
23-26 Embankment Place, Northumberland Avenue, WC2N 6NN (7930 2525/www.actionbikes.co.uk). Embankment tube. Open 8am-7pm Mon-Fri; 9.30am-5.30pm Sat. Hire £15/day. Deposit £300.
The only wheels on offer at Action Bikes are yellow-painted Brompton L6s: if you decide to buy one afterwards, the hire fee is taken off the price.
Other locations *across the city.*

City Bike Service
2 Fairchild Place, EC2A 3EN (7247 4151/www.citybikeservice.co.uk). Old Street tube. Open 8am-6.30pm Mon-Fri; 9am-5pm Sat. Hire £15/day. Deposit £150.
Seven-speed hybrid bikes, with helmet and lights included in the hire price.

> ## City Secret
>
> For an old-fashioned steed, visit Clerkenwell's **Bobbin Bicycles** (31 Eyre Street Hill, EC1R 5EW, 7253 1058, www.bobbinbicycles.co.uk). The workshop sells a gorgeous range of elegant, Dutch-made bikes to those for whom graceful gliding is more important than speed. Prices are very reasonable (from £250) and, in keeping with the personal service ethos, visits are by appointment only.

Go Pedal!
07850 796320/www.gopedal.co.uk. Open 8am-8pm daily. Hire £20-£32/day. Deposit £150.
Rates drop over longer hire periods, or for several bikes. Delivery and collection are included, along with helmet, lights and locks.

London Bicycle Tour Company
1A Gabriel's Wharf, 56 Upper Ground, SE1 9PP (7928 6838/www.londonbicycle.com). Waterloo or Southwark tube. Open 10am-6pm daily. Hire £3/hour; £18/day. Deposit £180 cash; £1 by credit card.
Bikes, tandems and rickshaw hire. Lights are included, but helmets and panniers are extra.

London Recumbents
Ranger's Yard, Dulwich Park, SE21 7BQ (8299 6636/www.londonrecumbents.com). Herne Hill rail. Open 10am-4pm Mon-Fri; 10am-5pm Sat, Sun. Hire £7-£12/hr.
Speed through the park in a sleek recumbent trike. Too wacky? The company also hires out standard bikes, tandems and trailers.

OYBike
0845 226 5751/www.oybike.com. Open 24hrs daily. Hire £2/hr, £8/day. Deposit £10.
To rent a bike 24/7 from OYBike's 40 pick-up points, pre-register with £10 credit, then call up to electronically release the lock. At the end of your ride, return the bike to a stand; trips of under half an hour are free.

Velorution
18 Great Titchfield Street, W1W 8BD (7637 4004/www.velorution.biz). Oxford Circus tube. Open 9am-7pm Mon-Fri; 10.30am-6.30pm. Hire £15/day.
Choose between a Brompton or Dahon Vitesse with the 'Rent-a-Folder' scheme: for £20, local delivery is included.

Bike shops & repairs

In addition to the following shops, **Action Bikes** and **Velorution** (for both, *see left*) also offer good repair services.

If you're miles from home and in need of help, try the **Mobile Cycle Service** (0800 321 3303, www.mobilecycleservice.co.uk), whose mechanics will come to the rescue for surprisingly reasonable rates.

Bicycle Workshop
27 All Saint's Road, W11 1HE (7229 4850/ www.bicycleworkshop.co.uk). Westbourne Park tube. Open 10am-2pm, 3-6pm Tue-Fri; 10am-6pm Sat (earlier for repair drop-offs).
You can book in for repairs on weekdays, but will have to join the queue for the Saturday no-bookings workshop: doors open at 7am in summer and 8am in winter. This place has an excellent reputation, and places soon fill up.

Bikefix
48 Lamb's Conduit Street, WC1N 3LJ (7405 1218/www.bikefix.co.uk). Russell Square or Holborn tube. Open 8.30am-7pm Mon-Fri; 10am-5pm Sat.
The shop sells classic city bikes, fold-ups, recumbents and accessories galore: nip round the back for the workshop (closed Saturdays). Word-of-mouth has built up a loyal following, but there are no appointments, so get there early.

Bikemech ✈
Castle Climbing Centre, Green Lanes, N4 2HA (07762 270616/www.bikemech.co.uk). Manor House tube. Open 9am-7pm Mon-Thur; 10am-5pm Sat.
Jon Chapel's skills as a mechanic come highly recommended, along with his wheel-building skills (a hard thing to find in London). At £30 plus parts, a general service is great value, while brake replacement starts at a mere £5.

Brick Lane Bikes
118 Bethnal Green Road, E2 6DG (7033 9053/www.bricklanebikes.co.uk). Liverpool Street tube. Open 9am-7pm Mon-Fri; 11am-7pm Sat; 11am-6pm Sun.
With its sleek frames and elegant custom builds, this track and fixed gear specialist is, according to one admirer, 'like a sex shop for fixed gear bike nuts'. It also offers hybrid and city bikes, plus vintage town bikes (£80-£120). The workshop offers a quick turnaround, and is open Sundays; a full service is £30.

Brixton Cycles
145 Stockwell Road, SW9 9TN (7733 6055). Brixton tube. Open 9am-6pm Mon-Wed, Fri-Sat; 10am-7pm Thur.
This place is known for its knowledgeable, friendly staff; if you buy a bike, you get a year's free servicing (parts not included). The workshop offers a same-day service, but soon gets booked up. There's also a daily walk-in emergency repair service during the first hour of opening; get here early.

Cycle Surgery
44 Chalk Farm Road, NW1 8AJ (7485 1000/ www.cyclesurgery.com). Chalk Farm tube. Open 9am-6pm Mon, Wed, Fri; 9am-7pm Tue, Thur; 10pm-6pm Sat; 11am-5pm Sun.
Prices are fair (£40 for a service), and certain staff members offer various areas of

specific expertise (ask for Peter for road racers, and former pro-rider Kris for BMXs). Repairs must be booked ahead at the weekdays-only workshop.
Other locations *across the city.*

London Bicycle Repair

Units 2-3 Benson House, Hatfields, SE1 8DQ (7928 6898/www.londonbicycle.com). Southwark tube. Open 9am-6pm Mon-Fri.
Regulars praise this cheap, efficient repair centre, where owner Rob Graham aims to fix your bike within eight hours. His team will take on anything from a clapped-out £5 bike to a £3,000 road racer; services start at £44.

London Fields Cycles

281 Mare Street, E8 1PJ (8525 0077/www. londonfieldscycles.co.uk). London Fields or Hackney Central rail/Bethnal Green tube, then 106, 253, D6 bus. Open 8am-6pm Mon-Fri; 10am-6pm Sat; 11am-5pm Sun.
The shop offers an excellent selection of bikes and accessories, while workshop services include a £30 tune-up, wheel-building and an 8am drop-in service for minor repairs. Queues start forming early, as only six repairs are taken each morning.

Two Wheels Good

165 Stoke Newington Church Street, N16 0UL (7249 2200/www.twowheelsgood. co.uk). Open 8.30am-6pm Mon-Fri; 9am-6pm Sat.
Bike brands include Puky, Gazelle and Gary Fisher, while the workshops in both branches are Shimano Service Centres, with Cytech-trained mechanics just as happy to do a custom-build as a £35 service. Staff will try to undertake emergency repairs on the spot.
Other location *143 Crouch Hill, N8 9QH (8340 4284).*

Maintenance

For free advice and minor repairs, seek out a **Dr Bike** clinic. The 'doctor' is generally a mechanic from a local bike shop or a cycling enthusiast, often setting up shop at cycling or green events to

check bike safety and carry out repairs out of the goodness of his or her heart.
Various **London Cycling Campaign** (*see right*) groups also run regular Dr Bike sessions; for details, see the website.

The following LCC groups also run regular cycle maintenance workshops, often charging a nominal fee to cover their running costs.

Greenwich Cyclists

Armada Centre, 21 McMillan Street, SE8 3EZ (www.greenwichcyclists.org.uk). Deptford rail.
Weekly two-hour classes (£5-£10) cover different areas of bike maintenance.

Hackney Cyclists

Kings Centre, Frampton Park Baptist Church, Frampton Park Road, E9 7PQ (07940 121513/www.hackney-cyclists.org. uk/workshop.htm). Bethnal Green tube, then 106, 254 bus/Hackney Central rail.
Twice-monthly workshops are led by a team of volunteers, running from 7pm to 9pm on the first and third Tuesday of every month.

Islington Cyclists Action Group

Sunnyside Community Centre, corner of Sunnyside Road & Hazellville Road, N19 3LX. (7272 3522/07810 211902). Archway tube/Crouch Hill rail.
Workshops are held 7-9.30pm on the fourth Wednesday of every month, bar August and December. You're asked to contribute £1.

Tower Hamlets Wheelers

Limehouse Town Hall, 646 Commercial Road, E14 7HA (07903 018970/www.tower hamletswheelers.org.uk). Limehouse DLR/rail.
These friendly, free sessions are held on the last Saturday of the month (11am-3pm).

Waltham Forest

Low Hall Depot, South Access Road, E17 8BS (8520 8858/ www.wfcycling.org.uk). Walthamstow tube.
Maintenance workshops are run 11am-3pm on the second, third and fourth Saturday of the month, by the Waltham Forest Council Bike Recycling Scheme (BRS).

Second-hand bikes

Avoid **Brick Lane** market, where the shiny sets of wheels suggest owners and cycles may not have parted ways willingly: instead, buy stolen bikes recovered by the police at **Frank G Bowen** (73 Sceptre Road, E2 0JU, 7790 7272, www.frankgbowen.co.uk). Auctions are held every other Thursday, starting at 11am: viewing is the day before. Expect up to 120 bikes, ranging from £5 for beat-up frames to £500 for gleaming racers.

For a full list of shops that sell second-hand bikes, visit www.lcc.org.uk.

Bob's Bikes
9 John Ruskin Street, SE5 0NS (7708 0599/ 07961 102072). Kennington tube. Open 9am-5.30pm Mon-Sat. No credit cards.
Bob sells a small range of second-hand bikes from around £40, which are serviced by him and come with a month's guarantee. Sellers must show three forms of ID.

Camden Cycles
251 Eversholt Street, NW1 1BA (7388 7899/ www.camdencycles.co.uk). Camden Town tube. Open 9am-7pm Mon-Fri; 9am-6pm Sat; 11am-5pm Sun.
There's a great selection of reconditioned bikes here, with prices from around £60. Sellers must give two forms of ID, and the shop keeps a regularly updated stolen bicycle database. Bikes come with a one-month warranty.

Edwardes
221-225 Camberwell Road, SE5 0HG (7703 5720). Elephant & Castle tube, then 12, 40, 35, 45, 68, 148, 171, 176, 468 bus. Open 8am-6pm Mon-Sat.
Around 20 second-hand bikes go from £50 upwards every week at Edwardes, with a good range of makes on offer.

Everything Cycling
530 Forest Road, E17 4NB (8521 5812). Walthamstow Central tube/rail. Open 10am-5.30pm Mon-Wed, Fri; 9.30am-5.30pm Sat. No credit cards.

Prices for second-hand bikes (bought from verified owners) start at around £49.

Recycling
110 Elephant Road, SE17 1LB (7703 7001). Elephant & Castle tube. Open 10am-7pm Mon-Fri; 9am-6pm Sat; 11am-5pm Sun.
Second-hand wheels cost from £69, with an emphasis on old-fashioned models such as Mayfairs and a 10% discount if you pay in cash. All bikes are guaranteed for a month.

Smith Brothers
14 Church Road, SW19 5DL (8946 2270). Wimbledon tube. Open 9.30am-5.30pm Mon-Sat.
Second-hand buys are guaranteed for up to a year. Prices range from £89 to £300, and as most bikes are acquired via part exchange you've no need to worry about their history.

Training

It's not widely known, but every London borough (bar, at the time of writing, Redbridge, Harrow, Hillingdon and Bexley) offers heavily subsidised or free cycle training to adults who live, work or study in the borough, in addition to in-school cycle training for children. What's on offer varies: in Hackney, for example, anyone aged over 11 is entitled to two hours' free training. Find out what you're eligible for by checking on your local authority's website, or calling your local training officer: see www.tfl.gov.uk/ cycletraining for a full list.

Useful contacts

The **London Cycling Campaign** (www.lcc.org.uk) is an essential resource, providing information on everything from regular rides to theft and insurance. Meanwhile, **Transport for London** (www.tfl.gov.uk) offers a printable route-finder for cyclists, along with 14 free cycling maps of various areas and information on subsidised cycle training.

GOING OUT

BEAUTY

FASHION

PARTIES

FOOD

HEALTH

ECO

OUTDOORS

HOME

CHILDREN

PETS

TRANSPORT

RESOURCES

Driving

From the perils of clamping to the rise of the car club.

Congestion charge

Driving into central London any time between 7am and 6pm Monday to Friday incurs an £8 fee, payable online at www.cclondon.com, by phone on 0845 900 1234, or at shops and petrol stations displaying the congestion charging sign or paypoint logo.

The area is defined as within King's Cross (N), Old Street roundabout (NE), Aldgate (E), Old Kent Road (SE), Elephant & Castle (S), Vauxhall, Chelsea, South Kensington (SW), Kensington, Holland Park, North Kensington, Bayswater, Paddington (W), Marylebone and Euston (N). You can pay any time during the day of entry, or until midnight on the next charging day after you entered the zone – although the charge then increases to £10.

Expect a £50 fine if you fail to pay (rising to £100 if you delay payment). For a map of the current congestion charge zone, see www.tfl.gov.uk. The charge doesn't apply on public holidays, or between Christmas Day and New Year's Day.

City Secret

If that one after-work drink spiralled and you're in no fit state to get behind the wheel, call on the nifty **Scooterman** (0870 242 6999, www.scooterman.co.uk) service. A chauffeur will arrive on a foldaway scooter, which he'll stow away in the boot of your car before driving you safely home.

Lift shares

Save money as well as the environment by sharing lifts. **Transport for London** have set up a journey match-up service at www.londonliftshare.com for lift-seekers and providers, where options range from cost-sharing on regular commutes, to one-off trips to Brighton, Bristol and beyond. Always use your common sense, and follow recommended safety precautions.

Parking

For parking in central London, visit www.westminster.gov.uk/parking, which has a map of parking bays plus details of car parks and special offers. Westminster Council also produces a handy, free **Park Right** guide, available on its website.

Another useful resource is www.park-up.com: type in a London street name and postcode for a map marked with car parks and street parking, along with charges and maximum parking times.

STREET PARKING

Parking on double yellow lines and red routes is illegal at all times, but in the evening (from 6pm or 7pm in much of central London) and at various times at weekends, parking on single yellows is legal and free. If you find a clear spot on a single yellow line during the evening, look for a sign explaining the regulations for that area.

Meters also become free at certain times during evenings and weekends; otherwise, they cost from £1 for 15 minutes, and are generally limited to two hours. In central

GOING OUT
BEAUTY
FASHION
PARTIES
FOOD
HEALTH
ECO
OUTDOORS
HOME
CHILDREN
PETS
TRANSPORT
RESOURCES

JOIN THE CLUB

Being a full-time car owner in London is often more hassle than it's worth – which is where car clubs come in. You get to use a car whenever you want, without any of the worries about insurance, MOTs and parking permits.

The major car clubs are **City Car Club** (0845 330 1234, www.citycar club.co.uk), **WhizzGo** (0844 477 9966, www.whizzgo.co.uk), **Streetcar** (0845 644 8475, www.streetcar.co.uk) and **Zipcar** 0800 011 2555, 7940 7499, www.zipcar.co.uk). Deals vary, but most clubs charge a joining fee or annual membership fee (or, with Whizzgo, a refundable deposit), then charge around £5 an hour for car

usage: you book the nearest car, swipe your card to unlock it, then drive off.

The only disadvantage is that you have to return cars to the designated space you picked them up from – so one-way trips aren't an option.

To see which club has the most cars available in your area, check out www.carclubs.org.uk.

If you had more glamorous motoring in mind, sign up for a supercar club and get behind the wheel of sleek, shiny Lamborghinis and Aston Martins. **Ecurie25** (7159 2543, www.ecurie25. co.uk) charges a joining fee of £1,500 and annual membership of £11,495, for an average 40 days' driving.

London, meters are being phased out in favour of a new pay by phone service (0870 428 4009, www.westminster.gov.uk): after registering your car licence plate, you can make payments over the phone, using a credit or debit card.

CAR PARKS

It's worth noting that Vauxhall Bridge Road, Grosvenor Place and Park Lane are a designated congestion zone through-route – which means certain car parks are also outside the charging zone. **Mayfair Car Park** (Park Lane, W1K 7AN, 7499 3725) charges £16 for four hours, while at **Masterpark Park Lane** (Park Lane, W1K 7TY, 0800 243348), prices start at £6 for two hours; take care to exit the right way to avoid entering the zone.

Elsewhere in town, London's major car park operators include:

Masterpark *0800 243348/ www.westminster.gov.uk/carparks.*

NCP *0845 050 7080/www.ncp.co.uk.*

Transport for London *0845 330 9880/www.tfl.gov.uk.*

Parking tickets & clamping

If you feel you've been given an unlawful parking ticket, contact the **Parking & Traffic Appeals Service** (7747 4700, www.parkingandtrafficappeals.gov.uk) to register an appeal.

If your car has been clamped, a notice will tell you which payment centre you need to phone or visit. You'll have to stump up a £70-£80 release fee and show a valid driver's licence. The payment centre will de-clamp your car within four hours, but won't say exactly when. Wait by your car: if you don't move it at once, it might get clamped again.

If your car has disappeared, it's probably been taken to a car pound. A release fee of £200 is levied, plus £40 per day from the first midnight after removal. To add insult to injury, you'll also probably get a parking ticket of £60-£100 when you collect the car (which will be reduced by a 50 per cent discount if paid within 14 days). To find out how to retrieve your car, call the 24-hour **TRACE** service hotline (7747 4747).

GOING OUT
BEAUTY
FASHION
PARTIES
FOOD
HEALTH
ECO
OUTDOORS
HOME
CHILDREN
PETS
TRANSPORT
RESOURCES

River services

Taking the scenic route isn't just for tourists.

For commuters, **Thames Clippers** (0870 781 5049, www.thamesclippers.com) runs a regular, reliable service between Embankment Pier and Royal Arsenal Woolwich Pier; stops include Blackfriars, Bankside, London Bridge, Canary Wharf and Greenwich. A standard day roamer ticket (valid 10am-5pm) costs £8, while a single from Embankment to Greenwich is £4, but Oyster travelcard holders get a third off. **Thames Executive Charters** (www.thamesexecutivecharters.com) also offers travelcard discounts on its River Taxi between Putney and Blackfriars, calling at Wandsworth, Chelsea Harbour, Cadogan Pier and Embankment, meaning a £3.75 standard single becomes £2.10.

Westminster Passenger Service Assocation (7930 2062, www.wpsa.co.uk) runs a scheduled daily service from Westminster Pier to Kew, Richmond and Hampton Court from April to October. At £12 for a single it's not cheap, but it is a lovely – and leisurely – way to see the city, and there are discounts of between 30 and 50% for travelcard and Freedom Pass holders.

Thames River Services (www.westminsterpier.co.uk) operates from the same pier, offering trips to Greenwich, Tower Pier and the Thames Barrier. A trip to Greenwich costs £7.50, though £10 buys you a Rivercard, which allows you to hop on and off at will. There's a third off for travelcard holders.

For all commuter service timetables, plus a full list of leisure operators and services, see www.tfl.gov.uk.

Tube & bus

See the city from a scenic bus route, or avoid the tube's worst interchanges.

Bikes on the tube

You can take folding bikes on the tube at any time, but standard bikes are only allowed on certain sections of the line, outside peak times (7.30-9.30am, 4-7pm, Monday to Friday). A map showing where cycles are allowed is available at larger tube stations, online at www.tfl.gov.uk, or by calling 7222 1234.

Interchanges to avoid

Bank/Monument: Central – Circle
There are few London interchanges that can match the sheer confusion and length of the Bank to Monument changeover. One to avoid.

Green Park: Piccadilly – Victoria, Jubilee
The interchange tunnel is spirit-crushingly long, while the head-spinning confetti pattern adds a suitably nightmarish vibe.

Hammersmith: District, Piccadilly – Hammersmith & City
The less-than-speedy line change involves going up a flight of stairs, through the ticket hall and shopping mall, across two busy pedestrian crossings, and into another station.

Paddington: Circle, District, Bakerloo – Hammersmith & City
Two stations made into one back in 1947 mean a very long walk from one to the other.

Shepherd's Bush: Central – Hammersmith & City
An escalator, a brisk six-minute walk, a four-road junction and a set of stairs lie between the two lines.

Waterloo: Northern – Victoria, Jubilee
The trek between lines here is so great, it's covered by an achingly slow airport-style travelator – the only one on the underground.

Lost property

If you lose something on a bus, call 0845 330 9882 and ask for the phone numbers of the depots at either end of the route. If you leave something on the tube, pick up a lost property form at any station.

Lost property found on tubes and buses is generally held locally for a couple of days before being sent to Transport for London's main **Lost Property Office** (200 Baker Street, NW1 5RZ, 7918 2000, www.tfl.gov.uk), open from 8.30am to 4pm Monday to Friday. A small fee is made for reuniting you with your lost property: from £1 for an umbrella to £20 for a laptop.

Underground times

Tube trains run daily from around 5.30am (except Sunday, when they start an hour or two later, depending on the line). The only exception is Christmas Day, when there is no service. Generally, you should not have to wait more than ten minutes for a train. Times of last trains vary, though they're usually around 11.30pm to 1am every day except Sunday, when they finish 30 minutes to an hour earlier. Other than on New Year's Eve, when the tubes run all night, the only all-night public transport is by night bus. For details of last first and last trains for each line, and night bus route maps, visit www.tfl.gov.uk.

GOING OUT

BEAUTY

FASHION

PARTIES

FOOD

HEALTH

ECO

OUTDOORS

HOME

CHILDREN

PETS

TRANSPORT

RESOURCES

When to walk

Lovely as Harry Beck's tube map is, it's not designed to show the distances between stations – so you're often better off walking between certain stations, as all smug Londoners know.

The classic is, of course, **Charing Cross** to **Embankment**: a mere skip, hop and a jump down Villiers Street. **Covent Garden**, meanwhile, is also a short stroll from Charing Cross – far easier than the tube journey, which involves changing from the Northern to the Piccadilly line. From **Covent Garden**, it's a quick flit along Long Acre to **Leicester Square**:

a mere 340m, in fact. **Leicester Square** and **Tottenham Court Road** are also near neighbours, divided by a short (if busy) walk down Charing Cross Road.

Another easy amble is from **Cannon Street** to **Mansion House** or to **Monument**: with either walk taking around four minutes, why wait for a train?

Finally, if you're prepared to put in a bit of extra legwork, it's possible to avoid one of London's most exasperating stations. If you're making for **South Kensington**, but can't face the thought of the hordes of tourists and kids heading for the museums, spare yourself the headache by getting off at **Gloucester Road**: small, peaceful and an eight-minute walk away.

BEST BUS ROUTES

Why get the tube when you can enjoy the fresh air and fine views from London's finest bus routes?

The **11** is the classic tourist route for people too canny to pay for a proper sightseeing bus. Handily, it ticks off most of the building blocks of history on its Fulham Broadway to Liverpool Street jaunt: consumerism at Sloane Square, democracy at Westminster, militarism at Trafalgar Square, the press at Fleet Street, the church at St Paul's and commerce at Bank. That's all the world in a 90p package, with a sniff of everything important except culture.

For that, try the **360**, which links the museums of South Kensington with the Imperial War Museum, or the **14**, which goes from South Ken to Russell Square, home of the British Museum. You might also be missing some fresh air: the **W3** will take you all the way from Finsbury Park to Alexandra Palace, somewhere no tube will venture, while the **3** stops outside south London's lovely Crystal Palace Park. And for one of London's last great wildernesses, east Londoners can pick up the **20**

outside Walthamstow tube and go all the way to Epping Forest.

If you prefer the river, the **RV1** is a great route that circles the Thames from Covent Garden to Tower Hill, via Tate Modern and the Tower of London.

There are also routes that pay tribute to one of London's departed icons, the Routemaster. Both the **9** and **15** offer truncated 'Heritage' routes, with Routies operating alongside the usual upstart buses: the 9 goes from Kensington's Royal Albert Hall to Aldwych, and the 15 from Trafalgar Square to the Tower.

Buses can also link up parts of the city that aren't easily visited by tube. The **31** cuts through north-west London from Camden down to Shepherd's Bush, while the **210** does the same further north from Finsbury Park to Brent Cross. In the south, the **37** does a similar job between Peckham and Clapham. And don't forget the **73**, one of London's most popular and unexpectedly iconic routes, which bustles many times daily between Victoria Station and the tube-free oasis of Stoke Newington.

Events

Quirky, idiosyncratic and sometimes downright weird,
London's lesser-known events reflect a unique city.

JANUARY–MARCH

London International Mime Festival
Various venues across London (7637 5661/
www.mimefest.co.uk). Date mid-late Jan.
Established and edgy companies from across
the globe perform innovative shows that,
thankfully, don't involve people pretending
to be trapped behind a sheet of glass.

Chinese New Year Festival
Around Gerrard Street, W1, Leicester
Square & Trafalgar Square, WC2
(7851 6686/www.chinatownchinese.co.uk).
Leicester Square or Piccadilly Circus tube.
Date last wkd Jan.
In 2009, the Year of the Brown Earth Ox takes
over from the Year of the Rat, an event that
will be celebrated through Chinatown with a
colourful children's parade, traditional
dances and spectacular firework displays.
Expect dense crowds.

Great Spitalfields Pancake Race
Dray Walk, Brick Lane, E1 6QL (7375 0441/
www.alternativearts.co.uk). Liverpool Street
tube/rail. Date 24 Feb (Shrove Tuesday).
If you like the idea of flipping a pancake or
two for charity as part of a four-strong relay
team, call in advance to register. If you're
simply in need of some silliness and cheer,
just turn up on the day.

London Lesbian & Gay Film Festival
BFI Southbank, Belvedere Road, SE1 8XT
(7928 3535/www.llgff.org.uk). Embankment
tube/Waterloo tube/rail. Date late Mar/
early Apr.
The UK's third-largest film festival is still
going strong after 20-plus years, screening an
evocative, sometimes provocative mix of
films from around the globe.

APRIL-JUNE

Spring Loaded
The Place, 17 Duke's Road, WC1H 9PY
(7121 1100/www.theplace.org.uk). Euston
tube/rail. Date from mid Mar.
This seven-week festival celebrates the best
British-based contemporary dance talent.

La Linea
Various venues (8693 1042/www.comono.
co.uk). Date Apr.
Now in its ninth year, La Linea celebrates
Latin American music with a lively line-up of
guests; past attendees have included Bebel
Gilberto, Gotan Project and Lalo Schifrin.

East End Film Festival
Various venues (www.eastendfilmfestival.
com). Date mid Apr.
Founded in 2001, the East End Film Festival
is dedicated to new film-making, often
exploring cinema's potential to cross social
and political divides.

Camden Crawl
Various venues (www.thecamdencrawl.com).
Camden Town tube. Date late Apr.
A two-day showcase of around 80 new bands,
most of them wielding jangly guitars, in a
dozen venues around Camden. Buy a one- or
two-day pass and see as many as you can.

Alternative Fashion Week
Spitalfields Traders Market, Crispin Place,
Brushfield Street, E1 6AA (7375 0441/
www.alternativearts.co.uk). Liverpool Street
tube/rail. Date 3rd wk Apr.
Check out London's new generation of design
talent. Catwalk shows are held at 1.15pm
every day and feature more than 70 original
collections, from the sublime to the surreal.

London Marathon

Greenwich Park to the Mall via the Isle of Dogs, Victoria Embankment & St James's Park (7902 0200/www.london-marathon. co.uk). Blackheath or Maze Hill rail or Charing Cross tube/rail. Date 26 Apr (2009).

Apply by October if you want to be one of the 35,000 starters. If admiring from the sidelines is more your cup of tea, the front runners usually reach the halfway point near the Tower of London at around 10am.

Playtex Moonwalk

Starts & ends Hyde Park, W1 (01483 741430/www.walkthewalk.org). Date late May.

Raise funds for breast cancer research by power walking through the night in your best brassière: choose from either the marathon or half-marathon route.

Jazz Plus

Victoria Embankment Gardens, Villiers Street, WC2R 2PY (7375 0441/www. alternativearts.co.uk). Embankment tube. Date June-July.

Lunchtime concerts from contemporary jazz musicians take place in the gardens on Tuesdays and Thursdays, with free entry.

Coin Street Festival

Bernie Spain Gardens, (next to Oxo Tower Wharf, SE1 9PH (7021 1600/www.coin street.org). Southwark tube/Waterloo tube/ rail. Date June-Aug.

Free live music events, plus a sprinkling of theatre and dance performances, are a lovely way to while away a sunny afternoon.

Watch This Space Festival

Outside the National Theatre, SE1 9PX (7452 3400/www.nationaltheatre. org.uk). Waterloo tube/rail. Date June-Aug.

This lively theatre festival brings an eclectic array of performances to a large square of artificial grass by the river.

Spitalfields Festival

Various locations across east London (7377 1362/www.spitalfieldsfestival.org.uk). Date 1st 3 wks June, 2nd wk Dec.

Spitalfields comes to life with a wide mix of concerts and events, with everything from classical music in churches to electronica in the market – or even a spot of bell-ringing.

Open Garden Squares Weekend

Various venues (www.opensquares.org). Date early June.

Almost 200 private gardens, squares and roof gardens are opened to the public for one weekend a year, from secret 'children-only' play areas to prison gardens.

World Naked Bike Ride

Hyde Park, SE3 (www.worldnakedbikeride. org). Hyde Park Corner tube. Date June.

Bicycles and nudity come together as part of a protest against oil dependency and car culture. Meet at 3pm on the day near the Achilles Statue off Broad Walk, Hyde Park, and prepare to bare.

Meltdown

South Bank Centre, Belvedere Road, SE1 8XX (0870 380 0400/www.southbank centre.co.uk). Embankment tube/Waterloo tube/rail. Date last 2wks June.

Londoners get as excited about the line-up of this brilliantly unpredictable music festival as the rest of the country does about Glasto. Previous directors have included Massive Attack, David Bowie and Patti Smith.

Pride London

Parade from Oxford Street to Victoria Embankment (0844 884 2439/www.pride london.org). Hyde Park Corner or Marble Arch tube/Charing Cross tube/rail. Date late June/early July

The colourful parade is preceded by Festival Fortnight, a mix of performances and cultural events around the city. The central section of the parade route, around Soho and Leicester Square, is the best place to head on the day, with cabaret, dance stages and a food festival.

Greenwich & Docklands International Festival

Various venues in Greenwich & Docklands (8305 1818/www.festival.org). Date 3rd wk June.

GOING OUT

BEAUTY

FASHION

PARTIES

FOOD

HEALTH

ECO

OUTDOORS

HOME

CHILDREN

PETS

TRANSPORT

RESOURCES

An innovative blend of free and family-friendly theatrical, musical and site-specific events. Community projects are mixed with large-scale and often visually stunning events.

London Festival of Architecture
Various venues (7436 8625/www.lfa2008. org). Date late June/early July.
A month of architecture-themed installations, events, film screenings, workshops, cycle rides and guided walks.

JULY-SEPTEMBER

Chap & Hendrick's Olympics
Bedford Square, WC1 (8332 1188/www. hendricksgin.com). Tottenham Court Road tube. Date mid July.
It's all terribly silly and terribly English: 'sports' include umbrella hockey, the three-trousered limbo and the pipe smokers' relay; and there's – hurrah! – free G&Ts.

Dance Al Fresco
Regent's Park, NW1 (www.dancealfresco. org). Regent's Park tube. Date July-Aug.
Held over three weekends, here's your chance to ballroom dance (usually on the Saturday) or tango (Sunday) outdoors to your heart's content. The dancing runs from 2pm to 6pm; novices can join the lessons at 1pm.

Somerset House Summer Series
Somerset House, Strand, WC2 ILA (7845 4600/www.somersethouse.org.uk/music). Temple tube/Charing Cross tube/rail. Date July.
The courtyard at Somerset House provides an impressive outdoor setting for live music; last year's headliners included Duffy, Justice and the Feeling.

Rise Festival
Finsbury Park, N4 (7983 6554/www.rise festival.org). Finsbury Park tube/rail. Date last wk July.
This large-scale free music festival used to promote anti-racism, but under Mayor Johnson this message has been dropped. However, it continues to showcase the best of London's multicultural music talent.

Rushes Soho Shorts Festival
Various venues in Soho (7851 6207/ www.sohoshorts.com). Date last wk July.
Free screenings of short films and videos.

Innocent Village Fete
Regent's Park, NW1 (8600 3939/www. innocentvillagefete.co.uk). Regent's Park tube. Date 1st wk Aug.
Sponsored by a smoothie company, this is the mother of all fetes, with thousands of punters enjoying live music, morris dancing, duck herding, children's activities and more.

Carnaval del Pueblo
Floats from Elephant & Castle to Burgess Park; festival at Burgess Park, SE5 (www. carnavaldelpueblo.co.uk). Date 1st wk Aug.
Europe's largest Latin American festival features colourful floats, bull riding, food and dancing, while past all-star performers have included Oscar D'León and Willie Colón.

Notting Hill Carnival
Around Notting Hill (7727 0072/www. nottinghillcarnival.biz). Bayswater, Notting Hill Gate, Queensway or Westbourne Park tube. Date Sun & bank hol Mon Aug.
London's most famous and flamboyant carnival takes over Notting Hill for two days every year; expect giant floats, pounding drums, exotic dancing and lots of food.

Portobello Film Festival
Various venues around Portobello Road (8960 0996/www.portobellofilmfestival.com). Date Sept.
Screening over 800 new films from around the world, Europe's largest indie film festival also hosts talks from top directors; best of all, entrance to every event is free.

Regent Street Festival
Regent Street, Soho & Mayfair, W1B 4JN (7152 5853/www.regentstreetonline.com). Oxford Circus or Piccadilly Circus tube. Date early Sept.
This annual event sees the horribly busy shopping street closed to traffic for the day to make room for fairground rides, theatre, street entertainers, storytelling and music.

GOING OUT BEAUTY FASHION PARTIES FOOD HEALTH ECO OUTDOORS HOME CHILDREN PETS TRANSPORT RESOURCES

London Gathering

Inner Temple Gardens, EC4 YBT (www. thelondongathering.com). Temple tube or Blackfriars tube/rail. Date early Sept.

Scotland comes to London in this two-day knees-up, celebrating culture north of the border with literary, culinary, historical and musical events, plus a whisky marquee.

London Freewheel

Across the city (www.londonfreewheel.com). Date mid Sept.

A one-day celebration of cycling, Freewheel sees thousands of cyclists turning central London into a huge car-free festival of entertainment, picnics and stalls.

Great River Race

River Thames, from Ham House, Richmond, Surrey, to Island Gardens, E14 (8398 6900/ www.greatriverrace.co.uk). Date mid Sept.

Around 300 vessels, from Chinese dragon boats to Viking longboats, vie for victory in this 22-mile 'traditional' boat race. The prime viewing points are Richmond, Hungerford, Millennium and Tower Bridges.

Spitalfields Show & Green Fair

Allen Gardens & Spitalfields City Farm, Buxton Street, E1 (7375 0441/www. alternativearts.co.uk). Whitechapel tube. Date mid Sept.

This annual horticultural shindig brings bucolic displays of home-grown produce and handicrafts, plus stalls offering fairtrade goods and promoting green living.

Mayor's Thames Festival

Between Westminster & Tower Bridges (7983 4100/www.thamesfestival.org). Blackfriars or Waterloo tube/rail. Date mid Sept.

Celebrating the Thames, this free two-day festival gets more spectacular by the year. Festivities culminate on Sunday with an illuminated night carnival, a lantern procession and a dazzling firework finale.

Open House London

Various venues (0900 160 0061/www.open houselondon.org). Date 3rd wkd Sept.

Peek behind doors that are usually firmly closed with Open House, which gives free access to more than 500 private buildings, from historic palaces to cutting-edge office spaces. Apply for a guide from the end of August and book ahead for certain buildings.

OCTOBER-DECEMBER

Raindance

Various venues across the West End (7287 3833/www.raindance.co.uk). Date 1st wk Oct.

Britain's largest independent film festival has been running for over a decade and a half. Check the website for screenings and events.

Diwali

Trafalgar Square, WC2 (7983 4100/ www.london.gov.uk). Charing Cross tube/ rail. Date Oct.

London's Hindu, Jain and Sikh communities celebrate the annual Festival of Light with sumptuous fireworks, food, music and dance. Everyone's welcome to join the festivities.

London Film Festival

BFI Southbank, Belvedere Road, SE1 8XT (7928 3535/www.lff.org.uk). Embankment tube/Waterloo tube/rail. Date end Oct- early Nov.

A stellar array of actors and directors attends the LFF, which screens around 180 new British and international features.

London Jazz Festival

Various locations (www.londonjazzfestival. org.uk). Date mid Nov.

This renowned ten-day jazz festival joins the dots between trad jazz and the avant-garde, and between America, the West Indies and Africa, attracting a splendid line-up.

Bankside Frost Fair

Tate Modern & Shakespeare's Globe, Bankside, SE1 (7525 1139/www.visit southwark.com/frostfair). London Bridge, Southwark & St Paul's tube. Date Dec.

Held by the river, London's largest free winter event attracts over 100,000 visitors. Expect stalls, music, food and workshops, plus plenty of mulled wine for the grown-ups.

Websites

The city in cyberspace.

BLOGS

www.diamondgeezer.blogspot.com
London's most interesting blogger has been posting since 2002 – and is a worthy online successor to the likes of Pepys and Ackroyd.

londonist.com
Describing itself as 'a website about London and everything that happens in it', Londonist takes a lively look at what's going on in the capital, covering everything from politics to club nights. Don't miss the map of free Wi-Fi spots; new suggestions are always welcome.

www.londonreviewofbreakfasts. blogspot.com
Deliciously entertaining and unfailingly astute reviews of breakfast establishments across the city. It's worth a gander just for the testers' pseudonyms (HP Seuss, Hashley Brown et al).

www.london.thewayweseeit.org
This inspired collaborative photo blog showcases contributors' snaps of selected parts of London. Head out with your camera and join the fun.

www.london-underground. blogspot.com
The best blogs have a tinge of obsession about them, and Annie Mole's tender paean to the biggest underground transport system in the world has it in spades.

www.onionbagblog.blogspot.com
Mr Onionbag takes some lovely shots of obscure corners of London, and has a wonderfully engaging written style. His tales of woe from south London always make our sorrows feel as nought.

pigeonblog.wordpress.com
A unique blog, purportedly written by a pigeon, with some great pictures and a surreal 'pigeon that looks like' section – squint hard enough and the most unlikely of resemblances really do start to emerge.

www.sub-urban.com
Snoop around the city's underground complexes (storm drains, tunnels, sewers) and derelict buildings with daredevil Londoners Jondoe and Stoop.

COMMUNITIES

www.gumtree.com
Founded as a community site to welcome new arrivals to London (in particular, Aussies, Kiwis and South Africans), Gumtree has become a mecca for flatshare-seekers – and a rich source of sold-out gig tickets.

www.kudocities.com
Members of this close-knit site pose questions about London life – such as where to eat in Chinatown, or the best place to woo a first date – which other users then answer.

www.urban75.org
This Brixton-based, non-profit community site is strong on protests and activism, with bulletin boards and listings for upcoming marches, talks and rallies.

GOING OUT

www.dirtydirtydancing.com
Alistair Allan spends his evenings at some of London's hippest club nights and fashion gatherings, snapping his fellow party people. Gawp (and sometimes giggle) at the beautiful people and their after-dark attire.

www.gingerbeer.co.uk
A vibrant guide to lesbian London, listing everything from bars to book launches, plus a guide to the capital's 'Gaybourhoods'.

www.londonisfree.com
A godsend for impecunious Londoners, this useful site lists free exhibitions, events and activities across town. It's particularly good for finding live radio and TV recordings and free instore gigs.

www.run-riot.com
This fast-paced, blog-style guide is excellent for hunting out alternative events. It grew from an informal text-only bulletin and is popular with London's creative types.

scene-out.com
An online community of London's gay clubbers, the site offers news, listings and photos of previous nights' debauchery, plus user reviews of music, film and theatre.

HISTORY

www.classiccafes.co.uk
Pay your respects to the capital's inimitable vintage caffs. The blog features some superb photography, and reviews of the old stalwarts that are still going strong.

www.derelictlondon.com
Paul Talling's huge and deservedly popular online album documents the city's fast-disappearing past, with an amazing photo-catalogue of dereliction and decay.

www.pepysdiary.com
Get a daily dose of Pepys at web consultant Phil Gyford's pet project, in which the great man's diary entries are presented in real time, starting in 2003. We approve.

www.untoldlondon.org.uk
This impressive site delves into the archives to document the history of the capital's ethnic and cultural groups – so you might find a multimedia record of the Greek Cypriot community next to a talk by ICA director Ekow Eshun on growing up in '70s London.

users.bathspa.ac.uk/greenwood
This interactive map of 1827 London is oddly engrossing, covering from Earl's Court to the River Lee, and Highgate to Camberwell.

LONDON LIVING

www.fixmystreet.com
Report neighbourhood nuisances such as abandoned fridges and missing paving slabs, and the team at this inspired website will pass your complaint on to the relevant authorities, and file updates on the outcome.

www.timeout.com/london
Head here for all things relating to the Big Smoke. The search facility helps you find out what's on, fast, from classical concerts to kooky cabaret nights or family-friendly events.

www.walkit.com/london
This user-friendly site encourages Londoners to get walking. Enter the start and end points for your journey and it'll give you a map, full directions and an estimated journey time – and tell you how many calories you'll burn.

SHOPPING & SERVICES

www.lynku.com
Thrifty types will love Lynku, which lists designer fashion and furniture sales across London. It offers free weekly update emails and alerts on sales and promotions.

www.mypropertyspy.co.uk
Property sale prices in London, some dating back to 2000, make for compulsive reading: now you can find out exactly how much your dream house went for when it was gazumped.

www.propertysnake.co.uk
First-time buyers take note: this site charts falling prices across town. Homeowners may find it makes for rather depressing reading.

www.streetsensation.co.uk
Offering a a virtual tour of London's busiest shopping streets, with photos and links to more than 3,500 shops, restaurants and bars, the site gives a whole new meaning to déjà vu.

GOING OUT

BEAUTY

FASHION

PARTIES

FOOD

HEALTH

ECO

OUTDOORS

HOME

CHILDREN

PETS

TRANSPORT

RESOURCES

GOING OUT
BEAUTY
FASHION
PARTIES
FOOD
HEALTH
ECO
OUTDOORS
HOME
CHILDREN
PETS
TRANSPORT
RESOURCES

Notes

Notes

GOING OUT
BEAUTY
FASHION
PARTIES
FOOD
HEALTH
ECO
OUTDOORS
HOME
CHILDREN
PETS
TRANSPORT
RESOURCES

Notes

Notes

Notes

Advertisers' Index

GOING OUT

BEAUTY

FASHION

PARTIES

FOOD

HEALTH

ECO

HOME

CHILDREN

PETS

TRANSPORT

RESOURCES

londontown .com	IFC
Life's 2 Short	10

Going Out

Cousin Jill's	15
Mucky Pup	15
Mudchute Park & Farm	144
Ribon	15
Up the Creek	8

Beauty

Rosebery Rooms and Hair Station	42
Strip	42
Toni & Guy	38

Fashion

Doors by Jas M.B	15
Kirk Originals	63
Lesley Craze Gallery	63
Portobello Green	IBC

Parties

Clerkenwell Kitchen	73
Profi-Dance Studios	73

Food

Brilliant Kids	94
El Faro	89
Gaby's Deli	94
Lodge Tavern	100
Mangal 1	10
Providores and Tapa Room	89

Sacred Café	94
Sagar	100

Health & Fitness

Arthur Murray	112
Paraiso School of Samba	112
Westway Sports Centre	112

Home

All Go Plumbing	10
Home Jane	154
Hossack & Gray	144
House Directory	8
Jennie Mann Flowers	154
Rebel Rebel	154
Robert Loomes	144

GOING OUT

BEAUTY

FASHION

PARTIES

FOOD

HEALTH

ECO

HOME

CHILDREN

PETS

TRANSPORT

RESOURCES

Index

GOING OUT

BEAUTY

FASHION

PARTIES

FOOD

HEALTH

ECO

HOME

CHILDREN

PETS

TRANSPORT

RESOURCES

GOING OUT
BEAUTY
FASHION
PARTIES
FOOD
HEALTH
ECO
HOME
CHILDREN
PETS
TRANSPORT
RESOURCES